The New Wave in Information Technology

The New Wave in Information Technology

What it Means for Business

Heinrich Steinmann and
Dimitris N. Chorafas

Based on an intensive research project in 1993/96 in the USA, Japan and Europe among computers, communications and software vendors – and leading user organisations

CASSELL

Cassell Plc
Wellington House
125 Strand
London WC2R 0BB

127 West 24th Street
New York
NY 10011

First published 1996

British Library Cataloguing-in-Publication Data
A catalogue record for this book is available from the British Library.

ISBN 0-304-33607-6 (hb)
0-304-33608-4 (pb)

Typeset by Action Typesetting, Gloucester
Printed and bound in Great Britain by
Redwood Books, Trowbridge, Wiltshire

Contents

Preface

During the last ten years, we think of telecommunications as a tool of business rather than an ancillary service. Telephony is no longer subordinate to a paper-based office system; it is the pivot point around which other networks grow and new applications develop.

Another important factor is that in the business of telephony the players are changing, and will continue to change since the stakes are high. The new product line of the telephone companies (telcos) is no longer limited to voice systems, but includes computer-based solutions, involves increasingly sophisticated software and targets multimedia.

By focusing on the new wave of communications and computers – and quite evidently on software problems – this book appeals to two populations: one is the academic world, particularly graduate students in engineering and telecommunications; the other is designers and developers of new systems – the people behind the very advanced communications networks of the mid- to late 1990s.

The book also carries a valuable message to company executives, project planners and government agents responsible for funding major new programs such as the information superhighway. To address in a comprehensive way the problems facing communications technology today, the 12 chapters of this book have been divided into three parts:

- Part 1 focuses on the search for efficient communications solutions.
- The theme of Part 2 is the challenge of a business systems architecture.
- Part 3 presents practical examples on how communications companies solve network design problems.

By addressing the pace of new development in network solutions, in Chapter 1 we explain the role of the telecommunications infrastructure in a modern society and review the challenges and opportunities presented by globalization. This chapter also stresses the software requirements which increasingly constitute the competitive edge of networks.

Today, it is nobody's secret that the communications and computer systems which we use have to be architectured. By far the better alternative is that of an open architecture, and in Chapter 2 we discuss why. The chapter also places emphasis on critical network decisions which have a long-term impact on communications.

In Chapter 3 we take a practical example with Internet and trace Internet's evolution since the time of Arpanet, explain how users can take advantage of its services and document why competitive pricing is the best policy. But we also lament the lack of global telecommunications standards – and, in Internet's case, the absence of security.

The synergy of many subjects which enter into communications solutions is the focal point of Chapter 4. Here we explain the practical value of the projected information superhighway in America, not just what the term means, and place emphasis on the goals of the National Information Infrastructure (NII) and on the diversity of required services. Many telecommunications experts, however, consider NII to be still just 'pie in the sky'.

Value added services will characterize the rest of this decade and constitute the competitive edge of network providers. Practical examples on value differentiation are provided in Chapter 5, in terms which emphasize the need for new network design. Basic principles characterizing a business systems architecture are presented in reference to the goals which the architecture sets for itself.

Practical applications which in their way reflect most or all of these principles start to appear; banking is a first-class example. Based on the best references available from the financial industry, in Chapter 6 we review the role of telecommunications in banking, introduce the concept of realspace as an evolution of realtime, and examine what can be done with virtual reality as well as virtual environments generally.

Since a business systems architecture has to continue to be dynamic, it needs to be periodically re-engineered. Object-oriented solutions are a good way to modernize a complex system, and in Chapter 7 we discuss how this can be done. The text also examines the role frameworks can play and brings into perspective practical applications, such as risk management.

While the applications perspectives examined in Chapter 7 are management oriented, those on which Chapter 8 concentrates concern transaction management. In this case, the merger of computers and communications is examined by means of desk area networks and client-server solutions. Emphasis is placed on the role of networks in promoting as well as effectively sustaining peer-to-peer solutions.

In Chapter 9 we bring the reader's attention to the advantages to be obtained through new network designs and more efficient protocols. We pay attention to the need for a steady renewal strategy, explain why telcos are now using fibre optics in the loop, introduce frame relay and asynchronous transfer mode (ATM), and underline the importance of sophisticated communications software.

All new developments require a significant amount of research. In Chapter 10 we say that much, but also present an infrastructure for resource sharing, explain why it is important to target solutions which are knowledge- and innovation-intense, and advise the need for cultural change – which is the only way to obtain a high return on investment.

The steadily more advanced services which have been presented by the first ten chapters of this book will be fulfilled by projects which are on their way to completion at the laboratories of major telephone companies. We build upon this notion in Chapter 11 by discussing some of the outstanding projects at the NYNEX laboratories and explain what the new generation of high performance networks has to offer.

The theme of Chapter 12 is networks for intelligent buildings and intelligent cities. By paying attention to community intelligence, at the level made possible through interactive networks, the reader is confronted with some social aftermaths. This concludes the vision of the new wave in telecommunications.

On several occasions in this text reference is being made to opinions expressed by reviewers. These are experts in communications and networks who have kindly read through several chapters of an early version and commented on what they found. In a number of cases, the authors agreed with the expressed opinions; in others this has not been the case. Divergence of opinion is, in fact, a most healthy business. If everyone agrees with everybody else, there will be no progress in technology or in commerce. Whether characterized by agreement or disagreement, these expert opinions have been most valuable in focusing this text, restructuring its contents and making it more appealing to the reader. Therefore, even in the case of disagreement, the reviewers' comments have been welcome.

The authors wish to express their appreciation for the reception reserved to them and the collaboration they received on behalf of 300 senior executives, systems designers, computers and communications specialists and other experts in the USA, the UK, Germany, Austria, Sweden, Denmark, Switzerland and Japan.

Ninety-four computer manufacturers, communications companies, financial institutions, service companies and university laboratories participated in this effort. A personalized list can be found in the Acknowledgements.

Let us close by expressing our thanks to everybody who contributed to this book: to our colleagues for their insight, to the company executives and technologists as well as the university faculty for their collaboration, to Naomi Roth for seeing this book through to publication, and to Eva-Maria Binder for the drawings, typing and index.

Dr Heinrich Steinmann
Dr Dimitris N. Chorafas

Part 1

The Search for Efficient Communications Solutions

1

Network Solutions Today and Tomorrow

1. Introduction

For more than 100 years, communications media have been designed for voice traffic, primarily through analogue transmission. Message switching, as implemented with telex/TWX, was a late 1940s development. Twenty years later, packet switching associated conventional communications techniques and computers,* essentially changing the emphasis from voice traffic to data transmission by:

- providing a platform for more reliable services at greater efficiency than that of bisynchronous and start/stop protocols
- assuring a line discipline which operated in a way transparent to the contents of the message.

This made feasible economies of scale and led to the building of networks able to operate in an applications-independent manner. The second significant contribution of new switching technologies has been a radical change in architecture. The aftermath included:

- increased functionality
- more flexible implementation
- the coverage of wider areas
- competition towards greater efficiency and hence lower costs.

The original computer-oriented networks, of the mid-1960s, were star type. Their terminals were linked to one central resource through point-to-point or multidrop lines. This network design lacks both flexibility and polyvalence. It is also bound to become obsolete since basic functions such as:

- line control
- access methods

* See section 5.

- terminals handling
- character control

are more or less intermingled. With star networks, the protocols are asymmetrical, based on telephone line properties. These networks do not have their own structure as they mix terminal, application, and computer constraints in an *ad hoc* implementation.

The contribution of new network architectures starts by eliminating these weaknesses. Modern peer-to-peer networks act as an *information freeway*. In a manner transparent to the attached resources, they transport *multimedia* bit streams: text, graphics, voice, image and animation. They also:

- disconnect sender from receiver through storage and forward capabilities
- provide for error detection and correction
- assure greater dependability and network performance, as well as better load balancing, through alternate routing.

However, sophisticated networks pose significant demands in terms of design and implementation. The transition from pure voice switching and transmission to full-blown business communications has been made possible by developments in computers, software and protocols – but this transition also affects each of these component parts in a significant way.

2. The Development of a Telecommunications Infrastructure

Telecommunications infrastructures are in full evolution. The earliest model, which dates back for more than three decades,* has been that of computers and terminals attached to classical analogue lines by means of modulators/demodulators (modems).

While they were pioneering at their time, these solutions had the defect that throughput was low, first measured in bauds then in kilobits per second (KBPS). The earliest *kilostreams* featured 1.2 KBPS. Then, as modems improved, we had 2.4 KBPS increased to 4.8 KBPS, 9.6 KBPS and 19.2 KBPS – practically applied on the same old telephone lines.

In the mid-1980s with the integrated services digital network (ISDN) agreement between post, telephone and telegraph companies (PTTs) and telcos, a communications channel featured 64 KBPS. This choice of digital transmission rates was not random but for a reason: the 64

* See also section 5.

KBPS channel results from pulse code modulation (PCM) which represents 8000 8-bit (one byte) samples every second.

The first available megastream channel operated at the rate of 24 x 64 KBPS = 1.53 MBPS (megabits per second); which characterizes T1 lines. Other megastreams are in multiples of T1, but as we already saw ISDN operates in kilostreams. It supports two 64 KBPS channels and a 'return wire' of 16 KBPS – hence 144 KBPS in total.

Today the concept of a *broadband* telecommunications infrastructure underpins new network designs. It also characterizes the platform upon which, in a post-industrial society, the whole economy will depend. The keyword is *megastreams* (megabits per second) but by the end of this decade it will be *gigastreams*. The proper infrastructure:

- enables vast quantities of multimedia information to flow freely and rapidly around the globe
- positions itself to support new services and applications that can be tailor-made to users' needs, supported by appropriate bandwidth.

Bandwidth is the range of frequencies characterizing transmission performance and its specific limits. It is the bit rate in a signal line and therefore the speed at which information flows.

Bandwidth is a vital metric of the capacity of a network, the other crucial reference being *bit error rate* (BER) characterizing the quality of the line. In terms of bandwidth we distinguish kilostreams, megastreams and gigastreams, as mentioned earlier.

The standard for broadband changes over time, depending on the growing user requirements. Communications solutions are dynamic, and as new applications are found the need for bandwidth increases.

- Many more issues characterize modern communications networks than bandwidth capacity.
- Telecommunications is no longer a matter of flicking switches to route telephone calls.
- Both telephone companies and equipment manufacturers spend large amounts of money on software, because that's 'where the action is'.*

User workstations (WS) will be connected to global networks through gateways, or will interface directly if they can handle the protocol(s) characterizing such networks. This is typically the case of intelligent terminals – including desk area networks** – as well as local area networks

* See D.N. Chorafas and H. Steinmann, *Intelligent Networks* (CRC Press, Boca Raton, Fl, 1990).

** See Chapter 8.

(LAN), supercomputers, database servers and personal computers, through to smart television sets.

Modern business information systems are built with intelligent devices. Increasingly, the same is true of consumer electronics. But technology is only part of the solution. An open market environment promotes the development of new services and ensures that they are adopted at a rapid pace. The issues here are political and have to do with *deregulation.*

Current and new players in the telecommunications industry would find it difficult to offer their services if their access to the network continues to be restricted and different monopolies are able to price them out of the market. All service providers must benefit from open access to other networks, at low cost, as well as being able to build and operate their own networks.

- The fact that telecommunications is characterized by constant change and rapid technological progress, adds to this statement.
- Only in a free and *open environment** driven by market forces, can enterprises achieve the degree of flexibility necessary to adapt to new developments and react quickly.

The flexibility achieved in an open market is therefore all the more essential because companies must be allowed the freedom to try out alternative routes towards new business opportunities, better solutions and more advanced applications. This is the role a telecommunications infrastructure must not only support but also actively promote.

3. A Steady Evolution in Communications Solutions

To appreciate the contribution of communications to our work and to our life, it is wise to briefly look back in time. After 1832, the telegraph made possible the first efficient text and data transmission system. It also facilitated direct manufacturing operations. Before the telegraph, for instance, success in multinational banking operations required having a large number of brothers or cousins, operating as a network with a single combined interest and being capable of thinking more or less alike. This helped to solve the agency problem and provided a means for management control. Subsequently, telephony brought people nearer together in a communications sense and, most importantly, it created a capillary network which spans the whole globe.

The rise of direct national and international investments, as well as

* See Chapter 2.

the multinational corporation, improved after the basic long-distance communications problems were solved. Spectacular flowering awaited the spread of the continental and transatlantic telephone in 1931, as well as of commercial air transport at about the same time.

But telecommunications really picked up momentum after World War II. Even in the immediate postwar years, telephony was considered to be a luxury and some socialist governments – as, for instance, in France – were thrifty in spending money to expand the telephone network. Also, for the better part of the last 50 years neither the interest nor the skills necessary for system integration were present. Telex was established as a separate network necessitating both an own infrastructure and the proliferation of terminals.

Only in the late 1960s after the now famous Carterphone decision broke the monopoly of Ma Bell* in America, and by extension that of other telcos, started a wave of change – first in the USA then in the UK and Japan. Technology played a key role in the new environment, and it provided the means for telecommunications suppliers around the world to ensure their cross-border services.

- One of the visible aftermaths of technology has been the computer-based public exchanges and private branch exchanges (PBX).
- Another aftermath is the increasingly vital role played in telecommunications by sophisticated software.

There are many reasons why we need intelligence for the networks as a whole, at the switching centres and at the end-user level. One reason is the ability to accommodate differences in sending and receiving messages, documents, formats, data types, codes, and representations. Such differences may exist not only between heterogeneous terminals but also between processes operating on the same host.

- To accomplish integrative functions in an able manner, we must pay attention both to the system and to the terminal.
- While messages and files are of network-wide interest, the object at the transmission and processing levels is specific to each applications field.

For a bank's current accounts protocol, for instance, the object of interest is customers, accounts, balances, deposits and withdrawals. A manufacturer's order entry protocol will focus on customers, sales orders, products, inventories, in-process orders, bills and receivables.

In all applications, a key point is file access. The concept of networks

* The old AT&T (American Telephone & Telegraph).

is indivisible from that of databases, and vice versa. For a distributed database access protocol, the object is not only the transport of information but also:

- data formats and their interpretation
- session and presentation control services
- integrity and security assurance.

A host of issues must be taken into consideration including their extent, design, implementation and further impact. Many activities relating to network management bring into play routines involving codes transaction requirements, record handling, files exchanges and program control.

From file transfer to user interaction, integrity considerations have to be given due weight. Solutions must be provided on a network-wide basis. It is therefore necessary to specify sets of rules by which the information transferred between processes and/or devices will be formatted, exchanged and interpreted.

High-level language interfaces for queries and analytical purposes, are other references to look for. The use of analytics also concerns network management as, for example, in the case of knowledge artefacts autonomously testing lines and switches as well as exploiting quality databases.

All these references help to document that telecommunications at large, and telephony in particular, have progressed a long way since the time of Alexander Graham Bell. The change which has taken place during the last 40 years is most impressive – but it is also only a prelude to what lies ahead.

4. The Transition from Current to Future Systems

A vital issue in telecommunication is that of providing sender and receiver with a very realistic sensation of a shared environment between the communicating parties. One of the recent goals is to achieve this communication realism in the visual media through the use of three-dimensional (3-D) imaging and presentation technologies, including:

- automatic acquisition of 3-D images
- their realtime modelling and display
- creation of an interactive envircnment for the communicating parties
- techniques for processing, manipulating and displaying 3-D objects.

The whole sense of the *Information Superhighway*, and the services it is projected to support, revolve around this concept.* The Japanese Advanced Telecommunications Research (ATR) Laboratory, for example, works on non-verbal interfaces such as the capture and interpretation of facial expressions, gestures and hand movements which – its researchers suggest – will characterize communications before this decade is over.

The goal of this and similar projects in America and Europe is to incorporate non-verbal methods in the communication system and its environment. The means is to use a visual language to give specifications accurately through a knowledge-based solution able to represent the information capture, processing and interpretation mechanism.

By investing in intelligent machines which emulate the way humans process visual information, and applying the results, we can create a system capable of automatic pattern cognition and synthesis. Applications in *virtual reality*** have the goal of presenting to the user realistic environments, significantly enlarging the input/output communications bandwidth between computers and their users.

Significant advances in this direction can only be interdisciplinary, as research projects are conducted at the frontiers of knowledge; ATR, for example, is currently engaged in psychological experiments aimed at clarifying the detailed characteristics of human motion and depth perception in order to:

- produce more advanced technologies in character and pattern recognition
- take a closer look at human perceptual, cognitive, and memory mechanisms.

It is also necessary to model the human character recognition process, an approach today taken by using neural networks.*** The reader will appreciate that these references are a world apart from what is usually thought to be 'telecommunications'. Yet, they are the key to the transition from current to future systems.

One of the most challenging issues with modern communications is to project a transition path from past to future systems which is rational, affordable and does not create service discontinuities. Such strategy requires that the technologies that will drive this transformation become widely understood with emphasis placed on:

- developing systems designs that are robust

* See also Chapter 4.

** See D.N. Chorafas and H. Steinmann, *Virtual Reality: Practical Applications in Business and Industry* (Prentice-Hall, Englewood Cliffs, NJ, 1995).

*** See also D.N. Chorafas, *New Information Technologies – a Practitioner's Guide* (Van Nostrand Reinhold, New York, 1992).

- assuring a steady stream of novel functions
- coping with unforeseen variations in usage characteristics.

Far from being in the form of some static parameters, these characteristics express service specifications in terms of dynamics. Examples of variables which change dynamically include call patterns, call duration, signalling load and geographic market development.

Most of these patterns can only be determined by considering the applications themselves and their evolutions, accounting for the novelty of different implementations as well as the variations in cultural communications habits characterizing the strata of society and the industry sectors.

Modern telephone companies appreciate that a user-centred process of experimentation is required, permitting exploration of the impact and potential use of new technologies. Models allow people involved in telecommunications network development to verify the fit of their intended designs to the projected communications patterns – a process now considered by many laboratories to be pivotal to the ability of meeting market demands.*

5. The Crucial Role of Network Protocols and Bit Error Rate

Data transmission first became a topic in the late 1950s, with a military project, the Semiautomatic Air-to-Ground (SAGE) equipment, for air defence. A few years later, in 1960, civilian projects also looked into data communications – but it was a slow beginning.

Only after 1963, did interest in data transmission grow rapidly, receiving a stimulus from time-sharing developments, by attaching a number of terminals on the same host. Since then, there has been steady progress – starting however, with transmission rates as low as 70 bauds, on analogue voice-grade lines.

Because the capillary plant that telephone companies have in place is old and of fairly low quality, there were doubts about the adequacy of classical phone lines for data transmission from the start. It was feared they would turn out to be too noisy and too liable to interruption. This happened in some countries more than others, and in some areas within the same country – as for instance in Sicily, Italy:

- The quality of a transmission line is measured in bit error rate (BER), as already stated in section 2.

Sicily has a BER of 10^{-2} which means that, on average, one out of 100

* See Chapter 11 on the experience in the NYNEX laboratories.

transmitted bits is erroneous. By contrast, Northern Italy features a BER of 10^{-4} to 10^{-5}, like the rest of Western Europe.

- As the speed of data transmission increased, due to better modems (modulators/demodulators) the BER problem became more severe.

As we have seen in section 2, the mid-1960s saw a transmission rate of 1.2 kilobits per second (KBPS), after graduating relatively rapidly through 200, 300 and 600 baud. By the early 1970s, as data transmission speeds reached 2.4 KBPS and, in exceptional cases, 4.8 KBPS, it became evident that a better solution than the plain old telephone system (POTS) was necessary.

- Data grade quality was provided in the mid- to late 1970s with new public networks featuring a BER of 10^{-7} to 10^{-8}.
- It also became apparent that not only BER had to be significantly improved but so did the protocols – or line disciplines – used in data transmission.

The protocol which was exclusively used in the late 1950s and early 1960s was *start-stop*. It was followed in the mid-1960s by the *bisynchronous communications* (BSC) protocol, which was an improvement over start-stop but still left much to be desired.*

The need for more efficient protocols increased as telephone lines improved over the years, particularly in connection to new installations, and mechanical switching gave way to electronic switching. Adaptive modems could squeeze a great deal of bandwidth out of a voice-grade line, changing the users' perspective of what was doable.

This development pressed further the need for a still better protocol, and an answer was found in *packet switching*. Already in the 1968–70 time frame, work on a new network by the Advanced Research Projects Agency (ARPA), of the US Department of Defense, had applied a packet-switching protocol combining principles from BSC and message switching used for telex.

The result was ARPANET which employed lines having a data rate of 56 KBPS.** The demand for higher data rates continued, though until the mid-1970s business applications were content to use the telephone company's offerings at what was then 4.8 KBPS or 9.6 KBPS.

- The lines used for transmission from 1.2 KBPS to 9.6 KBPS were practically the same.

* See also D.N. Chorafas, *Handbook of Data Communications and Computer Networks* (McGraw-Hill/TAB Books, New York, 2nd edn 1990).

** Arpanet today is operating world-wide and has been renamed Internet. See Chapter 3.

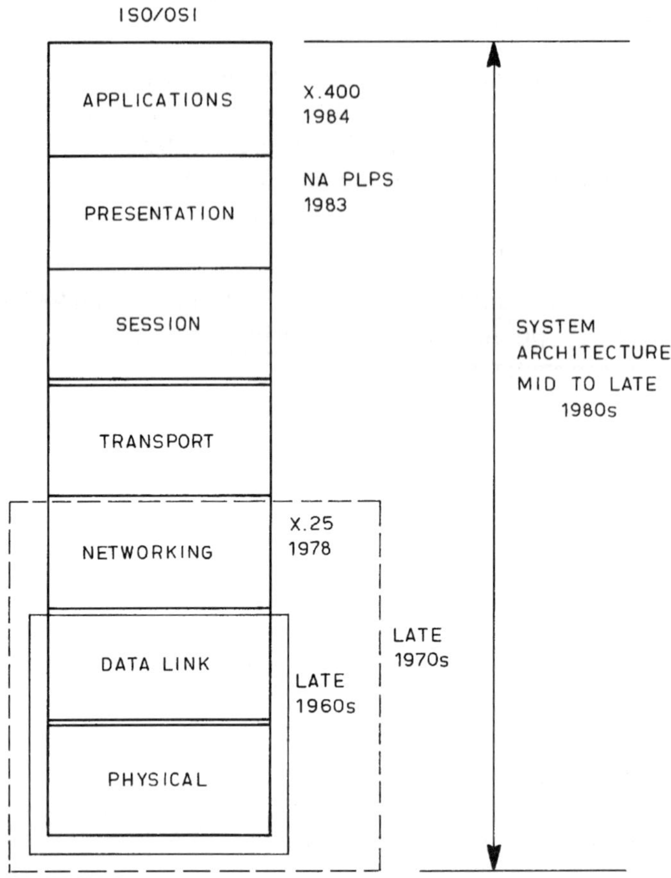

Figure 1.1 Layered structure of ISO/OSI

- Higher transmission rates cost more money because the modem was so much more expensive.

In terms of protocols, start-stop was mostly used for low data transmission rates and low-cost applications. BSC and subsequently packet switching were applied to higher transmission rates. In May 1978, under the auspices of the Consultative Committee for International Telephone and Telegraph (CCITT), was signed in Rome – the X.25 agreement – which, up to a point, provided a standard for packet switching.

The X.25 protocol is a packet-switching line discipline which addresses the networking layer of the International Standards Organization/Open Systems Interconnection (ISO/OSI) model. Figure 1.1 shows where exactly the networking layer fits on the layered structure of ISO/OSI.

For any practical purpose, the ISO/OSI model is the first flexible and modular architecture concerning computers and communications. As a *systems architecture*, it assures a layered approach by separating functions (and protocols), into consistent levels independent from one another – but interconnected through interfaces.

This architecture permits various computers as well as both intelligent and non-intelligent terminals to be connected and share a common communications network. As such, ISO/OSI has been a huge improvement over IBM's System Network Architecture (SNA), which was centralized and inflexible. The same reference is valid regarding ISO/OSI versus the architectures offered by other computer vendors.

6. Bottlenecks in the Implementation of Global Network Solutions

Telecommunications change people's lives in more important ways than just talking over the line, and will begin to show significant effects in new social habits well before the turn of this century. Broadband solutions will reduce traffic congestion; they will also enable more people to work at home, and may make business more efficient by squeezing out the 'dead' time in a number of ways. For instance:

- communicating rather than commuting to work
- doing away with letters sitting in the mail
- providing the means for a steady optimization of productive processes.

Cellular and satellite phones will link companies and individuals wherever they are. Vast new capacity will push down prices as both governments and business come to realize that flexible, high-speed, and reliable telephone networks are critical to economic growth.

Making these plans come true will, however, require hundreds of billions of dollars' worth of new installations – from infrastructural investments to telephone equipment. Critical to success will be a new generation of telephone switches and transmission gear that telcos will use to modernize their networks.

- Advanced software and hardware is needed to complete the broad telecommunications superhighways which are currently planned and, to a lesser extent, budgeted.

- The prognosis is that over the coming years, private and public switched telephone networks will undergo the most radical technological transformation in history.

Today's networks are built around the central-office switch – the telecom equivalent of a mainframe computer. This is a multimillion-dollar monster housed in a fireproof building and tended to by technicians around the clock. It is also a solution whose time has irrevocably passed.

Like mainframes, central-office switches are not so easily adapted to changing market drives and requests for new, more complex services. Large-scale switches remain so difficult to program that new features take years to deliver. Not only is this not competitive, but in a dynamic, competitive market it can be suicidal. The new solutions have to be fully distributed and benefit from knowledge-enriched software.

Digital telecommunications are propelled by technology advancements, but are also forcing changes in how business is conducted and how society progresses. Digitalization is driving internationalization and globalization, which demand much more competitive environments than those prevailing in the past.

In a global systems sense, a similar reference can be made about integrative solutions – even if some telecommunications equipment manufacturers and telcos continue to provide awkward approaches to integration, which multiply attendance requirements and costs. Figure 1.2 comes from a recent audit, and provides an example from an incompletely considered solution which, at work area level, requires the doubling of the number of terminals. Ironically, this approach was advertised by the vendor as a 'new epoch' in system design, but in reality it is a patching up of an old idea.

Both *integration* and *flexibility* are now at a premium. With the new telecommunications technologies, users should have the opportunity of trade-offs between processing, assembling, reassembling and transferring information through their chosen centres of operation – within their networks. Assistance in doing so in an able manner will create significant customer–supplier partnerships.

In terms of impact on system design, as well as on the facilities to be provided through its implementation, flexibility and integration are joined by another crucial subject: *universal numbering*. There are today serious numbering problems in connection with the global network, and no easy answers are in sight.

Simply stated, the telecommunications world is running out of telephone numbers. Not only countries asserting sovereign rights ask for new identification numbers, but also global network operators require access to the existing public network through appropriate numbering –

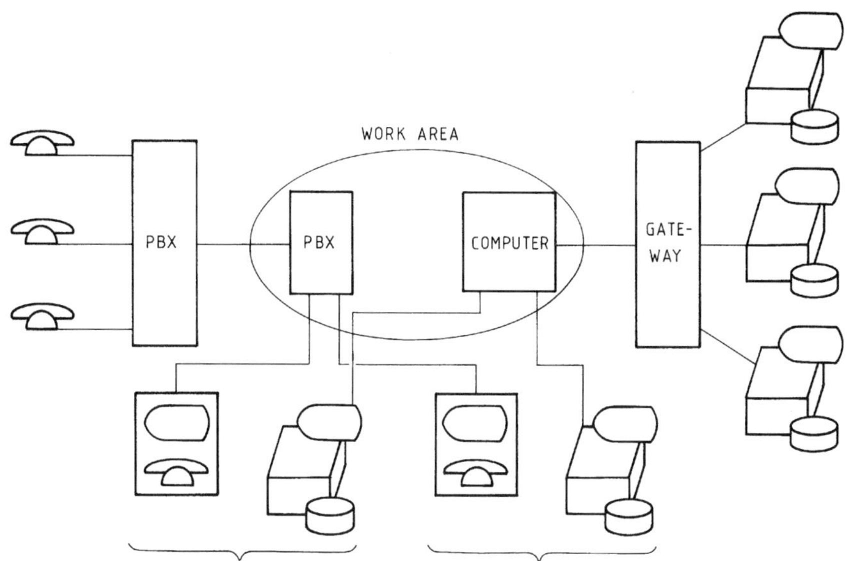

Figure 1.2 Flaws in design due to the lack of a systems integration concept

and so does the introduction of a myriad of new services. This has placed a heavy load on a numbering system designed in the late 1950s:

- Since December 1991 the CCITT has been calling for an overhaul of the world's telephone numbering plan.
- CCITT says the current scheme, which it administers, is in danger of coming apart as demand for new numbers proliferates.

Currently, all codes available are in use, but without an international access code for billing purposes it is impossible for national operators to negotiate bilaterally for telephone revenues. Not only is this quite a complicated issue, but also solutions have to look long term into tomorrow's challenges.

Part of the problem lies in the fact that current CCITT recommendations have been established on the basis of state-run monopolies – which after all constitute its membership. At present, in most countries the dominant telephone operator undertakes the roles of allocation and management of the numbering capacity for all operators and all services sharing the numbering scheme. This contrasts badly to the evolving multi-operator, multiservice environment, where numbering is emerging as a key enabling factor – not only in the growth of existing services, but also in the introduction of new services and operators.

What the different telco monopolies need to understand is that numbering has become as much a part of deregulation and globalization of communications as the technical fabric underpinning telecommunications services. Like frequency spectrum and transmission parameters, numbering must now be seen in the context of a scarce and finite communications resource. And there are global number portability requirements for the future Universal Personal Telecommunications system.

7. Learning from Local Area Networks and Their Megastream Solutions

As section 5 underlined, the generalization of the packet-switching discipline has been based on the original work done in connection with Arpanet. By 1978, it had been adopted by telcos for long-haul data transmission but on kilostream circuits. At about the same time, different variation of packet-switching protocols became available on *local area networks* (LAN) – but in connection to megastream channels.

At the end of the 1970s, a project at the Xerox research laboratories brought to life a new protocol specification projected for local area networks: the *carrier sensing multiple access/collision detection* (CSMA/CD), which constituted a new line of discipline.*

- Ethernet operated at 10 MBPS on coaxial cable, and this was a 'first'.
- Till then, the twisted pair of the telco's local loop was used for wide areas at kilostream.

When Xerox Ethernet was announced, interest in coaxial cable for data communication became the 'in' thing – but not all LANs run on coaxial. Others, like Omninet and Nestar used twisted pair cable and operated at 1 MBPS.

- One thing Ethernet, Omninet, Nestar and other LANs had in common was that they used variations of the carrier-sensing, multiple access/collision detection protocol.
- Another characteristic they shared is that they worked in megabits per second (MBPS) versus the KBPS transmission rate of POTS.

First, LANs found a niche in helping to share computer resources between workstations and servers – and then a broader market into which they fit. Local area networks' advantages closely matched what the computer community needed to use, and by the late 1980s the implemen-

* See also D.N. Chorafas, *Designing and Implementing Local Area Networks* (McGraw-Hill, New York, 1983).

tation concept evolved into client-servers.

The contention principle, on which CSMA/CD is based, served many applications and the bandwidth was more than adequate for that time. But the overwhelming attraction of the early LANs was their simplicity:

- They were one-level interconnect systems, with flat addressing and no routing problems.
- Shortly thereafter, methods of interconnecting LANs became available and, while not without their constraints, they are adequate for present-day requirements.

By the late 1980s, the fibre distributed digital interface (FDDI) protocol started being applied with optical fibres and coaxial cables. It works at 100 MBPS, while the subsequent version, FFDI II, features 150 MBPS. We are also beginning to see experimental versions of LANs operating in the gigabit per second (GBPS) range.

Gigastreams are the way of the future and it is not surprising that new protocols like *frame relay* and the *asynchronous transfer mode* (ATM) have been developed for more efficient long-haul communications. Frame relay is an intermediate state while the asynchronous transfer mode has been described as the technology that allows total flexibility to be achieved in broadband multiservice, multimedia networks:

- ATM is the CCITT standard for cell relay where multimedia information is conveyed in small, fixed-size cells consisting of a 5-byte header and of a 48-byte user information.*
- *Multimedia* applications are supporting the display of many types of information like moving images and animation along with the more classical voice, text and data.

Perceived benefits from ATM implementation have caused this protocol to receive a great deal of attention, particularly with regard to integrated services and universal connectivity. The goal is to enable time-critical applications to reach workstation or server level at high speed. In regard to the ISO/OSI model, ATM and frame relay substitute the aging X.25 protocol. They also collapse the second and third layer of ISO/OSI into one level.**

8. Communications Challenges Implied by Multimedia

New developments both in protocols and in line capacity are necessary to handle multimedia. Compound electronic documents are structures in

* We explain more about the technical aspects of ATM in Chapter 9.

** The second layer of ISO/OSI was served by the HDLC data link protocol.

which data, text, voice, graphics and images integrate. The requirements they pose go well beyond what has, so far, characterized data transmission.

Images, especially moving images and animation, require a vast number of bits, even if compression techniques are used. When the passing of multimedia documents between one computer site and another becomes a frequent operation, the load imposed on networks is considerable and old solutions are no longer good enough.

In other areas, too, developments tend to increase the traffic on networks. For instance, the growing use of virtual reality, modelling and realtime simulation in engineering and science – as well as their recent migration in finance and in management.

- Top-flight banks ensure that the results of complex calculations are transmitted and displayed in 3-D colour graphics.
- From capillary data collection to realtime reporting, the load increases the amount of traffic carried by computer networks.

The growing use of automatic methods for acquiring tick-by-tick, subsecond data is leading to new traffic characteristics which tend towards data loads that so far have been the exclusive property of satellite sensors. At the same time, scientific data capture is achieving a quantum leap in volumes.

Working with various other space agencies, the National Aeronautics and Space Agency (NASA) has announced plans for putting up an earth orbiting system (EOS). The new system is projected to send a huge amount of data to the Earth every second, but may also create the test bed for business communications problems by the end of this decade.

Some communications experts may say that EOS is a one-off example which will not repeat itself so often. If so, they are wrong. Major banks are interested in tick-by-tick data collection, and the February 1995 collapse of Barings because of deficient management controls will encourage the use of this path much faster than was thought just a year ago.

Multimedia is a fusion of technologies and its advent will have a tremendous impact on the way information systems are designed and built in the future. To better appreciate this reference we must consider that network implementation is spreading like an oil spot:

- Voice networks were integrated with data networks during the 1980s, leading to computers and communications aggregates.
- During the 1990s we are experiencing the integration of computer, communication and consumer electronics.

The networks and their protocols that we now have are not designed for the sort of traffic heralded by the integration of services. New design perspectives are needed and there exist two types of evolving data transmission requirements which are contrasting to one another:

- subsecond handling of short messages, a process of paramount importance to engineering and finance
- a steady growth of bulk data traffic, which must be transmitted in real-enough-time.

Database-to-database communication fits the second group. It will be augmented by document traffic, including reference material – largely handled by multimedia servers throughout the networks.

The current networks were not designed for demands posed by either traffic. Hence many existing solutions will become useless for the new purposes. New solutions will need to be built, alongside the existing networks, optimized for the mission which we have just seen and other goals they will be projected to serve.

Both optical fibres and satellites, particularly hybrid solutions combining the advantages of both, will provide enough bandwidth for both types of service. This is one of the goals the information superhighway aims to fulfil, as we will see in Chapter 4.

9. The Cost of Developing New Technology in Telecommunications

One of the major advantages of telecommunications which is not readily apparent to the untrained eye, is their any-to-any, ephemeral hierarchical structure. Networks usually offer channels which are not hierarchized in one direction from the beginning and, therefore, are inflexible:

- A telephone line has two or more users with similar privileges who, through switches, are connected any to any.
- All types of conferences, whether realtime or time asynchronous, offer equal or relatively similar privileges for all participants.

Due to these systems features, the nature of the communication channels does not favour long-term hierarchical network structures – even if some vendors go out of their way to provide them, as has been the case with SNA.

But peer-to-peer networks pose other prerequisites, one of the more challenging being the ability to assure a seamless passthrough among heterogeneous networks. Figure 1.3 brings this subject under perspective and it suggests a solution by means of *mapping units*.

Mapping units are emulators operating at gateways. They help to provide an infrastructure for flexible interconnect situations, where we can identify, define and solve differences in protocols. This solution helps to

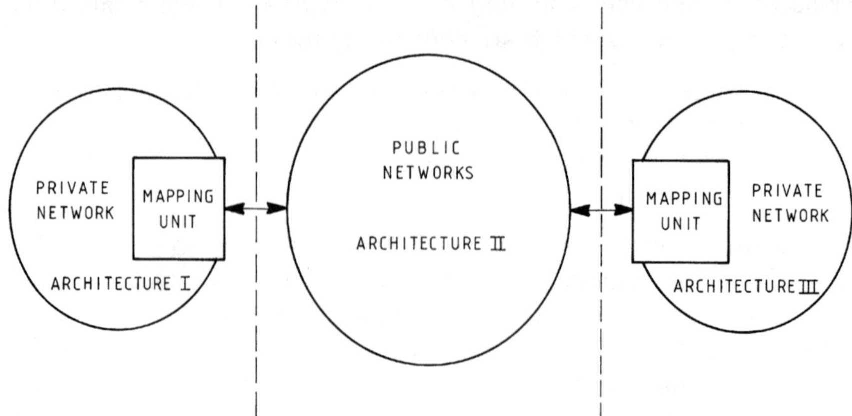

Figure 1.3 Ensuring seamless passthrough among heterogeneous networks

provide passthrough in a much more flexible way than has been available so far. Seamless approaches in connection with heterogeneous networks are vital to *federated* organizations, and therefore to virtual offices and virtual corporations. We discuss much more about federated organizations in Chapter 5.

Seamless solutions are supported not only through protocols but also by means of knowledge engineering artefacts; they are steadily improved by means of competitive research. To maintain vitality and a stable, balanced growth, communications companies must continue to expand interdisciplinary research as well as strengthen their development resources.

An example will help to better explain this reference. In section 4 we mentioned research work carried out at Japan's ATR Laboratory, which includes models of human auditory processing and their applications to speech recognition and signal handling. These are studied through psychoacoustic and speech perception experiments:

- Adaptive functions of the human auditory systems in various environments are investigated.
- Speech perception/recognition processes are studied to yield an integrated model of information processing in humans.

The knowledge gained by telephone companies from over 100 years' of experience is still necessary in telecommunications, but it is not enough. For instance, the able handling of multimedia poses problems never before encountered with pure voice telephony – or with pure data transmission among networked computers.

Provided research and development (R&D) is properly directed, the cost of developing new communications technology is largely compensated by the fall-outs from the market drive to globalize the world of computers and networks. Freer trade of communications gear has a stimulating effect on further spending, as well as on more sophisticated implementations.

Telecommunications vendors make such investments – at a level of 12 per cent to 17 per cent of their yearly business – because they appreciate that dynamic organizations today must aim to become truly global. The minimum step is to go for three major regions: Western Europe, North America and the Pacific Basin. But to do so successfully, they must develop, produce, market and distribute in each one of these three economic blocs. This is the only way to guarantee to themselves and the market a steady stream of sophisticated products and services sold at an affordable cost. Co-ordination requires a global view of markets, as well as a first-class intelligent network.

Fast and reliable communications permit companies to move production around the globe without succumbing to centrifugal forces. The precondition is fast, reliable timing in information exchange and in management decisions:

- Quick product development and immediate efficient marketing are at a premium.
- Long timetables result in loss of market share and financial troubles.

From R&D laboratories, to manufacturing plants and marketing efforts, networks have been playing a key role in *product turnarounds* – as they assist management with knowledge information and decision power. In this connection, their role in the mid- to late 1990s will be even greater, but it is just as true that a number of problems will have to be solved – including software challenges.

10. Software Requirements for Telecommunications Equipment and Networks

As happened with distributed computing in the 1980s, telecommunications increasingly takes on integrated software-driven operational functions. Sophisticated software is necessary for supporting the globalization of world business, providing intelligent network services which eventually lead to total restructuring of the way in which companies operate.

- It matters less and less where organizations and people work.

- What is crucial is how to maintain flexible network connectivity.

An increasingly greater flexibility in network connectivity is required to obtain the maximum advantage from information transiting on networks or stored in databases. This has to be accessed in an any-to-any fashion – at any time anywhere in the world.

The message is that in terms of communications, computers and software, the rules of the game from design to the way applications are implemented have radically changed. The old pre-1950s telecommunications switching systems cost about $10 million to develop and had a market life of about 25 years. In the 1980s, when the digital solutions started getting established, development costs had risen to $1 billion for a life expectancy of eight to ten years.

Digital development costs of $1 billion require roughly 8 per cent of the world market share just to recover the investment. At the same time, software not hardware underpins market success of a digital telecommunications switching system. For example:

- With Siemens's Hicom, 75 per cent of the R&D budget went into software.
- Northern Telecom adds 500 new software modules to its private branch exchange every year.*

The interest which currently exists in communications software, and most particularly in *agents*,** can be judged by the fate of the stock of General Magic. A $13 stock price would give this company a market value of some $300 million. Yet it has revenues of just $2.5 million from two products largely unproven in the market.

Magic Cap software for *personal communicators* lets people send and receive electronic mail and faxes by tapping on the screen of a handheld device. Telescript*** is a programming language for communications software that enables agents to zip along the network to retrieve information elements from distributed databases.

General Magic still has not produced the business miracle many expected, but investors' interest for new and innovative telecommunications start-ups remains in high gear. When in August 1995 Netscape Communications, a tiny maker of software to navigate the Internet,

* See also in Chapter 4 for reference to the money telephone companies are spending on software.

** Agents are knowledge artefacts resident in nodes of the network which, contrary to expert systems, are proactive. They prompt their users and take their own initiatives.

*** On Magic Cap and Telescript see also Chapter 2.

went public, it had no profits to its name yet racked up a market value of about $2 billion. There is demand for:

- browsers to view material on the World Wide Web
- the behind-the-scenes programming needed to help businesses set up shop on the Internet.

Advanced software is needed to keep track of billing in a network-wide sense, make transactions safe and cultivate virtual communities on-line. That is where Netscape expects to strike it rich: its Internet server programs sell for thousands of dollars while it mostly gives its browser away. This evolutionary process in intelligent software development – as well as the redirection of investments and refocusing of management attention it makes necessary – follows the frame of reference in Figure 1.4.

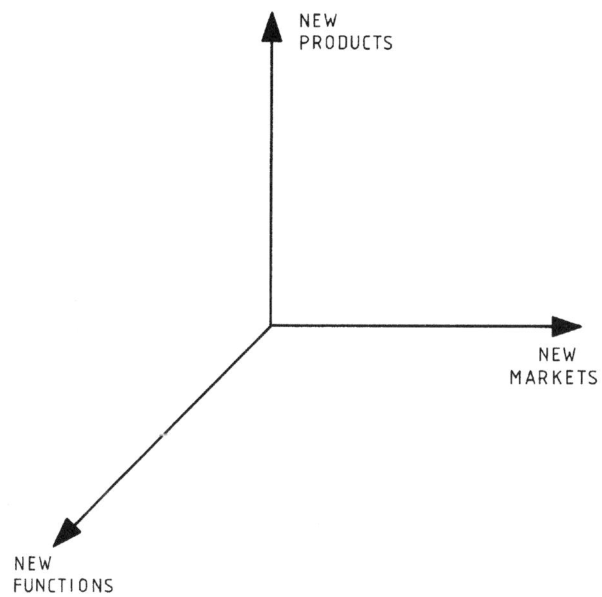

Figure 1.4 Frame of reference for business practice

This figure presents in a nutshell the co-ordinate system into which companies increasingly fit their strategy – whether in hardware and software for networks or in any other line of business.

No wonder that, in order to survive, telephone equipment manufacturers are increasingly software oriented, in the same way as they are depending on advanced switching technology for sending the reams of data and video needed for the information superhighway:

- These manufacturers are putting together a line of switches and other products ideally suited for the modern voice and data networks that corporations are building to link global operations.
- By the end of the decade, some of this same switching technology will help in bringing a flood of digital programming to millions of homes.

Telephone operators, other industrial companies, merchandisers and financial institutions are slowly appreciating that very significant investments are so much more necessary as, in the emerging global market, the focus of competition is shifting to high technology.

In plain terms, in the context of advanced telecommunications solutions, high technology means *agents* which are proactive, residing in nodes and switches; expert systems for network diagnostics and maintenance purposes; quality databases and reliability models. Failure to continue moving ahead destroys the technology base:

- Protectionism and strong ties between local telephone companies and equipment suppliers still linger.
- It becomes increasingly evident that no nation can afford to oversubsidize equipment makers or live with outdated telephone technology.

High technology is the only way to unlock the huge world-wide telephone equipment and communications market. This market features many players and not all of them can be Number 1. Neither is everybody now in the telecom business going to make it to the twenty-first century.

The cost of developing a new generation of switches is tremendous, as researchers push close to the frontiers of physics, working with atoms, picoseconds and gigabits. The next generation of advanced optical information processing devices demands new materials and new design concepts which harness the potential of non-linear optical phenomena. In research on new device concepts – theoretical analyses, computer simulations and interactive experimentation – are combined in investigations of applications of non-linearities such as those present in *optical chaos*. The times of the nationalized PTT* being called 'Petit Travail Tranquil'** are irrevocably past. Those who stumble backwards into the future are going to disappear.

Costs are even more staggering in software development which, as we have seen, now accounts for 75 per cent of the switch-makers' R&D

* Post, telephone and telegraph.

** Work which is small and quiet.

budgets. Investments in intelligent software are a 'must' because the network will be called upon to carry just about anything that can be digitized – from voice to multimedia.

Telephone companies are making huge investments in broadband by replacing copper wires with fibre-optic cables – but much more is needed to keep the digital flows going smoothly over fibres.

The foremost telephone companies come to appreciate that building bigger, faster versions of today's equipment is far from being the solution. Present network switches, which route calls from place to place, wastefully reserve a fixed pathway between two points even if the circuit is idle for most of the call. In a typical voice call:

- The two-way circuit is idle about 60 per cent of the time.
- Valuable seconds are wasted in setting up a circuit which may handle a split-second data burst.

Assisted by knowledge artefacts, the new generation of switches breaks down all messages into packets of digital information mailed at light speed over the network and reassembles them into a coherent stream at the other end. As we have seen, both the asynchronous transfer mode and frame relay are efficient, streamlined versions of the packet-switching technology now used in networks. For businesses, the advent of new generations of superfast switches built on high technology means competitiveness.

2

Macroengineering and Open Systems Architecture

1. Introduction

Professor Terano, president of LIFE,* advises: 'The first step in a successful project is the *macroscopic* view. Most systems designers are so involved in the details that they lose track of the project's grand design.' Fine details make sense only when the direction we have chosen is right.

During the last five years, a similar concept to the grand design has developed in America, applicable to all engineering projects. Known as *macroengineering*, this new discipline is the science of large-scale systems – their:

- study
- development
- deployment
- operations
- maintenance.

This science also includes the analysis and evaluation of the evolution that large systems cause, including the way in which it impacts on the design approaches we should take and the solutions we should provide. Big systems are not small systems which have grown up; they have totally different perspectives and requirements than small systems – and these have to be studied in a rigorous manner.

Telecommunications, and most particularly global communications, is a big systems science. A macroengineering approach is that much more important as today's model of relationships between the network, its computer-supported services and its software will not work so well for tomorrow. Both conceptual and design changes are necessary because:

- during the next ten years, the roles of computers and communications will be reversed

* Laboratory for International Fuzzy Engineering, Japan.

- instead of ever faster computers connected by relatively slow copper wires, we will have very high capacity fibre networks linking what will seem to be slow computers.

Not only are fibre communications significantly cheaper for a given level of bandwidth, but also they impose new implementation requirements. As a result, much of the skill which today exists in terms of system design will be obsolete.

Closely connected to this proposition is the fact that proprietary and parochial architectural solutions, the way we have known them for over 20 years since IBM's announcement of SNA, are no more affordable – or for that matter welcome. A *system architecture* is for any practical purpose a *business architecture*, therefore a self-respecting company:

- should neither be locking itself into somebody's else business architecture
- nor can it expect to answer its fast evolving requirements through prepackaged solutions.

This notion is elaborated to a considerable extent in Chapter 5. Practical examples will be provided to substantiate the statement which has been made. By contrast, this chapter focuses on the concept of an *open architecture* – or, more precisely, the standards which, when observed, lead to an open vendor policy.

2. Concepts Underpinning Open Systems Solutions

As we have seen in the previous section, the macroengineering characteristics of telecommunications networks have been instrumental in making us revise the way we look at communications and computers – as well as the architectural solutions we are adopting. Promoted by the search for steadily greater cost-effectiveness, many factors have been gradually improving the state of the art in architectural solutions.

One of the key concepts in new architectural approaches is to permit increased use of technology in the solutions which we adopt. Macroengineering has been of great help in this evolution, opening horizons which call for new departures in the way we put systems together, and make them work.

Since parochial approaches present many bottlenecks to the efficient use of resources, the drive has been towards *open architectures*. By definition, an open architecture is non-proprietary, where the user organization has available a range of design choices, and procurement options.

An *open system* implements specifications for interfaces, protocol services and supporting formats established by international standardization bodies. The benevolent aspect of these norms is that they enable application software to:

- be ported across implementation platforms
- interoperate with applications in a network-wide sense
- interact with users in a comprehensive style thanks to normalization.

Defined in January 1990 by the Institute of Electrical and Electronics Engineers (IEEE) the concept of an open architecture makes feasible the use of applications on different system levels exploiting central, departmental and workstation/server resources. It enbales applications to migrate from one platform to another, of the same or different vendors, as well as integrating applications of different vendors.

While the adoption of an open architecture does not automatically ensure effective communications between heterogeneous systems, its absence makes such communication costly, slow, error-prone or unfeasible. The lack of open systems perspectives is the reason why today 70 per cent of every dollar spent on corporate information systems goes towards maintaining the old mainframe-based infrastructure. As a result, only 30 per cent is available for developing new applications, and this is rarely well spent. By contrast, as we see in Chapter 8, with client-server systems which are observing an open architecture, and with distributed networked databases such systems make feasible, this unfavourable ratio is turned on its head.

However, able solutions require a cultural change key to the implementation of client-servers in the development and maintenance of a sound migration policy. Leading-edge organizations found by experience that a smooth migration policy will seek to maintain operating integrity while creating a flexible new architecture and moving to it. In this point lies the whole wisdom of a smooth transition in systems solutions. This reference also hints at the policies which should be followed in order to capitalize on the use of international standards and norms.

Chapter 3 explains how Internet has been able to establish itself as the first open network in the telecommunications world, particularly in terms of interconnection of heterogeneous equipments and data transmission. As we have seen in Chapter 1, Internet developed from Arpanet – but as it expanded world-wide it had to face the problem of open access to the network. This was achieved by establishing and following a *de facto* standard.

The Internet example helps document that an effective policy in information technology is one able to handle the challenges before they arise, in order to avoid 'fire brigade' approaches and associated disasters. In a business sense, for example, a global analysis of transactional

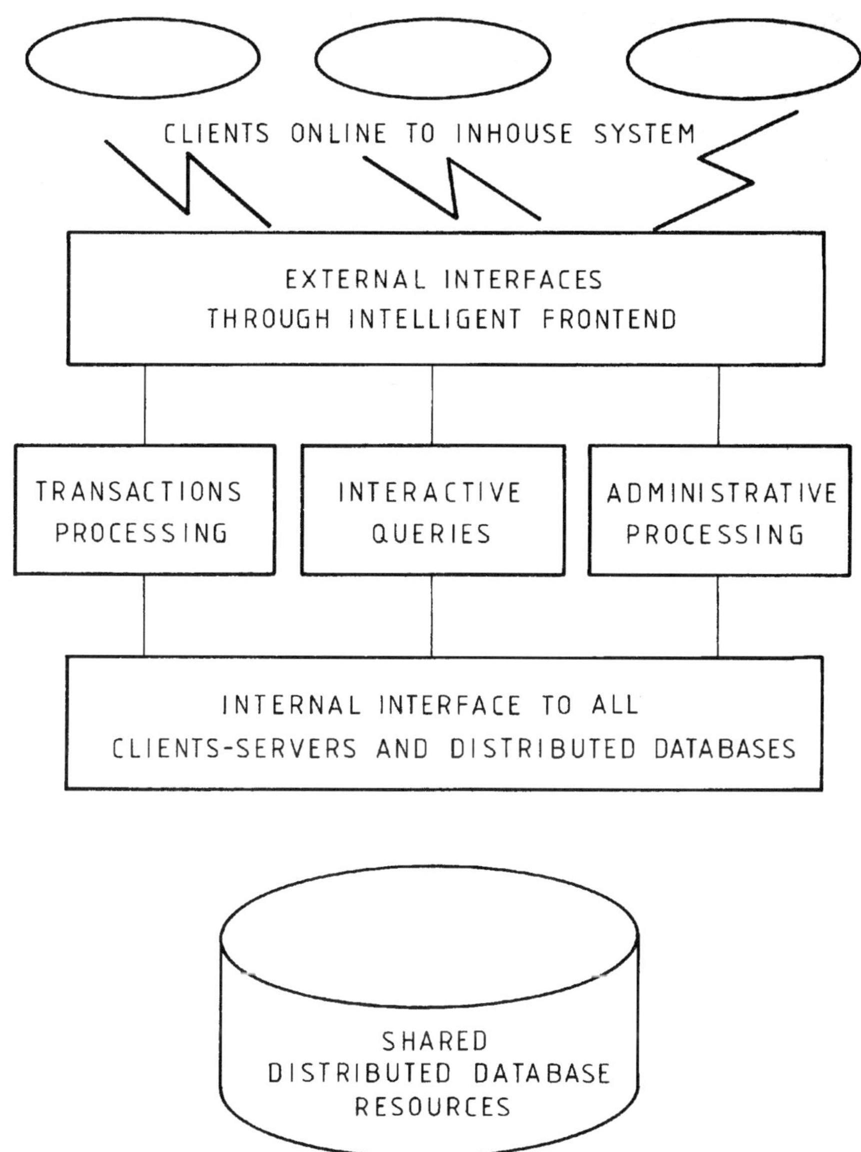

Figure 2.1 An interactive concept for in-house dataflow

requirements – both current and future – should cover all corporate needs. This should be followed by:

- detailed design of transaction and query solutions regarding each functional area, and
- transition to a fully parallel processing mode of operations, which is interactive not batch.

Systems analysts and designers should keep in mind that, as Figure 2.1 demonstrates, most real-life database management problems in the 1990s and beyond will be multidimensional involving transactions, queries and administrative chores. They will rest on fully distributed solutions, both in processing and in databasing. Our clients will communicate on-line with our company, hence the need for first-class service interfaces:

- Our clients and suppliers will have complex transactions to handle as well as analytical queries – to which they need on-line response.
- Able answers to business partner needs will call into play a range of administrative chores, which should be fully automated through agents.

Valid solutions will involve knowledge engineering artefacts, or agents, not just legacy data processing. They will increasingly call for object-oriented approaches in response to interactive requirements – and will require superior analytical skill. While these concepts will be sufficiently underlined throughout the present book, it is wise to present them concisely at this point.

In conclusion, an open architecture consists of technical standards but also of procedural approaches able to address business problems in an efficient manner. The technical norms are elaborated by standardization institutes and more or less represent compromises on which most vendors and users can agree. By contrast, the procedural solutions which we adopt are custom-made. They provide the muscle to the skeleton established by norms – and are every company's own business architecture.

3. Software for the Integration of Telecom and Broadcasting

One of the most imaginative macroengineering projects of the mid- to late 1990s is that addressing the integration of telecommunications. It is also one of the most demanding in terms of open architectural solutions into which can converge programming companies, broadcasters, cable television firms and the rejuvenated plain old telephone utilities.

Throughout the First World, and most particularly among communications companies, there is growing interest in the integration of telecom and broadcasting. At the physical level, this can be done through the deployment of broadband fibre-optic cable, but the greatest challenge is at the logical level served through increasingly complex software.

The technical reason behind this statement lies in the fact that communications technology is largely computer based. However, there have been many failures with software over 40 years of computer usage, recently augmented by business reasons due to the uncertainty over the future demand for services, such as videotelephony and high-definition television (HDTV). Wide area broadband communications, metropolitan area networks and HDTV are interrelated. They are also in great demand for new departures in regard to the nature of supporting software and the evolution to which it must respond.

Few companies appreciate that the most imaginative software for multimedia communications will be the product of start-ups which have found a niche in the market and rush to fill the demand in an able manner. California-based General Magic provides an example.

In 1990 General Magic came to life as a project undertaken by Apple Computer, but was soon given independence to encourage the support of other companies. Apple, AT&T, Matsushita Electric, Motorola, NTT, Philips Electronics and Sony all own equity stakes in the company – and expectations run high even if this niche has not yet become a wide market.

This multivendor environment is a foundation for an open architecture. The product all these companies are after is known as Telescript, a multimedia operating system for personal communicators particularly oriented to mobile communications systems. Telescript is software aimed to link personal digital assistants (PDA) world-wide. But is there a market for this type of basic programming product?

In 1994, Dataquest estimated that at $1000 per unit PDA shipments will boom. There were 250,000 in 1992, 400,000 in 1993, and were expected to jump to 850,000 in 1995. But in 1995 these estimates have been lowered, and there is no more talk about the market doubling over the following couple of years.

In Chapter 1 we mentioned Netscape, another start-up with great hopes for a swinging market response. Unlike Telescript, it appeals to Internet users,* but like General Magic doubt remains that it will really carry the day and make investors rich. Today:

- There are hundreds of companies who can be classified as network software hopefuls.
- Most are still tiny and mainly privately held – though some, like Netscape, go public.

Some financial analysts believe that they recognize the syndrome: it is a technology bubble, a late twentieth-century version of tulipmania. Just

* See Chapter 3.

as in the 1620s the Dutch wildly bid up the prices of tulip bulbs, only to watch them crash later on, so investors today snap up technology stocks.

Other financial analysts are of the opinion that the current rush to investing in unknown networking companies is akin to the railroad-building of the late 1800s and the automobile investments of the early twentieth century. Railroads went bankrupt and auto companies merged, but in the meantime, a new economy was built. Today companies are spending huge sums to develop a telecommunications infrastructure – and this will be the foundation of the twenty-first century economy.

Enough about the investment perspectives. Investments in new companies can prove either to be sound or unsound, depending on the technology underpinning products and processes, their market appeal, the market's own response and management's ability to pull a rabbit out of a hat. Let's not forget that when, at the beginning of this century, J.P. Morgan formed US Steel, the company's stock opened at $19.50 and soon increased in price, reaching a peak of $29. However, within ten years the value dropped to $9. It then recovered and eventually became the darling of Wall Street.

The company was nicknamed 'Big Steel'. It was the largest steel producer in the world – until, in the 1960s, its fortunes changed and US Steel started a long track into decline.

Will Netscape have a similar future? We shall see. As J.P. Morgan once said: 'The stock will go up if there are more buyers than sellers.' This is precisely what has not happened with General Magic. Two years after the euphoria about its wares the company seems to have faded from attention, and is now being restructured, and a new management has taken over – but it is doubtful whether the situation can be redressed.

Yet, the original idea made sense. In terms of the software technology itself, the heart of the General Magic Software is Magic Cap, where 'Cap' stands for Communications Applications Platform which:

- is an object-oriented operating system (OS) optimized for both wireline and wireless communications
- features a user interface and application hooks designed to make it easy to use by both consumers and software developers.

The kernel is Telescript, a programming language with communications routines that allow various networks and applications to work co-operatively. Through it, users were to be able to personalize the functionality of networks and their services.

While General Magic was expected to concentrate on developing system-level software and licensing, some of the basic applications were supposed to be produced by third parties. Still other applications were to come from the same company which made the OS.

The first, known as Magic Mail, is a wireless email application differing from others in the sense that it enables users to send messages that include graphics as well as text, and leads towards the on-line handling of compound electronic documents at personal digital assistants' level.

What went wrong with General Magic? We asked this question in our research in Silicon Valley, in January 1996, and here are the top five answers which were given by cognizant people in this field:

1. The technology was not mature
2. The product was difficult to use
3. The product had a lot of rough edges
4. Sales did not focus correctly on a market
5. The targets were too generalized.

In other words, the company did not focus on any specific industry such as, for instance, health care. This would have allowed it to tailor the product, remove its rough edges, smooth the linkages to other packages and add functionality without inordinate complexity.

The same aims could have been sought if the PDA market was targeted in a forceful manner. While PDAs were said to be at the centre of General Magic's marketing picture, technical developments and the sales effort did not convince investors that there was a future in Magic Cap. Those investors who rushed into acquiring equity were deceived.

Looking at this case study postmortem, the lesson to be learned is that nothing is sure with investments in new software companies. Most or even all of the top five reasons for General Magic's failure apply to a large number of new start-ups. Some, indeed most, will become part of the dust of industrial history. Others will live to become the sort of company US Steel used to be.

4. Accessing the Network from Anywhere at Any Time

The reference to General Magic, its operating system and programming language serves a dual purpose: it exemplifies a real-life solution to open architecture challenges, and suggests a procedure which might become the norm in accessing multimedia network resources.

Both issues are vitally important since, as we saw in Chapter 1, one of the crucial questions today in communications technology is *how* will consumers access the information superhighway. Some experts think they will use a personal computer. Others say it will be a beefed-up cable-TV converter box. Still others look to knowledge engineering artefacts (agents) which can reside in anything from handheld devices to high-performance computers and also use the network services.

- Many user organizations believe that the first step toward multimedia messaging would be to have a single electronic *in box* for all email, voice and fax messages.
- All information in databases will be accessible from a single device: a personal digital assistant, smart telephone, or personal computer.

The crucial issue is to have a single platform for all media, with the user depending on visualization for communications reasons. This is, more or less, a generally accepted principle.

Computer companies suggest that a screen-based interface is generally better suited than a telephone interface as a multimedia messaging platform. But telephone companies answer that the telephone, too, is moving in this direction and voice communications are a better bet.

The aftermath of a fast-moving technology is that the main issue today is much less centred on the platform than on how vendors of different messaging media will build bridges between their products. The range of facilities which need to integrate into an open architecture involves:

- personal computers and local area networks
- voice, fax and electronic messaging
- a great deal of intelligence-enriched software.

Having overcome the constraints of parochial vendor approaches through an open architecture, user organizations will define the exact nature of this new type of software, and its agents, according to dynamically defined applications environments.

As Figure 2.2 suggests, within the perspective of an open architecture, the solution space will find itself in a triangle delimited by planning tasks, dynamic operational requirements, diagnostics and maintenance for high uptime. Agile approaches will be assisted through expert systems:

- The solution space so defined is valid for practically all communications, databasing and processing activities.
- Ingenious engineering studies will ensure that available facilities can be effectively used in a cross-product sense.

The first applications of this type are already on hand. Links with fax messaging are now available from most email and voice mail systems. With an estimated 40 million fax machines world-wide, fax is going to remain a basic service. An integrative solution should allow users to:

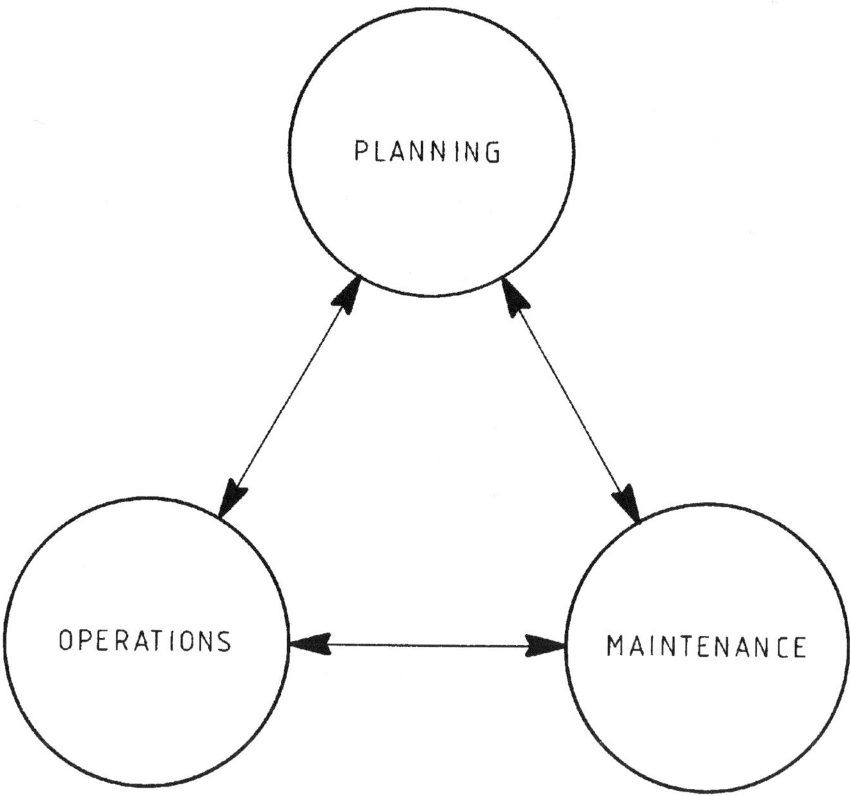

Figure 2.2 Layers of support for able network management

- dial into a multimedia mailbox from a touchtone telephone
- listen to how many faxes and telephone messages there have been
- direct the output operation at any time to any platform the user wants.

Indeed, this may be happening faster than many people think. In January 1994, a release by American Telephone & Telegraph (AT&T) suggested that consumers would tap into NII by the most ubiquitous of communications gear: the telephone.

Under Project Sage, AT&T engineers are now in the process of reinventing the classical telephone set. The goal is to make it act as the central controller that will funnel information to and from a variety of platforms whose exact nature will be no constraint to the interconnect solution:

- personal computers
- fax machines
- television sets
- videogame players
- videotape recorders.

AT&T suggests that after Sage hits the market it is going to be increasingly difficult to figure out what is a game machine, a computer, and a telephone – thus providing platform independence within the context of an open architecture.

The newly designed polyvalent telephone set will pack the power of a personal computer and include both software and circuitry to manage the digitized information coming into the home. The Sage telephone will accept electronic plug-in cards slightly bigger than credit cards.

- Each will emulate an existing appliance or connect to one.
- A digital telephone-machine card will store messages.
- Another will function as the set-top control box for cable TV, and so on.

AT&T will also offer a card that enables the camcorder and TV to make video calls, and other vendors may offer a myriad of other solutions as this market opens up and attracts investments.

The software making all this possible comes from AT&T as well as from General Magic. The company, of which we spoke in section 3, has designed an agent that can perform such tasks as calling out across the information superhighway to find all the programs about the subject its user wants.

As they come on stream, such knowledge artefacts will find a myriad of applications, from manufacturing to banking. The service sector of the economy will stand to benefit the most. *Post mortem*, agents will answer in the best possible manner the silly argument of some intellectuals that 'it is ridiculous to talk of artificial intelligence applications in banking'.

5. Steps Leading Towards Interactive Computer Conferencing

The solution provided by AT&T for the mid-1990s goes well beyond what email-based services can support, even if the latter allow functional services from a screen, enabling users to retrieve or send faxes from their desktop. As many people, and surely AT&T, appreciate, both the facilitator and the bottleneck will be software.

Returning to the fundamentals, we should recall that the last couple of years have seen software that shows users a list of email, telephone or fax messages on their personal computer screens. They can then listen to a telephone message or obtain a copy of the fax on their personal workstation desktop screen by clicking on an icon.

- Some products provide links to the company's database that tells the user the number of the person calling in or sending a fax.
- Other software products assure pieces necessary for multimedia messaging, but also pose the challenge of integrating these pieces into one stream.

Some companies, like Intel, go well beyond what is needed for turning the PC into a *personal conferencing* product. By value-differentiating the personal computer with new application programs, hardware add-ons and design standards, they hope to make it as useful for communications as it is for data processing. However:

- An information appliance for the superhighway poses problems no data processing job ever faced.
- An information appliance for computer-based conferencing anywhere, at any time, compounds these problems.

We have seen what is behind this reference when we discussed the Shuttle, developed at the NYNEX laboratories. The Shuttle solution permits a network of teleconferencing stations but we should as well keep in mind that computer conferencing *focuses on topics* – not on individuals.

Therefore, computer conferencing has several similarities with mailboxes and tends to merge with them. In the way it has developed over the last ten years, computer conferencing is basically a store and forward operation supporting a group of communication processes. Valid both in the 1980s and in the 1990s, the goal with computer conferencing is participation capabilities:

- leading to fast and accurate conferences
- with efficient information exchange.

But the great difference between the 1980s and the 1990s is that now an *electronic meeting* involves a *virtual reality* setting – creating a virtual space in which the conferencees can meet in realtime.

Until a couple of years ago, the computers and communications-based store and forward facility formed a *virtual conference table* around which the participants could hold their meeting. Each member could also participate in other virtual conference tables, provided that:

- the topics were well defined
- the member could timeshare his or her personal attention.

This is known as *branching* and it enables addressing different interest groups. Joining is the ability of getting on selected virtual conference tables and being updated on the treatment of different subjects.

While all this is still a state-of-the-art reference, technology today permits more than the previous paragraphs have explained. This statement rests on breakthroughs concerning both software and microchips.

Based on these premises, Intel has launched an ambitious strategy, spending some 20 per cent of its research and development money (about $200 million a year), to turn Pentium-based PCs into communicators. The company is also proposing new hardware standards to get better video and multimedia performance out of PCs, including:

- a new bus to speed the flow of data between the microprocessor and other parts of the PC
- upgrading of other hardware and software platforms to handle video and audio more efficiently.

One of the new products, VideoSystem 200, consists of two add-on cards able to handle video, a tiny camera, a headset, and the ProShare software. This entry is in response to recent market projections which indicate that sales of computer-based video-conferencing systems will grow significantly over the coming years.

At the same time other companies (with many start-ups among them) are developing virtual reality solutions which will make computer conferencing even more realistic than the foregoing references indicate. They:

- introduce *virtual meeting places*,
- handle parametrically the *boundary conditions**
- assist through agents the administrative chores and the *Inbox*.

But while software and hardware are crucial, the organizational perspectives are even more important and they involve: purpose, duration, participation, access control, meeting cycle(s), and co-ordination effort. Adaptation to change is vital, and this is true for all new communications disciplines.

6. What Constitutes an Advanced Intelligent Network?

Many of the services which we have studied in the preceding sections will have to be supported through novel and sophisticated solutions which together contribute to an advanced intelligent network. This

* Which is a critical factor in computer conferencing.

means a layered structure where successive levels are built on top of the transport layer, the latter consisting of switching nodes and links for transmission:

- The top layer will concentrate on the creation of new, customized communications services.
- The next layer will contain knowledge artefacts and databases dedicated to implementing specific features.
- Other layers will be concerned with overall network management and will involve expert systems.
- The bottom layer will address the more classical aspects of transmission and switching, but with new technologies.

Figure 2.3 puts this open architectural approach into perspective. The top layer is necessary because the intelligent network of the mid- to late 1990s promises not only a host of significant communications facilities, but also the option to create new ones by the users themselves without the intervention of network operators.

Layered solutions are the best architectural approach in an environment of increasing liberalization of network services, able to specialize, contain costs and decrease the time it takes to develop new services. In addition, layered solutions can provide the platforms necessary for a growing range of income producing products and services.

Practically every expert in the communications field agrees that at the bottom layer advanced intelligent networks will involve both optical fibres, typically with asynchronous transfer mode (ATM) and photonics switches, and satellite communications. The latter will require radio relay centres. The network itself will support:

- multimedia nodes
- database servers
- number crunchers
- workstations
- videophones
- telephones
- facsimile
- high-definition television.

An integral part of these services will be databases. By distributing intelligence in its communicating databases, the intelligent network holds the promise to crack the software bottleneck that has delayed the introduction of new products. Hence, this solution is being heralded as the key that will unlock a new era of telecommunications economics.

Intelligent networks also introduce the concept of software portability to network-service provisioning while at the same time blurring the

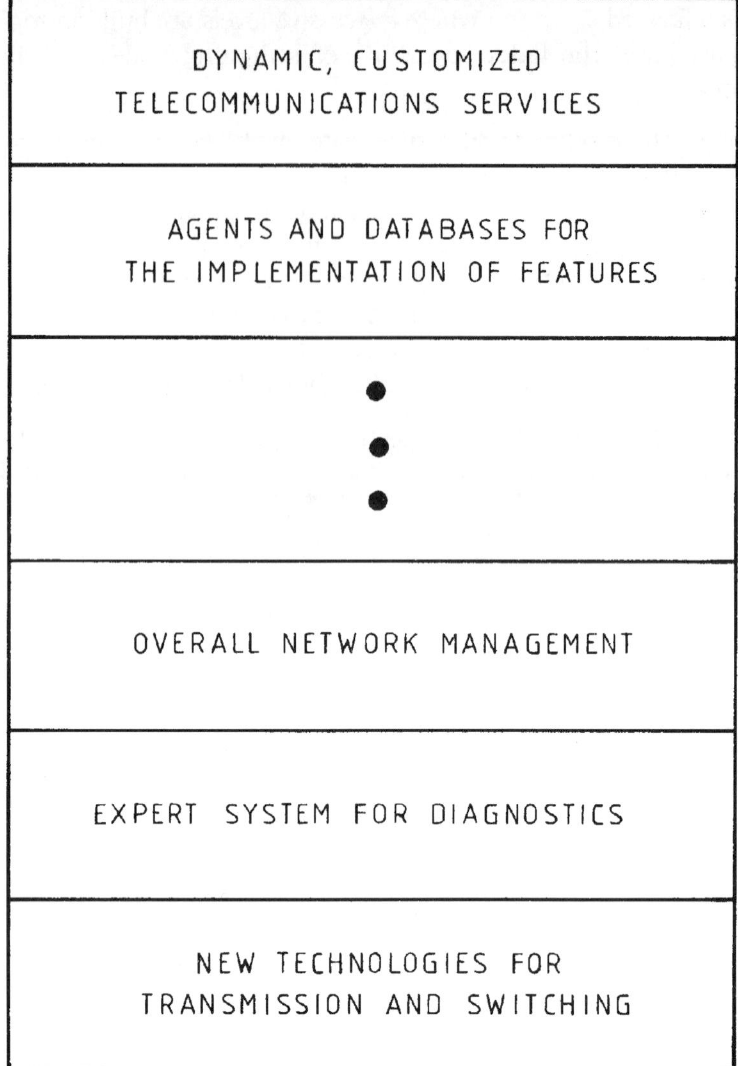

Figure 2.3 Telecommunications solutions are evolving well beyond the traditional switching system

boundary between public and private networks through the provision of virtual communications facilities in a way that is fast, flexible and economical.

With the use of intelligent multiplexers and fibre optics in the local loop, new flexible access systems hold the potential to deliver true customer control at a reasonable cost, and have the added advantage of almost limitless bandwidth available on demand.

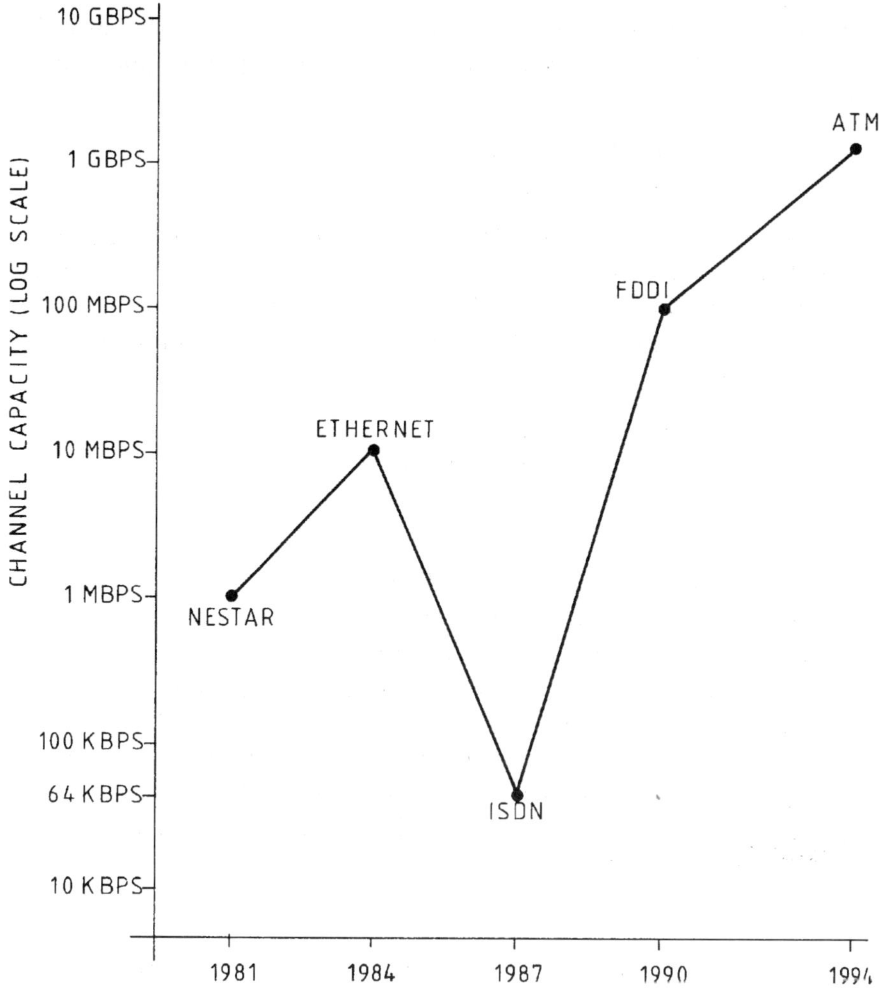

Figure 2.4 The evolution of transmission speeds in less than 15 years

- Intelligent networks will make it possible to switch among public network operators.
- Third-party software houses will create niche communications services for specific customer groups.

An intelligent network service logic should not depend on any single underlying technology. An open architecture should make it possible to decouple the software control of public networks from underlying access and transport technologies.

Wise implementors will use value-added features making it feasible to develop new communications environments. This reference leads into the theme of section 7 on software for intelligent networks, but also impacts on in-house services as those characterizing the functionality expected from:

- the private branch exchange (PBX)
- local area networks.

Classically, the function of a PBX has been to switch telephone voice, facsimile and low-speed computer data. The more recent solutions are using digital technologies, time division switching multiplexing (TDM), 32-bit microprocessors and lots of software. The current PBXs are powerful in terms of:

- transmission speeds
- numbers of lines accommodated
- application services
- media integration functions.

But the main contributor to the flexibility and functionality of a PBX is software. Software provides intelligent switching of a connection-oriented type. By contrast, the transmission characteristics are limited.

Local area networks transmission speeds run from ten to several hundred MBPS. Asynchronous transfer mode now handles 1 GBPS to 2 GBPS transmission speed. By contrast, PBXs usually manages up to 64 KBPS bit streams in the obsolete and inefficient ISDN mode of operations. Figure 2.4 documents how ISDN bends the growth curve of transmission speeds backwards.

7. Developing Software for Intelligent Networks

Companies manufacturing telecommunications equipment suggest that three-quarters of their R&D budgets goes into software. With intelligent networks, telephone companies say that software development accounts for about 60 per cent to 70 per cent of the development cost of their public private communication systems.

The introduction of knowledge-enriched functions and advanced services into networks and terminals, considerably increases the software content of communications solutions. Not only expert systems are necessary for network design implementation, diagnostics and management, but also highly functional user-oriented software which is a vital prerequisite for the communication industry as a whole.

The widespread applicability of knowledge-based technologies in all spheres of communications, requires the investigation of new development methods. The entire life cycle of communications products has to be addressed to enable taking full advantage of new techniques. A holistic approach is necessary to:

- specifications
- design proper
- prototyping
- verification
- installation
- run-time support.

Offering a steadily increasing transmission capacity at declining prices, fibre-optic transmission is forcing a change in the way public telecommunications networks are designed and built. It is a fact that commercial fibre transmission systems have more than tripled public network capacity in the past two years. But it is not less true that this is only part of a huge revolution.

A study which we recently carried out in the banking industry* reflects the major developments which have taken place during the last 30 years – and it is not surprising that all of them are underpinned by networks. Figure 2.5 highlights this transition through to mobile information systems which we discuss in the next chapter.

- Both satellite-based and optically-based connectionless switching schemes are blurring the boundaries between switching and transmission.
- By so doing, they are challenging long-held tenets about network planning as well as operational support, and the type of software needed to sustain it.

The pace at which intelligent networks and flexible access systems are being deployed varies considerably from country to country. But even those operators who lag behind accept that knowledge-enriched software solutions hold interesting implications.

Research and development of smart software is needed to enhance the utility of the visual and data communications facilities of the future integrated broadband network, for the benefit of both business and domestic customers. This is critical in providing an expanded range of services as well as producing economies for both network operators and their customers.

Any valid network design must be effected with a view to enable additional communication services to be created. For example, means for

* D.N. Chorafas and H. Steinmann, *Off-Balance Sheet Financial Instruments* (Probus, Chicago, 1994); and D.N. Chorafas and H. Steinman, *Database Mining* (Lafferty, London and Dublin, 1994).

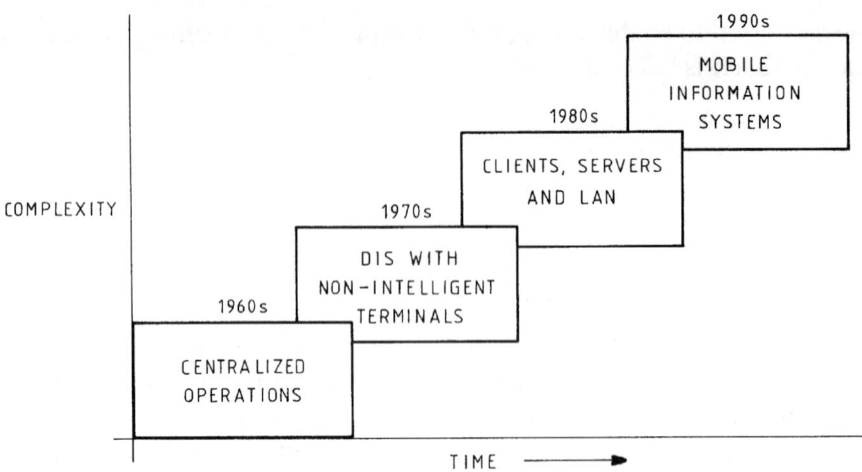

Figure 2.5 The evolution of information technology in banking: with networks at the hub

generating and transmitting economically 3-D representations of still and moving images will:

- ease the work of industrial designers and the medical profession
- provide the basis for new educational entertainment applications.

Both areas require knowledge engineering support and the same is true of day-to-day operations which stand to benefit from knowledge-enriched solutions. Distributed management solutions are another prerequisite.

Because of the deployment of intelligent networks, it will become necessary to delegate functions from the formerly centralized control centre to the nodes. This will help to minimize the amount of control message traffic and associated information processing. It will also enable dynamic allocation of the network resources with:

- realtime resource assignments
- dynamic routing criteria based on learning capabilities
- flow control applied broadly to a set of resources
- dimensioning criteria activated upon threshold triggering.

To realize such functionality it is necessary to study and outline relevant network performance parameters, taking into account the possibility of having polyvalent services. It is also necessary to determine the particular characteristics of each traffic flow and to develop models for performance evaluation.

To support interworking, information must be maintained on the quality of service provided by intercommunicating networks, traffic patterns and availability. Computers and software should handle traffic management functions in realtime – and this is as true of public networks as of the private network we discuss in the following sections.

8. Using the Network to Gain Competitive Advantage: an Example with Edward D. Jones

Founded in 1871, Edward D. Jones is a brokerage house organized as a communications network. Throughout the USA this network interconnects one-man offices serving private clients. The company has nearly 3000 branches and a little over 4000 employees, compared to Merrill Lynch which has a mere 531 branch offices in America.

A firm with 1000 owners, Edward D. Jones does not target the client base of Merrill Lynch and similar brokerage houses. Its focus is the population to whom appeal American Express, Ford Motor and Sears Roebuck, which constitute Edward D. Jones's main competitors for the small investor.

Business expands in the same way cells split. After four months of training, a broker moves to a new town. The broker is not allowed to work in his or her home town, thus avoiding becoming lazy and depending:

- too much on local friends
- too little on new connections

For the first six months of the assignment, the broker cannot open an office. Instead, he or she is expected to drum up interest by cold-calling and knocking on doors. Typically, the broker does not go home until he or she has given out 20 business cards each day.

- Large Edward D. Jones offices are usually staffed by one broker plus an assistant. The smaller offices have just one broker. The 1000-person head office at Maryland Heights, Missouri, provides backup, including a team of financial analysts.

What is particular about this company is that it *first* laid out its business strategy and *then* invested in technology. This is the right way to go, yet few firms take this path – only those able to guarantee competitiveness and return on investment in the huge expenses made in communications, computers and software.

To improve communications, which are crucial in so diffuse a firm, Edward D. Jones has invested in satellite technology. Every branch office has a satellite dish enabling the firm to run live television broadcasts throughout the network of branches. Data communications are also supported by satellite.

Hence, apart from being a first-class example of the precedence which should be given to strategic planning, Edward D. Jones also constitutes a good case study on how to capitalize on the advances in telecommunications – particularly in the multimedia domain. Behind the excellent applications example which we have seen lies rapid change:

- from electromechanical to digital switching and broadband channels
- the entry of new competitors with pioneering solutions to gain business advantage.

Taken together, these two facts are rewriting the rules of the networks game – from the manner in which alert user organizations benefit from communications technology, to the new strategic moves by network providers.

AT&T's long-distance arm expects to lay off thousands as computerized *voice recognition* systems replace droves of human operators. But this is only part of the story. At AT&T, GTE and other carriers, there has been a revolution with automatic diagnostics and maintenance – where expert systems are able to:

- increase quality
- reduce cost at the same time.*

With all these examples of technological breakthroughs, it is quite curious how and why senior people in management still fall for the old data processors rhetoric against new technology and, particularly, against the use of artificial intelligence artefacts.

Forty years ago at the University of California at Los Angeles (UCLA), Dr Louis Sorel used to say in his lectures at the Graduate School of Business: 'Even human stupidity has its limits, and where stupidity ends starts the conflict of interest.' This is the wrongly perceived self-interest of EDPers who are afraid that expert systems will replace them. The fact is that they will not be replaced by expert systems but by colleagues who know how to do a clean job – as the Edward D. Jones case demonstrates.

*See also D.N. Chorafas and H. Steinmann, *Intelligent Networks* (CRC Press, Boca Raton, FL, 1990).

9. Making Critical Network Decisions: from Banking to Engineering

The strategic use of technology has many aspects which show a surprising consistency in a cross-implementation sense. Many people think that the right solution differs in significant ways from one branch of industry to another and from one company to the next. This is nonsense. The truth is that:

- Good design rests on universal principles.
- Bad design is characterized by roughly the same failures.

To prove this point, in this section we will take two examples. The first comes from the banking industry and concerns a networking solution, which could be applied *as is* in engineering. The other comes from engineering file exchange standards, and can be ported with only minor changes to concurrent banking.

For its new telecommunications solution, the now defunct Barings Securities chose to build a global router network as the vital element in a three-pronged strategy to update its operations infrastructure:

- Main sites were to be linked using frame relay technology.
- Smaller sites would have been connected by means of leased circuits or X.25.
- But a separate network for voice communications was projected.

Ironically, the bankruptcy of Barings which resulted from losses of about $1.5 billion from Nikkei index derivatives traded in the Osaka stock exchange, out of the bank's Singapore office, underlines the need for a global network. Facilitated by this network, internal controls must operate:

- at any time
- for any product
- anywhere in the world.

This reference demonstrates that, though necessary, the network itself is not enough. The technological gear is the lesser half of the problem. The bigger half is the necessary organizational infrastructure, since in its absence there is no management control.

Not every financial institution or industrial organization appreciates this issue. Yet, without a realtime organizational system of checks and balances it is impossible to hold the company together: the left hand does not know what the right hand is doing.

As the case of Barings demonstrates, the technological gear more or less made sense, but internal controls were lacking. Typically, new network solutions are seen from a narrow perspective which, however, still has two goals: reliable higher-quality communications links interconnecting all centres of operations, and fully automated trading rooms.

A key element in Barings's decision to update its network was the growing demand for LAN-to-LAN connectivity. Distributed database applications are pressing for far more LAN interconnect than has been the case till now. With the installed base of LANs growing, the company wanted the same facilities between offices as within them.

- As information volumes increase, so does demand for higher speed and greater bandwidth through to the desktop.
- Broadband is helping both to spread and to consolidate activities across sites, and therefore, to improve productivity.

This is a situation faced by every broker, bank, merchandising firm or manufacturing enterprise. The counterpart is that *concurrent* financial work, like concurrent engineering, requires a great deal of normalization in files – bringing into the picture the work currently undertaken by standardization institutes.

- Whether in banking or in engineering, norms for the *exchange of files* have become an absolute necessity. *Concurrent work* cannot be achieved outside an open architecture, with parochial approaches reflecting the whims of the vendors but not the needs of the user organization.

Precisely because normalization is a pressing need, not long ago the International Standards Organization (ISO) released a draft international standard version of the Standard for the Exchange of Product-Model Data. Known as *STEP*, but officially named ISO 10303, this norm has the goal to facilitate computer-readable exchange of information used to describe and define an industrial product.

- Being a normalized method for digital product definition, STEP supports communications among heterogeneous computer environments.
- This makes it easier to integrate systems that perform various product life-cycle functions, such as design, manufacturing, logistics and banking.

Automatic paperless updates of product documentation are just as basic to concurrent engineering as they are to concurrent banking.

Therefore, the question is not whether STEP is necessary, but whether it will really become a unique standard.*

How do STEP and the Electronic Document Interchange (EDI) relate to one another? The unfortunate answer is: Not that much. And to confuse the issue, there is also EDIF.

The 'original' idea behind the Electronic Design Interchange Format (EDIF) of the Electronic Industries Association, was to facilitate exchange of information to silicon vendors under contract to fabricate application-specific integrated circuit (IC) chips. But there is as well the VHSIC Hardware Description Language (VHDL), owned by IEEE, which enables:

- capture of top-down design information
- simulation of digital electronic circuits independently of physical realizations.

Furthermore, there exists the IGES/PDES Organization which presently directs the Initial Graphics Exchange Specification (IGES) effort. Ten years after its introduction in the mid-1980s, this norm has still to establish itself. In the meantime, the 'standards' business has become critical to network decisions. 'My standard is better than yours' is quite common in these days.

10. The Challenging Issue of Wide Area Network Servers

One of the key factors why from engineering to banking applications it is so important to solve the problem of file normalization, is to be found in the challenges which are involved with network servers – from local area to wide area. Indeed, an interesting case in modern network design is that of *wide area network servers* covering a variety of media including sound, image and document transfer.

Part and parcel of the new equation is user control mechanisms that are easy to employ and at the same time provide high-level performance at an affordable cost. Issues to be addressed include:

- Bandwidth requirement within the range 2 MBPS (as minimum acceptable) to 2 GBPS for high-quality uncompressed digital streams.
- Distributed file servers providing the ability to participate in concurrent applications, including documentation and teleconferencing.

*In engineering for example there exist today a variety of other 'standards', including EDIF, VHDL, PHIGS and IGES. See also D.N. Chorafas and S. Legg, *The Engineering Database* (London, Butterworths, 1988).

- Interactive application access methods, taking into account security and other issues, as discussed in Chapter 1.

One of the challenging tasks under today's technology is to address the identification of network servers and their contents across the entire spectrum of applications. This issue must be dealt with at a sufficiently high level of quality and associated control procedures.

To underline the importance of *multimedia servers*, also known as video servers, in 1994 Bell Atlantic announced that it would spend millions for three new supercomputers plus software to build a first leg of the information superhighway. Two companies were awarded the $25 million contract: nCube and Oracle Systems. This award is pace-setting because it opens a new market: giant servers to feed compound electronic documents, complex business information, digitized movies, home shopping, and other interactive multimedia services to companies and homes across America.

Some of the best brains are being put to work to design new software for specialized multimedia servers which can respond in an able manner to the coming interactive-TV and other markets. The business of equipping cable and telephone networks with innovative network servers will start slowly but will grow.

- Industry specialists have set the first target over the next few years at the level of a $3 billion market.
- This is big and small at the same time. It is just 1 per cent of today's world-wide computer market – but is only the tip of an iceberg.

Which market will be first to offer the largest rewards: business or domestic? This is a query to which nobody can at this time give a precise answer. In a technical sense, the answer seems to matter little since the problems to be faced in the two markets are practically the same.

Designing and installing network servers for films on demand could help develop other markets such as video-based business information services. Those companies are expected to perform best that have a lot of multimedia, or joint service and networking experience. Such experience puts them in a good position for the coming market, which will flourish in the beginning of the twenty-first century.

In their initial phase, video servers could prove difficult to develop. In digital form, a feature film takes one billion bytes (GB) of computer storage. Just 400 tapes in any video store would, if digitized, exceed the 400 gigabytes featured by the larger airline reservation systems. But, unlike airline reservation transactions, video data streams can tolerate no more than subsecond delays in transmission. That is why only massively parallel computers will do the job in a neat manner – and it has to be performed at low cost.

Judging from what is being currently projected, advanced communications facilities will include from multimedia mail to complex compound electronic documents. Solutions will be hard to come by, and even the mixture of realtime voice and video communications with non-realtime requirements – such as still image and graphics – represents a significant challenge.

3

Internet and the Opportunity to Revolutionize Tariff Structures

1. Introduction

There are many forces that gradually and inexorably improve business performance, but also augment the risks from staying behind. One of the most important is the wide impact of telecommunications, tying together all operations into a single, interconnected and integrated virtual network.

But telecommunications solutions are not just a matter of putting together the lines and the nodes. Few people appreciate that for new departures we need new systems concepts and new standards. Otherwise, we cannot take advantage of the technological revolution and benefit from its fruits.

By and large adopting new systems concepts means turning computers and communications upside down – and doing so in an almost permanent manner because today's model of relationships between a network and computer services does not necessarily work tomorrow:

- The roles of computers and communications will be reversed in the next ten years.
- Instead of ever faster computers connected by relatively slow copper wires, we will have *very high capacity* fibre networks linking what will seem to be slow computers.

Because of this radical change, much of the skill which exists today will be obsolete in the new environment. Nearly all the experience and wisdom we have accumulated has been received during a time when computers went faster than communications. But, as we have discussed in Chapter 2, this relationship has already changed and by the end of this decade communications will work much faster than computers.

Furthermore, for the new generation of communications-intensive services to perform in an efficient manner, the price structure of the network providing them has to be right. Today's tariff model is wrong, because it makes false assumptions which are a mockery of competitiveness. Based on these notions, this chapter has two objectives:

- To examine whether there is or can be a global network standard.
- To review the tariff structure which will be wise to associate to this standard or standards.

A global standard for telecommunications and networking cannot be established in a theoretical way. It is always necessary to start from somewhere, with references made in a factual and documented manner. Therefore, for a frame of reference we have chosen Internet. The reasons are explained in sections 2 to 6.

Internet is currently the fastest-growing communication link, considered by many as being both the information highway governments are looking for, and a people's network. This is a statement with which it is rather easy to agree. However, it is more difficult to reach a consensus on how many people are networked on Internet at the present time.

2. A People's Network Called Internet

If the Internet was a publicly quoted company, its stock might be considered a market superstar, with sustained double-digit growth and no apparent end in sight to the upward spiral. Over 70 countries have full transmission control protocol/Internet protocol (TCP/IP) connectivity; some 22 others have at least email services through IP, or some more limited forms of connectivity.

A new, more agile as well as more secure protocol – IP version 6 (IPv6) – is in the offing. It had been originally known as IPNG (for New Generation) and its lead designer is Stephen E. Deering.

Practically every one of Internet subscribers is using electronic mail. News is regularly gathered and circulated on this first incarnation of a global information superhighway. But how numerous are the subscribers? And where will the next big expansion be located? This is where opinions widely diverge.

Some say that, as of January 1996 there were as many as 30 million subscribers in 92 countries. Others advance the number of 35 million or even 40 million. This opinion, however, is far from being universal. A number of cognizant people in telecommunications considered it to be hype, made up of wishful thinking rather than documented facts.

The opposite view is that the notion of tens of millions of consumers jumping on-line is grossly exaggerated. The number of *active* Internet users is less than 5 million.* This estimate rests on the fact that a little

* *Communications Week International*, 4 September 1995.

more than 4 million of an estimated 10 million clients with on-line access to Internet are using browsers to search the World Wide Web.* This is an ominous statistic for Netscape, UUNet and other browser vendors.

PaineWebber, the Wall Street investment bank, calculated that to sustain its $157 share price (at the end of 1995) Netscape would have to have an income of $2 billion by 1997. In fact, Netscape's price has sharply dropped since then to $50.

- Our prognosis is that the market for Internet software is much larger than Internet itself.
- The larger market is the *Intranets*, or Internet clones used as private networks – a modern Management Information System (MIS).

There are still other estimates of Internet users which do not necessarily agree with what has been said so far. In November 1995, the Communications of the ACM** reported that, according to a new poll, Internet's population has been down-scaled from its last estimate of 30 million. The new estimate is that:

- 5.8 million American adults are directly connected to Internet
- another 3.9 million use only commercial on-line services.

This estimate, too, some experts say is too high. But there is some truth in the statistic that there has been a 100 per cent growth of connectivity in the 1993–95 time frame. Subscriptions started to mushroom as interfaces to the network became a popular off-the-shelf commodity.

Another interesting statistic is file accesses and navigation traffic on Internet, which is said to have increased by approximately 7.6 terabytes per month in the last year. Such a guestimate looks a little too high, but it reflects the Internet community's diversity, which ranges from non-technical users, who concentrate on email and participate in news groups, to software developers and other companies employing the network for business reasons.

Because of the large population of consumers directly connected to on-line services or, in many cases, indirectly through America Online, CompuServe and Prodigy, Internet is today the people's network. As we will see in section 3, at its origin has been a project by the US Department of Defense (DoD), which, a number of years down the line, was turned over into the hands of the National Science Foundation (NSF).

With this, Internet became a university network. It provided an open architecture and, to a very substantial degree constituted the first incarnation of the information superhighway. This experience was

* See section 5.

** Volume 38, Number 11.

far-reaching because, among other positive fallouts, it constituted the first testbed of the new principle: 'The Network is the Computer'.

3. From Arpanet to Internet

People networked to Internet are to be found everywhere in industry as well as among consumers. It all began with some far-reaching decisions in the late 1960s, when the Department of Defense asked information scientists to find the best way for an unlimited number of computers to communicate – without relying on any single machine to be 'traffic cop'. A centrally managed network, defence strategists reasoned, would be too vulnerable to nuclear attack. A peer-to-peer architecture appeared the best way to increase significantly network reliability, which is crucial to a communications system.

Betting on the then new protocol for packet-switching, in 1969 the Pentagon funded the Advanced Research Project Agency Network, or Arpanet. Arpanet has been a trendsetter in the telecommunications industry. At a time when practically all networks were hierarchical, it introduced the peer-to-peer design and implementation principle.

The passage of Internet from military duty to NSF, and therefore to a university environment, is the second major milestone. Initially, it linked just four research laboratories but – as we briefly saw in section 2 – it expanded to dozens of universities and corporations, and added many refinements.

Renamed into *Internet* and practically decommissioned from military chores, the network expanded world-wide. Today Internet is struggling to contain the hazards associated with its rampant growth and put some order on assigned addresses which have mushroomed.

The explosion in assigned addresses is shown in Figure 3.1. The user community – a loose co-operative of research institutes, universities, commercial enterprises and other end-users – is currently drafting a new charter. Strategies followed to accommodate continued growth include the establishment of:

- new routing protocols and an expanded addressing scheme which will characterize global and national exchanges – starting with the US Internet
- one or more Internet exchanges necessary to handle world-wide routing – which involve governments and will be perhaps jointly owned with an international oversight group.

As a co-operative effort, Internet is overseen by the Internet Society (ISOC). This however does not mean that there is a central governing

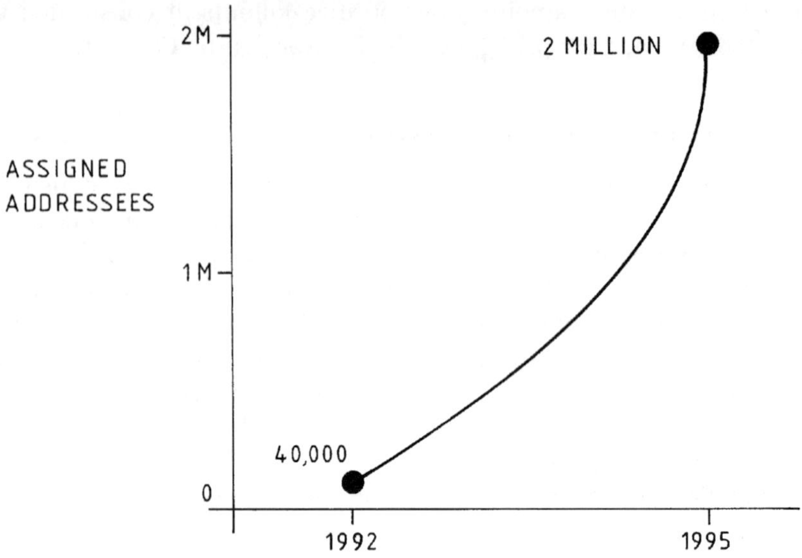

Figure 3.1 Internet's exponential worldwide growth

body. ISOC serves as an umbrella for developing new technologies, standards and applications for the global network.

In terms of routing protocols and other services, new standards are necessary, and they have to be dynamic because Internet is growing in complexity. Based on the transmission control protocol/Internet protocol as a *de facto* standard for linking computers and other devices, Internet gradually has to accommodate:

- other Open Systems Interconnection protocols,
- variable bandwidths on communications links,
- dynamically switched services,
- a whole new community of commercial users.

TCP/IP addresses the Transport Layer (fourth level) of the International Standards Organization/Open Systems Interconnection (ISO/OSI) reference model. But ISO/OSI itself is evolving as the Asynchronous Transfer Mode (ATM) collapses its second and third layers, respectively data link and networking, into one.

Since its original version IP has allowed any number of computer networks to link up and act as if they were one. It works just like the global mail system, in which dozens of independent authorities collaborate in moving and delivering one another's messages.

The IP gets the packets from sender to receiver. TCP manages the data flow. But the original Internet Protocol, or for that matter any other protocol, is no longer best fit to answer present-day requirements. Like people, products, processes, factories and companies, protocols die – hence the advent of IP version 6.

The strength of TCP/IP comes from the fact that over 20 years of growing usage it has proved to be a flexible and adaptable protocol. Therefore, it has been resisted by some mainframe vendors – but it has survived because it has been supported by the Defense Department.

In the 1974 to 1978 time frame, four successively refined versions of TCP/IP were implemented and tested by ARPA research contractors in academe and industry, with the fourth version being standardized. The protocol was used initially to connect:

- Arpanet, based on 50 KBPS terrestrial lines
- Packet Radio Net (dual rate 400/100 KBPS spread spectrum radios)
- Packet Satellite Net (SATNET) based on a 64 KBPS shared channel on Itelsat IV.

Today, there are millions of computers and tens of thousands of networks using TCP/IP, and it is from their interconnections that the modern, global Internet structure has emerged. This is an important reference because it identifies a solid user community which will not go away.

As we saw in section 2, designers are currently working on the next generation of Internet protocols, the IPv6. This is projected to run well on high performance networks, such as the ATM type, while meeting requirements posed by wireless and other low-bandwidth communications links:

- IPv6 is able to handle multimedia
- it addresses security, though the extent to which this happens has not yet been proven.

As the world's largest Internet backbone, the US National Science Foundation network handles much of the global routing and transit. For international interconnections, the Co-ordinating Committee for Intercontinental Research Networks has taken the initiative of concentrating international routing through one or more global Internet exchanges.

These exchanges are described as managed facilities housing a high-speed local area network. Technically, they are based on the fibre distributed data interface (FDDI) to which participants could attach routers and connect circuits. Performing a role similar to that of a telephone switching centre, the mission of the global exchange is to help in:

- establishing routine schemes
- maximizing connectivity
- enabling the sharing of available resources such as leased circuits.

Among the assets on which this effort capitalizes is the fact that, over the years, Arpanet users built an array of fairly sophisticated programs to help people exchange email, tap into remote databases, run wide area networks of computers and communicate over bulletin boards. All this already-acquired experience can be instrumental in promoting a process of globalization.

4. International Competition for New Communications Systems

With the globalization of the world's markets, there is international competition on practically every major product and service. Telecommunications is no exception to this rule. After a given solution takes a leading position, its hold on the market is not eroded easily – though eventually it might be. This reference includes standards, systems approaches, protocols and whole networks.

- Currently Internet comprises thousands of different networks around the world.
- Some networks cover entire geographic regions, while others connect only a single company or college campus.

Connected through Internet, computers work so well together that a researcher in England can browse the files of an information provider in New York or in Tokyo. He or she can practically do so as easily as a local user can. Until now, remote users have seen only a few seconds' delay as their messages move to and fro across a series of intermediary nodes and networks.

- By agreement, all of Internet's subnetworks handle each other's traffic at no charge to the others.*
- Users pay a flat fee, based on the length of time they are connected to a local subnetwork and the potential bandwidth of that connection.

Internet's unique technology and pricing assure that the network will be around, in one form or another, for many years to come. Its success, however, is not guaranteed in every area – one of the reasons being the different monopolistic regulations prevailing country by country, and by major region.

In the European Union, for example, the new backbone would be built by the Co-operation for OSI Networking in Europe (COSINE), along the principles and protocols of Open Systems Interconnection. The back-

* We will return to this issue when, in section 10, we discuss postal tariffs.

ground of this choice is not technology but politics. Several countries, notably France, Germany and the UK, have already invested substantially in academic networks based on X.25, and the European Commission has adopted a 'Buy OSI' policy.*

- The irony is that many national networks, research facilities and even Europe-wide communications structures have already been using the non-OSI TCP/IP.
- Therefore, even the EU directive had to accept both X.25 and TCP/IP; hence a multiprotocol network architecture.
- Besides that, the 'Buy OSI' policy will fall flat on its face as ATM comes along and displaces X.25 links.

Another key difference among countries is in carrier capacity. American researchers are planning their route from 45 MBPS to gigabits per second. But Europe's research networks have been projecting a 2 MBPS backbone – which is definitely substandard. They cannot be any more ambitious because, outside a few countries, higher speeds are not available or affordable.

- These are obstacles to state-of-the-art European networking that are beyond the realm of academics, scientists and some of the government officials.
- The power lies with the monopolistic carriers; they have resisted change so strongly that a leased line in Europe can cost five to ten times what it does in the USA.

It is self-evident that communications monopolies are inefficient. Their whole reason of being is to charge to others – companies and consumers alike – the high cost of their inability to manage their resources. One way the telco monopolies survive is through state patronage. One of the worst barriers they raise is their use of parochial protocols.

By contrast to the inefficient solutions discussed above, Internet features an *open architecture*, which was and continues being a key factor in guaranteeing its success. One of TCP/IP's most significant features is that it is not tied to any single computer or communications technology; or for that matter to the oligopolistic interests of major hardware manufacturers and vendors.

Internet traffic can move over almost any physical channel – telephone lines, high-speed fibre-optic trunks, cable-TV, satellite links, wireless telephone – taking advantage of every advance in microprocessor technology. Its shortcoming is the lack of security features in a network-wide sense which, however, up to a point could be taken care of at local

* Japan has taken the same unwise step.

nodes while capitalizing on a growing software endowment.

Internet has shown what can be achieved through an open architecture. Parochial solutions are not only retrograde but also damage the economy they are supposed to serve. Hanging on to past investments increases the costs of new investments – and reduces the quality of the services they are thought to promote.

5. Private Access Providers, Smart Software and the World Wide Web

Not everything connected to the Internet is running smoothly. There is still a number of issues which need to be stretched out, both in a technical sense and from a users' viewpoint. For instance, the network is not transparent. Nobody knows which part is owned by whom. Neither does anybody have a complete log of all information providers.

- On the assets side, while Internet is chaotic it is self-organised.
- In terms of liabilities, because of the unregulated volume of traffic it can simply reach meltdown.

This has not happened yet. There are, however, increasing delays in network traffic – and most particularly in connection to responses from databases. This is partly due to the fact that Internet nodes reflect the original design of the 1970s, where the same engine did the front-ending – therefore switching – and the data processing chores.

There are also problems connected to database updates, because nobody really supervises their accuracy. For instance, answers given to recent queries to the MIME reference dated back to September 1992, and the MPEG reference to January 1992 – while significant work has been done in the meantime.

These challenges are of an organizational nature. It is not enough that access companies provide services ranging from dial-up, text-based access to leased lines, point-to-point protocol (PPP), and serial line internet protocol (SLIP). PPP and SLIP take advantage of graphical Internet interfaces, and this is fine. But the keyword of business is confidence, and users must have confidence in database contents.

Other major technical queries which wait for a consistent answer include what happens if there is a major bottleneck? a partial or total breakdown? Somebody should provide an additional link – but who will be that somebody? and how fast will they act? Given that there is no central supervision and no network control centre(s) for Internet, will somebody know what happens, when it happens? Where and how should this party be located? How fast will it be able to respond? How dependable will be the solution it might provide?

Answers to these queries are important because of virtual company services offered on a global basis through Internet. Virtual companies and virtual offices are competitive ideas whose time is coming,* but for their success they depend so much on communications that they simply cannot afford uncertainties in networking.

In fact, Internet already features virtual company services, and some of them have so far been quite successful. Such services serve electronic commerce and some include 24-hour delivery – for instance by FedEx, DHL and other companies. But how will payments be made?

There are security problems, as we will see in section 8. Because of them, the payment system is not on-line, and this handicaps commercial operations. Security may not have a great impact on the California Yellow Pages, for example, but it does hold back activities on the Internet Shopping Network and similar ventures.

All this is a pity because the World Wide Web (WWW), the smart software which provides an efficient infrastructure for Internet's user community, has helped to produce a tightly-knit user interaction. Developed at the European Centre of Particle Physics (CERN) in 1992, by Tim Bernes-Lee:

- the Web is a wide-area hypermedia distribution system
- its pages benefit from hypertext links and can incorporate multimedia, including moving video.

The WWW is so successful because it is easy to use and it serves the goal many organizations have been seeking over the past several years: seamless on-line access. To a significant extent, the appeal of the World Wide Web lies in the fact that it is a collection of protocols enabling:

- communication across the Internet
- access to information by means of hypertext.

Multimedia information is linked and accessed by clicking on highlighted keywords with a computer mouse. The Web makes feasible direct access to many different files located throughout distributed databases that are linked to each other. What makes this approach powerful is that such files are accessed through one source and can contain text, graphics, sound, even animation, which traditionally had to be accessed via specialized software and complex commands.

One way of looking at this facility is to think of the browser** as a type of a TV set with, at the other end, the broadcasting station. The intelligent TV set is the client and the broadcasting station the server

* See D.N. Chorafas and H. Steinmann, *Virtual Reality – Practical Applications in Business and Industry* (Prentice-Hall, Englewood Cliffs, 1995).

** Be it Mosaic, Netscape Navigator, Microsoft Explorer, MacWeb, HotJava, Spyglass or another.

which lets people with TV terminals view their programmes. Thus, the individual with a Web page is broadcasting his or her page to anyone who wants to view it.

This reference to 'an intelligent TV set' is just a paradigm, and it should not be interpreted as espousing the idea of the so-called 'network appliance' which, in our judgement, is simply unrealistic. In the future, personal computers and workstations on-line to Internet will need more computing power, not less, and new applications like the popular programming language Java and its translator* act like cycle sponges.

In this discussion of new applications which come on-line to the service of Internet users, reference should be made to the Virtual Reality Modeling Language (VRML)** designed by Marc Pesce and Gavin Bell. This is the most promising of a variety of 3-dimensional modelling solutions, allowing Web users to navigate and interact with many realistic-looking places and spaces. Smart software can do a great deal in promoting the use of Internet.

6. Taking Advantage of the Polyvalence of Internet Services

One of the pieces of smart software available on Internet is the Archie service. This is a collection of discovery tools permitting users to locate information on the network. For its part, the wide-area information servers (WAIS) is a bundle of commercial software programs which also aim to assist users to look for information available in databases.

Veronica is an acronym for 'Very Easy Rodent-Oriented Net-wide Index to Computerized Archives'. Created at the University of Nevada, this tool searches throughout Internet for information by means of keywords. It can also find relevant files. Similar to Veronica, Jughead specializes on searches in a select group of sites.

There are literally hundreds of electronic subscriptions and other information providers on the Internet that can be found both for free and at a reasonable cost. An example is Dow Jones News/Retrieval, which provides fee-based access to the *Wall Street Journal* and the company's public database.

Newspapers are joining Internet as information providers. In January 1996, *The Sunday Times* launched its first Internet edition. This meant that the newspaper became globally on-line and can be accessed within minutes by anyone, anywhere in the world, through a personal computer and an Internet connection.

* Designed respectively by James Gosling and Arthur van Hoff of Sun Microsystems.

** See also D.N. Chorafas, *Visual Programming Technology* (McGraw-Hill, New York, 1997).

At about the same time, the *New York Times* announced a similar strategy with an Internet edition. This, too, is a databased comprehensive coverage of news to which subscribers will have direct access. Interactive newspapers open new horizons in end-user services. The same is true of interactive shopping.

The Internet Mall is a collection of shops each providing products or services for sale. There are also Gopher sites dealing with electronic versions of many journals. What all these efforts have in common is not only that they are databased but also that they can be accessed in seamless manner through the Web.

A Silicon Valley-based consortium of Internet users is offering services intended to make the world-wide computer network easier to use, more secure and suitable for conducting financial transactions. Based on the World Wide Web, the CommerceNet Consortium operates a server able to support electronic commerce.*

- CommerceNet provides starter kits, Mosaic-based directories, access control, a financial transaction platform, and public key encryption for two-way user authentication.
- Core members of the consortium are Enterprise Integration Technologies, the Bay Area Regional Research Network, Stanford University's Center for Information Technology, and several of Silicon Valley's high-tech companies.

While this not-for-profit consortium first focuses on connecting companies in Silicon Valley, it has the potential to address Internet users worldwide. CommerceNet says that it could link up to one million companies, interconnecting with user-driven electronic commerce projects in different regions.

San Francisco's Whole Earth 'Lectronic Link (WELL) provides an example of a virtual community. It is connected to Internet but protected by a gate that will not open without a password or a credit card. As long as the user community was relatively small, it could be self-policing, but now that the population is large, informal rules of behaviour are not enough. Hence the need for passwords and encryption.

Other astute companies, too, have taken advantage of the growing range of Internet facilities. Computers at Evergreen CyberMart, a consulting firm that has been hired to manage the Internet operations of Sundance (a mail-order firm), now complete the virtual paperwork in a matter of seconds. They check credit card limits prior to a sale and control Sundance's inventory database to make sure all items are in stock.

Networked procedures can cross-sell related items, remind a customer

* But as we will see in section 8, there have been security breaches.

of a past-due balance, or send other messages. When the transaction is complete, Evergreen's computer automatically updates Sundance's inventory, accounting and shipping subsystems. All this is done at sharply reduced cost when compared with facilities formerly provided by the local telephone company. Traditionally, it has cost mail-order firms from $10 to $15 to process a telephone or mail order. Over Internet, that cost falls to $4, representing, on average, a 65 per cent cost reduction.*

7. Expanding Business Perspectives

One of the most significant factors for the expansion of networked services lies in the fact that companies can use Internet as a public information highway, rather than creating their own expensive network. While the service is not cost-free, a company using Internet instead of creating a private network solution tends to reduce communications costs by 25 per cent to 70 per cent, according to some estimates.

Commercial use is further promoted by the fact that very little of the current Internet is owned by, operated by or even controlled by government bodies. Today, most of the funding for Internet comes directly from private sources, even if the educational community in the USA receives most of its research funding from the National Science Foundation and other governmental agencies.

- Value-added services provide Internet users with the ability to access directories, referral material, multimedia catalogues and product demonstrations – or solicit bids and place orders.
- Regardless of use, the provision of Internet communication services is increasingly being handled by commercial firms on a profit-making basis.

Currently available solutions make feasible collaboration on engineering and manufacturing projects through to scheduling production and transportation. Internet-provided services are also said to have been instrumental in flushing out Pentium's fault.

The whole affair of the fault located in some Internet chips proves that there are no black-and-white issues in terms of reliability, no matter how technical the subject may be. However, cognizant people believe that an interesting subject has been the fact that much of the fault-identification event played out on Internet.

According to some reports, discussions regarding Pentium's fault,

* *Business Week*, 14 November 1994.

including participation from Intel's CEO Andrew Grove, helped accelerate both the publicity of the flaw and Intel's final decision to replace all affected chips.* As the test bed for computer-based communications, Internet has indeed become a force that cannot be ignored.

The network is used also for legal purposes. Hale & Dorr, a Boston-based law firm, is using Internet to speed up operations and cut the costs of some routine work. If one of its clients needs a contract for, say, a foreign distributor, the client can fill out an electronic questionnaire and send it over Internet to a Hale & Dorr computer. An expert system then constructs a draft document from boilerplate text. A lawyer reviews the document, makes necessary changes, and ships it back over Internet to the client. This time around, the legal document is complete with a list of recommended lawyers in the other country.

The above example is one of many which help demonstrate that Internet provides competitive technology that is critical to delivering services to clients, thereby acquiring an edge. With over 30 million people reachable by electronic mail, the commercial domain of Internet's implementation now:

- makes up more than 50 per cent of the connected base
- represents the largest rate of growth for the years to come.

As cannot be repeated too often, crucial to Internet's success is its open architecture and widely accepted TCP/IP protocol which ensures that heterogeneous computers and networks using multiple technologies can intercommunicate. Equally impressive is the change taking place in public perception. The risks lie in security.

8. The Security Problems Will Not Go Away that Easily

Network security is not just an Internet problem; it is a world-wide problem confronting any and every network, even private ones. A Japanese government report recently raised security questions about personal computer networks, and also brought a new perspective to this subject.

According to the Posts and Telecommunications Ministry, computers give off electromagnetic waves that can be intercepted by industrial and military spies. Unlike mobile telephones that use security coding, PC networks don't have a common safeguard for emanations from electronic circuits, which creates severe security problems as the use of PC networks rapidly expands.**

Network-related crime is not new. What is new is that as more

* *Computer-Aided Engineering*, 4 February 1995.

** *Communications of the ACM*, January 1995, Vol. 38, No. 1.

businesses and private individuals discover the Internet, the opportunities for hackers multiply. Based at Carnegie Mellon University, the Computer Emergency Response Team reported 2241 Internet security breaches in 1994, twice as many as in 1993.*

Private networks in the financial industry and big industrial companies, use techniques to assure that the sender of a message is who it claims to be. An example is one-time passwords that cannot be reused. However, this is the responsibility of senders and receivers – not necessarily of the public network.

Hackers have a field day with public networks and Internet is no exception. Kevin D. Mitnick, who was arrested by FBI agents in February 1995, had in his record a string of network break-ins that included the pilfering of thousands of credit-card numbers from an Internet database. He frequently used the WELL, a San Francisco-based on-line service linked to Internet, as his hunting domain.

Before he was caught, Mitnick had cracked an account on the WELL, which became his downfall because the account owner – a researcher at San Diego's supercomputer centre – hunted him down. Credit-card numbers and subscribers' personal data were stored unprotected on a main server, but if this hacker did not tamper with this personal data, somebody else might.

To protect public networks from this kind of risk, experts suggest *firewalls*. The term stands for secured gateways that erect a wall between private networks and Internet. This is a way of keeping unwanted intruders out – but it does not offer 100 per cent assurance. There are no 100 per cent foolproof and fullproof secure solutions.

Firewalls consist of one or more dedicated computers running programs that screen incoming traffic. Theoretically, only trusted systems can gain entry. Practically, this is a partial protection at best, because hackers use *protocol spoofing* to fool otherwise secure computers into thinking that they are authorized users:

- By probing a remote computer, a hacker can glean information about other trusted computers.
- Then, the hacker masquerades as a trusted system to gain access, copy files, and even take control of part of the network.

The countermeasure for spoofing is the use of filters. They can help to assure that a message that appears to come from a trusted system did not actually originate elsewhere. Filters can also block unauthorized outgoing messages. But nobody said that filters are fullproof. If a hacker

* *Business Week*, 13 March 1995.

manages to seize control of a network or its computers he or she can move on to other computers and other networks. Besides this, filters do very little to defend privacy of information when a message leaves a computer to move across Internet.

The answer to that kind of challenge is *encryption*, scrambling messages such as electronic mail, credit-card numbers, money transfers or other sensitive information so they cannot be read by hackers. The most popular type of encryption is public keys, which use software to scramble and unscramble messages.

- The military and the foremost financial institutions have a policy to scramble everything that travels on their networks.
- But with public networks such as Internet, most information moving across is unencrypted and therefore vulnerable.

An often-used trick of hackers is to secretly install on networks programs known as *packet sniffers*. These record the contents of packets of information as they cross the network. Packets may include passwords and user names, which can then be employed to gain entry to a computer, send out messages regarding unauthorized fund transfers or do other illegitimate acts.

Internet is not yet a secure information superhighway. In terms of protection of its data streams it is rather like a trail in the Wild West. All public networks will have that feature till something consistent is done about security. Short of this, somebody suggested, they will be 'like a bad neighbourhood where a lot of people are looking for trouble'.

9. Is There a Global Telecommunications Standard?

It was not very long ago that Internet was viewed as a specialized network serving the academic and research communities. But, in the early 1990s, the public began to take notice of the potential ramifications of its communications assets. This helped to make Internet a standard computer network infrastructure – and therefore the first practical implementation of the information superhighway in a world-wide sense. There are two types of standards in technology: one is *de facto*, the other is developed by standards bodies.

De facto standards establish themselves by the weight of their implementation. But this does not exclude standards bodies that present their own, therefore leading to contradicting standards – some *de facto* others *de jure*.

In a meeting held in Tokyo on 14 February 1995, 37 telecommunications and information technology companies from America, Europe, and Asia formed a consortium to develop global standards for telecommunications software. These companies said that their Telecommunications Information Networking Architecture Consortium (TINA-C) 'will enable the efficient introduction and management of telecommunications services on a worldwide basis'.

As an architecture, TINA-C is based on advanced distributed processing and service delivery technologies. It is projected to incorporate several international standards; as well as provide means for testing their effectiveness through experiments and field trials, over a five-year period.

But the task is not necessarily going to be that straightforward. Whether in America, Europe or Japan, regulation regarding telephony services as well as data networks has not kept pace with innovation – and there are conflicting business interests:

- So far, efforts to spur competition have been bogged down by industry and partisan bickering.
- A balkanized system has taken shape, with freewheeling competition in a few countries, and regulatory straitjackets in the majority of cases.

The delay in overhauling telecom regulation is not a simple case of heavy-handed government bureaucracy, but a battle between different species of telecommunications giants. In the USA, for example, both the cable companies and the Baby Bells are giant, regulated monopolies, and AT&T still controls 60 per cent of the long-distance market. For their part, cable-TV operators manage a network that reaches the homes of 59 million Americans.

- Morgan Stanley calculates that telephone services should add 8 per cent to 10 per cent to a cable system's value.
- By offering telephone services Time Warner is expecting an extra $10 per customer each month.

Yet, CATV networks are local, not global. The interest in them lies in their capillarity, their relatively new plant (compared to telcos) and the fact that coaxial wiring can handle broadband immediately. Hence, it will be cheaper for cable companies to add voice than for telephone companies to add video and multimedia.

Top cable-TV operators such as Tele-Communications, Cox Enterprises, and Comcast, have formed an alliance with Sprint to build and operate a nationwide wireless telephone network. The group is the top bidder for licences to operate wireless telephoning in the form of personal communications services (PCS). The aim is to offer one-stop shopping for local calling, long distance, cellular, PCS, and cable. But the fact of betting $1.4 billion that the new technology can fill gaps in a national network, does not make this effort standards setting.

Evidently, each player wants to protect its turf while lobbying to eliminate regulations that prevent it from penetrating its rivals' territory. The Baby Bells say they want simultaneous entry for all players, but long-distance and cable companies want the Bells fenced until there is measurable competition in local telephone service.

Telecommunications standards aside, truly deregulating this massive industry has major implications for the entire economy. As an example, Americans dialled up some $160 billion worth of domestic calls in 1994 and analysts estimate that the figure will pass $200 billion by the year 2000.

An econometric study sponsored by the Baby Bells estimates that competition in local calling will spark so much demand for new services that there will be a net gain of 3.6 million jobs by 2003. Job creation, incidently, has also been the argument advanced by the Group of Ten (the ten most important industrial nations) when, in their February 1995 meeting in Brussels, they decided to finance 12 major projects in connection with the information superhighway.

10. Seeking Greater Competitiveness through Postalized Tariffs

Open markets and technologies such as fibre optics and wireless transmission may create significant demand but they also require big investments. Such investments must be recovered through pricing products and services and by means of deals which now cross every industry line:

- Pacific Telesis, Bell Atlantic, and NYNEX have formed a joint venture with Hollywood's Creative Artists Agency to develop new multimedia programming.
- Ameritech, BellSouth, and SBC have joined up with Walt Disney for the same purpose, targeting both the American and international markets.

This is done in the belief that the merger of entertainment and information networks is the wave of the future – and in the longer term such a future cannot be served only through Internet-type solutions. But these efforts also have immediate business objectives.

Time Warner Cable already supports bypass services in 15 cities and has applied to offer residential service across New York and Ohio. California regulators say they will let cable operators offer telephony as soon as any one telephone company in the state receives approval to offer TV. There is a fuzzy line dividing cable and telephone operators in regard to services – as well as in terms of tariffs.

Telecommunications companies investing large amounts of money in their networks want to see return on investment (ROI). Advanced applications are key to success, as documented by an example from Sprint. In the last two months of 1994, Sprint invited a host of US high-technology companies to develop applications over its 240-kilometre broadband network in California including:

- distance learning
- desktop video-conferencing
- transmission of dense graphics and video images.

Sprint's information superhighway begins at 45 megabits per second (MBPS). The company suggests that its service allows users to access the most up-to-date graphics and related software on-line, in a way eventually exceeding facilities provided by Internet.

Other applications address customers of Drums. This is an international project developed by Sprint and Silicon Graphics, that allows companies at different sites to work on-line to develop software for films and TV commercials. Notice the similarity between this and some of the other applications we have examined so far.

Such projects could succeed if they can fulfil two basic conditions: they have to be long on imagination and innovation – but thrifty on costs. This issue of costs applies through to *tariffs*:

- The old tariff structures are not only obsolete but also counterproductive, because they don't account for technological innovation and cannot exploit market potential.
- New telecommunications technologies ensure that distance is practically immaterial – a fact now reflected in *postalized tariffs*, such as those featured by Internet.

Postalized tariffs are distance-independent tariffs which apply the same charges to calls no matter over what distance they are carried. Such rates are now coming into force in the American long-distance market, revolutionizing the way user organizations look at telecommunications.

In January 1995, Sprint began offering nation-wide long-distance service for 10 cents per minute during off-peak hours, 22 cents during peak hours. Shortly before that, in December 1994, AT&T had received regulatory approval to offer postalized domestic rates of 15 cents per minute during off-peak hours and 26 cents during peak hours. Sprint undercut these prices.

A smaller long-distance carrier, LCI International, that has offered postalized rates since 1991, credits this pricing strategy with helping to double its revenue in three years – to $450 million in 1994. Telecom experts see postal rates as the trend for plain old services with carriers gaining market leadership by means of value differentiation.

Fundamentally, the dissociation of the distance a call is transmitted from the amount a customer is charged can be credited both to competition and to technology.

- In the mid-1980s transmission cost was a very important component of the cost of doing business.
- But as high-capacity fibre networks proliferate, that cost has significantly dropped.

Falling costs and increasing competition define the global telecoms market. Therefore profits are not going to be found in pure connectivity. Apart from value differentiation, the new strategy is to make consumers use the network as much as possible, not to charge them as much as possible – hence, the Sprint project.

But contrary to what happens in deregulated, and therefore competitive telecom markets, in the former PTT environments of Europe and elsewhere, the alliance of the still monopolistic carriers and their vendors attempts to buy privileges employing lobbyists. This complex alliance is sponsoring political rallies against deregulation, engaging in political bribes (such as hospitality) and instituting appeals procedures which may reduce the likelihood of deregulation.

11. Competitive Pricing is the Best Strategy

The examples we have seen in this chapter, from Internet and LCI International, show that competitive pricing is the best strategy. They are also a valid way to approach the issue of value-added services, for which no state-run telecommunication monopoly has a lock on the client base.

Current tariffs impede the flow of information both within the same country and across international boundaries. By being too high, they penalize many new business initiatives and discourage others because of their complexity.

- Large users are better able to evaluate the telecommunications service to employ in connection to a particular application, and they do not appreciate penalizing tariffs.
- Smaller companies do not have the necessary expertise for optimization and find the task of assessing the cost of public data networks daunting.

Granted, tariff principles, like the technology they are being applied to, are evolving – but in protected, monopolistic telecom environments they do not necessarily point in the right direction. For instance, they stiffen or swamp new developments rather than enable exploitation in an able manner of an increasing number of new business opportunities.

New business opportunities arise because telecommunications in all its forms, has become the nervous system of industry, through to the consumers. This will be even more true tomorrow since, in economic terms, the relative size of this sector of the economy is growing – though it is growing at a faster pace in deregulated countries.

A basic reason for this discrepancy in growth rates is tariffs, which in many countries are still crushing because of state monopolies. While the international growth of telecommunications is both an inevitable and a positive development, networks will not benefit every company and every country in the same way:

- Global competition encourages growth by increasing and diversifying the types of services available.
- Those who will gain the least are the telcos exploiting users through the short-sighted approach of high tariffs.

It does not take a genius to understand that high tariffs are uncompetitive. They don't allow user organizations to benefit from productivity gains, and they penalize most of all the telcos who apply them.

A few years ago, Fiat, the Italian automobile manufacturer, made a study of its telecommunications costs including connections, accesses and traffic for transmission of voice, data and images. The hypothesis being tested was: 'What if Fiat was based outside Italy?' The results are shown in Figure 3.2.

It is curious, indeed, that governments don't understand that high tariffs are crushing their native industries. Just as puzzling is the rush to miss the coming business opportunities which have in the background low-cost telecom services. It is now projected that in the coming years new business ventures will feature:

- resellers of simple bandwidths, including user organizations
- providers of managed end-to-end circuits
- operators of international gateways handling traffic from several carriers.

For each of these three classes, current tariffs are meaningless. Take the market for bandwidth resale as an example. The opening of the market for simple bandwidth resale will enable new service providers to:

- lease switching and transmission capacity in bulk, from existing carriers, and
- resell capacity to their own customers for voice, data and multimedia.

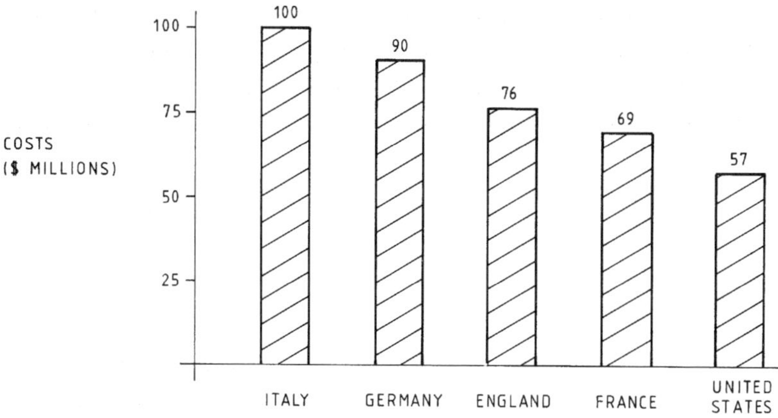

Figure 3.2 Fiat's telecommunications costs if it were to be based outside Italy

With competition steadily on the increase and *channel capacity* booming, experts suggest that there will be a spot market for future bandwidth traded as any other commodity in the exchanges. Options and futures will enter the telecommunications trade.

Also, groups of users will share facilities to increase network efficiency and reduce costs. There will be providers of discount telephone services; aggregators arbitraging capacity between carriers and resellers, or users; and facilities managers with solutions tailored to customer requirements.

At the bottom line, knowledgeable users will have plenty of opportunity in choosing the least expensive transoceanic link from any point to any point in a continent or region – and will do so at very significant cost savings. Cost reduction in transatlantic cables provides an example of forthcoming challenges because of technological advances:

- Each new installation costs half the money of the last one, therefore telcos need to write off the cable in practically one year.

Theoretically this is impossible because competition drives down prices. Practically it can be done by siphoning the most lucrative customers out of the hands of state monopolies or other companies which apply high tariffs.

12. Suffering from the Crushing Weight of High Tariffs

In mid-1993, in the wake of Europe's decision not to fully liberalize its voice telephony markets for another five to ten years, multinational corporations drew up plans to route their intra-European traffic via the USA. Underpinning this strategy are issues of cost control and quality of service confronting all financial, commercial and industrial companies.

Some cognizant people in telecommunications would suggest that a sharp reduction and eventual harmonization of tariffs is an impossible issue. Others consider it impossible only as long as the owner of the different telecom administrations is the state which also controls the postal service:

- Using a Europe-wide 64-KBPS channel, an average letter could be sent for 1/35 of the cost of a stamp.
- A letter of some 8000 characters or 64 kilobits could be sent in one second through such a network.

If privacy and security measures are also provided, this will reduce considerably the normal post operations in business and private mail. In fact, even with an irrational pricing of telecommunications, one-page letters cost less to fax than in stamp duties.

Matters are evidently made worse because of the European Union's failure to deregulate the telcos. Indeed, the news about a delayed liberalization came as a blow to major telecom users who had been pushing for:

- full, immediate deregulation of the voice services with emphasis on low costs and competition
- infrastructural investments – hence, markets – to rectify high tariffs, long delays in circuit provision and poor services.

Among the companies that said they are considering shifting their European telecoms traffic elsewhere were Shell, BASF, Lloyd's of London and American Express Europe. These are, however, only the tip of the iceberg.

It is not surprising that, with European governments set on maintaining existing telecommunications monopolies, business users are looking for ways to circumvent the ossified structures and avoid high tariffs. One of the key mechanisms to do this is by moving the telecom business to a US setting; another is *tariff arbitration*.

As we discuss in section 11, tariff arbitration exploits the intelligence and speed of digital networks to enable users to obtain telephone services from other sources, at much lower cost but without breaking the rules.

- Alternative services based on tariff arbitration represent a direct challenge to the business of European telcos.
- This switch of services will have a much more negative impact on telco revenues than the temporary income reduction from a strategic change.

At the core of looking for lower cost and higher efficiency solutions is the fact that, in Europe, tariffs for long-distance and international calls are likely to remain high in comparison to those in the USA. Since liberalization in telephone services, competition in America has relentlessly driven down costs and prices.

Open-eyed politicians should have expected user organizations to employ every crack in regulations as well as every opportunity. Alternative ways of securing telephone services can offer not only much lower costs, but also some of the facilities that are absent when competition in basic services is not available.

It is not surprising that users will increasingly turn to alternatives like global end-to-end managed virtual services which are now offered by competitive international carriers. The latter are the larger transnational companies which have most weight in communications revenues – and have the skill to examine competitive offering and capitalize on them.

- Financial analysts estimate that the 500 largest companies in Europe spend more than $1 billion a year on intra-European public switched telephone calls.
- This means that for every 1 per cent of traffic concerning these companies, which is shifted out of Europe, $10 million goes along with it.

American Express calculates that telecoms costs in the 12 countries of the European Union are on average four times as high as those in the USA. And American tariffs are falling so rapidly that this difference is sure to increase.

Most importantly, for private industry the existence of low communications tariffs is a matter of sustained competitiveness. If the costs of telecommunications remain the same as they are now, then businesses just can't afford new information technology which is necessary to regenerate the European industry and help it to face increasingly tougher competition. But is anybody listening?

13. Ways and Means for Tariff Arbitration

What governments do not wish to understand is that the longer they put off competition, the worse it is going to be for the victims, namely the fat and inefficient telecom administrations of Europe. The worst that can happen to the protected monopolies is to lose the richer part of their client base which has four principal ways in which to circumvent existing monopolies:

1. *Virtual private networks* (VPN), offered mainly to larger user organizations.
2. *Cellular or wireless bypass* of the national operator, wherever a competitive cellular operator exists.
3. *Country-direct services*, available by major telephone companies to both their nationals and to individuals and businesses in other countries.
4. *Call-back services*, which reverse the direction of a call to enable customers to benefit from lower tariffs.

In the years ahead, virtual private networks will have a large market impact. Transnational companies with subsidiaries around the world are keen to benefit from the various international virtual private network and freephone services, offered on intelligent network platforms. These businesses can already obtain access to VPNs linking to them their PBXs – directly or through a leased line.

Cellular and wireless bypass is also a wise strategy and many large companies are investigating the addition of data services on top of voice. The fact that the structure of telecommunications systems is so rapidly changing alters the interconnection perspectives. It introduces different types of radio links through to low Earth orbiting (LEO) satellites.

Country-direct services began as a scheme for Americans travelling in other countries. They offered access to an English-speaking operator, direct billing to a home or business address, and avoidance of the high local tariffs often charged in hotel rooms or telephone booths. In a few years:

- this type of service enjoyed rapid success
- thousands of companies have been subscribing to it.

With call-back services, the switching centre sets up a three-party connection then switches itself out of this connection. Such a procedure requires that three numbers are transmitted to a call-back computer: the calling party number, the card number and the number of the party to be called.

Currently, call-back is primarily used by private persons and small companies. Larger companies have made little use of this service because of the complication of dialling an additional code, while call-back cannot work via a PBX unless the caller has a direct dial-in number.

Eventually the combination of VPN and call-direct services could prove to be the ultimate nemesis of the bureaucratic and uncompetitive telecommunications administrations and their high tariffs. Virtual private networks:

- obviate the need to dial additional codes
- allow for shorter dialling sequences than those used on ordinary international calls.

Knowledge embedded into VPN removes much of the inconvenience of a call-back-type service. The larger companies are attracted by their features, and the same is true of the heavy users of international networking services.

It therefore comes as no surprise that a number of European telcos such as British Telecom, France Telecom, and Unisource* are actively looking to enter the VNP market. However, American companies already have many years of experience with intelligent network platforms which can effectively promote lower tariffs.

A very interesting communications scenario is developing on which competitive companies can capitalize. What the EDPers, the mainframers, the monolithic telco administrators, and the governments supporting them don't seem to appreciate is that there is no future for those who live in the past.

* Comprising PTT Telecom Netherlands, Swiss PTT and Sweden's Televerkert.

4

The Practical Value of the Information Superhighway

1. Introduction

Projects which are worthwhile, and bring lasting benefits, don't start at random. They typically require a planning and decision cycle which eventually brings commendable results and flourishing implementations.

- Valid projects call for foresight and for funding, as they usually involve complex relationships.
- Their macroengineering perspectives require many contributors, technological breakthroughs and return on investment in the medium to longer term.

Communications technology finds itself today at the crossroads. Research and development expenditures are necessary in telecommunications proper, broadcasting, intelligent switching, optical and radio transmission, as well as agile and friendly human interfaces.

Effective R&D efforts, crucial to future progress, proceed within a longer-term vision. As an example, Figure 4.1 presents the life cycle of a network from planning to maintenance and back to the drawing-board.

- A post-industrial society's economic growth is largely based on the development of applied technology, with telecommunications, computers and software being the mainstays of this effort.
- More than ever before, the new communications solutions transcend geography while at the same time they undergo unparalleled change.

Combined with broadband channels, digital fibre cables, powerful digital signalling techniques and computerized exchanges, huge reductions in international transmission costs enable astute carriers to offer a broadening range of telecommunications services, including plain old

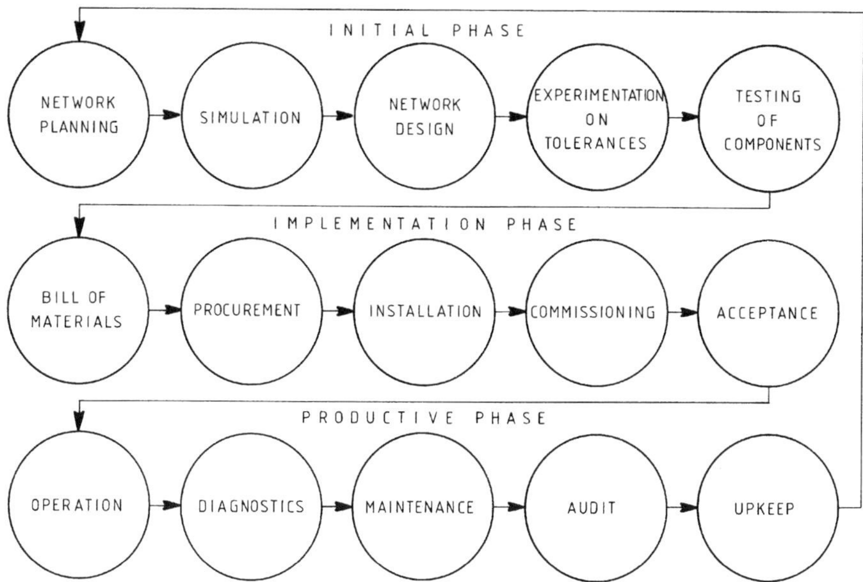

Figure 4.1 A network life cycle: from planning to maintenance

telephony. They do so for much less money than an inefficient carrier would.

Equipped with intelligent, digital customer premises equipment, users are increasingly employing larger bandwidths. The provision of advanced services and their exploitation for profits are interlinked. On this simple principle lies the whole effort behind what is now called the information superhighway.

2. The Changing Nature of Networks

During the 1990s, a great deal of the advances in telecommunications has been due to the boundaries between computers, communications and software becoming blurred. Areas where traditional distinctions no longer hold include:

- switching and transmission
- virtual and permanent circuits
- public and private network equipment
- information technology solutions
- sophisticated, computer-based telephony sets.

For both basic and value-added networks, a new environment has been created by advanced technology which brings its own challenges. Many of these challenges are often underestimated. Only the leaders appreciate their impact.

Opportunities for very competitive solutions as well as pitfalls from taking the wrong path, exist in many issues – some at end-user level, others more specific to telecommunications operators and information providers. As far as communications companies are concerned, major areas in which problems are likely to arise in the years ahead include:

- the planning and control of network resources for effective end-to-end management across multiple boundaries
- technical interconnection of multiple communications structures, including global allocation of network addresses and numbers
- consistent network quality and reliability in the assurance of universal service.

To a significant extent, in the coming years the possibility of managing across boundaries of different networks will determine competitiveness. A local or national telecommunications network can no longer be viewed as a single entity with one operator and one or two types of customers.

- The communications system is becoming stratified with networks within networks.

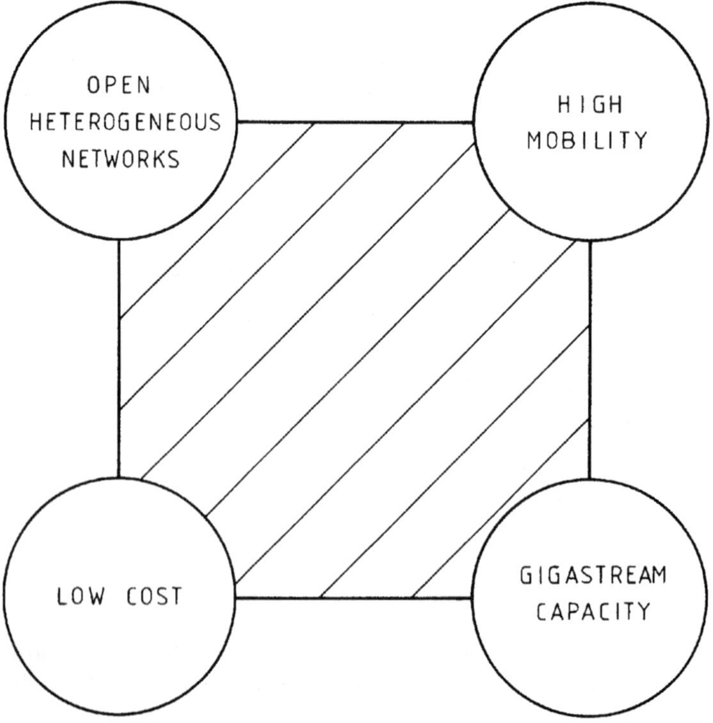

Figure 4.2 Solution space for telecommunications during the next five years

- Both the customers and the services they require will no longer be well-defined, as was the case in the past.

Therefore, planning has to be very flexible. In a world of multiple operators, carriers must plan for the lowest-cost, most efficient structures. They should always be on the look-out for the most modern facilities, and have the technical skills to cope with just about any change in the business environment.

In a coarse manner, Figure 4.2 shows the solution space for telecommunications. Within the broader perspective this figure sets, can be fitted different detailed designs. Ideally, these should be optimized to dynamically respond to business goals of a carrier, its main customers and of the market to which the network as a whole appeals.

Therefore, network planning and design have to be interactive and integrative. The simple, linear projections of customer demand traditionally used in network planning should be replaced by scenario analysis, in which different, even contradictory, outlooks are considered, evaluated and judged in terms of costs and performance.

Short of concurrent strategic business planning and engineering, the problems thrown up by the disappearance of the old concept of a telephone company could destabilize its management with the net result of:

- paralysing major investment efforts due to loss of direction and loss of money
- holding back the implementation of new communications technologies such as broadband and multimedia.

Because the new wave in telecommunications demands heavy up-front investment and long-term planning, those committing themselves to capital expenditures need longer-term market perspectives and some assurance of returns. But at the same time:

- the traditional function of telecommunication companies (or administrations) as guarantors of universal service will be less and less appreciated
- as competition intensifies due to deregulation, the spread of new carriers and third-party operators will jeopardize revenues.

This is the way the industry goes and there is nothing that can be done (or should be done) to reverse such a trend. Reverting back to the old ways will be uncompetitive and unrewarding, will reflect a state of bureaucracy in which progress is downplayed in favour of decay.

3. The Target is Leadership in Cross-Border Operating

According to fairly dependable estimates made by the leaders in the telecommunications domain, cross-border broadband operators capitalizing on optical fibres and satellites – as well as network pluralism – will leave no room for the classical functioning of public networks. But the transition will not be easy, as not only political roadblocks but also long chains of command and control created by heterogeneous networks are likely to lead to major problems.

Until a new definition of telecommunications is effectively established, and a new order in network operators settles, lack of clear responsibility could lead to network breakdowns. This will be partly due to the fact that as networks become more complex, they also become more vulnerable. Sophisticated, knowledge-enriched software is the answer to the vulnerability issue. As a result, not only the definition of targets and the mode of operations but also the type of investments in networks is bound to change.

British Telecom (BT), for instance, now spends the biggest chunk of its research and development money on software for network management. By contrast, just five years ago, most of BT's money went into technology research in areas such as optical fibres and broadband communications. AT&T has made a similar shift and the same is true of the Baby Bells and their joint Bellcore Laboratories, and of Canadian Bell and its Northern Telecom subsidiary.

Telecommunications has become a major software application domain. It is not surprising that, currently, some of the world's most complex software systems support communications. This is most definitely the trend.

Siemens, the main supplier of Deutsche Telekom and a world-wide vendor of communications equipment, was mentioning in a meeting in Munich that 75 per cent of the R&D money for its newest PBX went on software. This does not mean that the budget for R&D in hardware shrank, only that by far the main expense is now software.

Figure 4.3 shows this transition, based on the input received from three different PBX vendors. With ATM technology and multimedia, the trend towards a growing emphasis on sophisticated software is going to increase, and will tend to dwarf hardware R&D. However, as many telecommunications companies start to discover:

- in developing and maintaining communications software, feature interaction proves to be a severe problem
- feature interaction concerns the observable behaviour of a telecommunications system and is therefore an integral part of technical specifications.

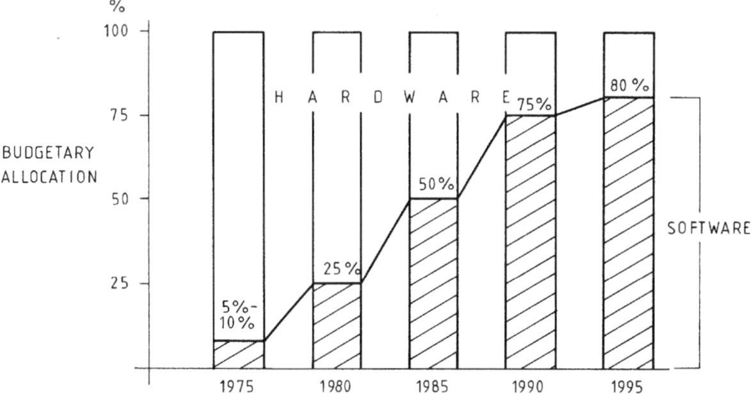

Figure 4.3 Trend in R&D money for communications hardware and software over a 20-year period

Able solutions to feature interaction get that much more complex as we move towards cross-border systems. The different user communities have significantly varying requirements due to business reasons, cultural background, regulatory norms and other factors.

No matter how big or how small this variation may be, the fact remains that to effectively exploit the new technologies we must move away from the concept of communications as a plain old telephone service. The new environment is one of prolonged and continual technological change.

We must think of advanced techniques for formal specification of functionality, executed in a dynamic manner but also benefiting from a suitable amount of foresight. And we must appreciate that there exists a number of complex communications issues that current software techniques cannot handle satisfactorily.

The objective of the change in investment strategies towards a more sophisticated software, is to exploit what high technology has to offer as well as to enable control of end-to-end network resources notwithstanding the:

- diverse requirements of customers
- need to cross many network boundaries – new and old.

This will be in all probability, the most significant challenge to strategists and development engineers over the next few years. A basic requirement is to assure consistent presentation of services to customers in a situation in which end-users will themselves be among those creating the services.

4. Goals of the National Information Infrastructure

The telecommunications world as we understood it over the last 30, 20 and even 10 years, is gone. By the end of this decade it will not be possible to remember which companies were telcos, which were cable operators and which were computers and software outfits:

- Intelligent networks will radically change the landscape the telcos considered to be their rightful property.*
- In the most advanced countries the regulatory divisions between telephony, television and information networks will disappear.

Such a major change will require a radical rewrite of 60-year-old or older communications laws, which is both doable and coming. In the USA, for instance, Congress and the Clinton Administration are hard at work on this project of a totally revamped legislation; pending bills aim to break down outmoded barriers that separate local service from long-distance, telephones from cable TV, and programming owners from delivery systems. But without a grand vision such large sweeps in legislature could also turn out to be unsettling, as they touch many embedded interests. Named National Information Infrastructure (NII), this grand vision constitutes a multimedia broadband strategy. Its characteristics and associated technology policy were launched by the US government in September 1993, as an agenda for action.

In all probability, a nationwide and eventually transnational information superhighway will be a powerful photonics and electronics network capable of delivering vast amounts of multimedia business information to companies, as well as entertainment and business data to homes. It will provide the infrastructure for applications ranging from 24-hour banking to two-way television and remote medical diagnosis.

These polyvalent cross-border solutions will also pose significant requirements in terms of uninterrupted services while the network providing them steadily evolves. This is neither a policy nor a practice classical telcos and their bureaucratic, slow-moving structures know by experience.

The adaptation period will be long and painful. Therefore the best way out is a *metamorphosis*. But are the managements of the different telephone companies, which for over a century operated as regulated monopolies, up to the task?

In principle, the private sector will build the NII, with the government acting as a catalyst through legislation and seed money. However, the

* See also the forecasts made in D.N. Chorafas and H. Steinmann, *Intelligent Networks* (CRC Press, Boca Raton, FL, 1990).

details of how this will happen are still rather obscure. The leading thought among the main competitors is that the government should do everything possible and:

- provide the seed money but stay far away from making any decisions on NII
- avoid any involvement with respect to the implementation of the national information infrastructure.

Assuming that something like this might happen, how far will the support for multimedia services, wide-ranging business information and two-way entertainment solutions go? The most likely scenario is that, in the long run, no single type of application is going to provide the great motivation to go ahead.

Polyvalence, therefore the capability to handle many applications, will be at a premium. The strength of American industry is independence of action, and the motivation for implementation investments is basically going to be scale economics.

But there is a hinge. If for the domestic market American vendors can develop concepts, software and generally intellectual property that are applicable on a global basis, they will automatically become world-wide franchisers. This will provide the basis of an enormous industry exporting intellectual property the world over – and can be seen as the secret goal of NII.

5. From Leadership in Telecommunications to the Challenge of the Audiovisuals

The merger of telephone companies and cable television operators can open wide new markets challenging local telephone monopolies by providing services well beyond the more classical TV and voice services. Programming solutions will include video-on-demand, home shopping, educational and other channels.

Not everything will be technology-driven and among the programming products for a vast national market many parts may not be directly exportable. But there is no denying that NII will give the American industry a tremendous lead, compounding the effects of current market control in the audiovisuals, which has become a major point of friction between America and Europe.

To a significant extent, which way the die falls will depend on new legislation in America – and on both deregulation and legislation in Europe. As long as in the old continent the telco monopolies swamp initiative, the future of European business will be bleak.

Cognizant executives from different business lines who participated in this research expressed the opinion that much of what needs to be done would require legislative action and even in the USA the new legislation will not be settled in one go. There are many issues still open:

- Will the projected information superhighway both start and continue to be built by private industry, with a minimum of government intervention?
- If and when the existing regulatory restrictions on telephone companies will be lifted, how many will have positioned themselves to capitalize on the opportunity?
- Will the new regulatory policies assure open access to the information highway – making sure that the new digital networks don't bypass poor and rural America?

The risk of bypassing is real. The crucial question is: 'Who will pay the cost – perhaps $1500 per home – to extend the high-speed network to each and every user?' And what, precisely, will comprise basic service in the year 2000?

Social groups in America will start being worried about possible discrimination regarding socially beneficial services, such as electronic access to libraries. Who is going to pay the bill for many people unable to afford the most advanced and expensive services?

These are but a few examples of the NII challenges in other than purely technical domains. While it is said that the legislation would require each service provider to pay a portion of its revenues into a pool, administered by an FCC-headed federal-state board, the mechanics of how this will be done – as well as the amounts to be involved – are not at all clear.

A leading thought is that the money coming from a portion of the revenues still to be defined, would subsidize those subscribers-to-be who cannot afford to pay the full cost. This would apply to whatever is defined as 'an essential service'. But nobody:

- has yet spelled out what is meant by essential services, describing their possible contents
- can really foretell the cash flow, and whether the still to be defined percentages will be adequate or short of goals.

These and many more questions are still to be answered. Therefore, on 15 September 1993, the White House unveiled an agenda for the national information infrastructure by setting up a task force to study the 'thorny' issues. The panel's charge includes:

- figuring out who can send what in the network

- who should pay for its use and how
- how security and privacy can be assured.*

Sorting out the conflicting interests of business, the local telephone companies, long-distance providers, cable operators, different contractors, business users, academe and households is and will remain a major challenge for the task force – as well as for everybody else.

Among the concerns that need to be addressed by the US government's task force is whether the Bell companies' $12 billion in overseas investments is detracting from the development of the American network infrastructure. Some state regulators and public interest groups fear that foreign investment diverts funds that would otherwise go to:

- the modernization of domestic infrastructure
- the development of innovative communications services.

The only confident statement at this moment is that a significant number of issues remain wide open. As another example, the architects of the future multimedia industry cannot yet agree on whether it will be the residential or business customers who will drive network development. Or, whether wireline or wireless applications would be the 'killer domain' in the convergence market.

6. The Services of NII are for the End-Users

On the positive side of plans and projects regarding NII lie a number of concepts and initiatives that can help in choosing the future course of action. A keyword is *synergy*, and lessons can be learned even from deals which did not go through.

For instance, the Bell Atlantic-TCI merger which was contemplated in late 1993 and early 1994 was abandoned on 24 February 1994. A focal point in this deal had been that of exploiting areas where TCI operated but Bell Atlantic did not. The main strategic scenarios were that the projected company:

- would or could install switches so that telephone calls could be delivered to homes over TCI cables in competition to the local telco
- the video cable network could be upgraded with new computer servers and switches to deliver interactive communications media.

This may well become a daily scenario on how the information superhighway across America will be built. The challenge is significant, but

* We discuss these issues further in sections 11 and 12.

in a way it is quite similar to that of constructing the railroads after the American Civil War and the interstate highway system after World War II.

Hopefully, the same or similar types of major mistakes which took place with the interstate highway system will not repeat themselves with NII. For instance, the fact that the height clearance of bridges was too low and when the time came to transport missiles from Southern California to Cape Canaveral, in Florida, many bridges had to be demolished and rebuilt.

To err is human and that's precisely the reason why we need foresight. With NII, there will be plenty of opportunities for failure by misjudging the requirements of critical factors, the most important among them being:

1. Private citizens and their future needs.
2. The ever expanding business horizon.
3. The virtual company and virtual office where items 1 and 2 above merge.

As an example which helps to convey how important the planning task will be, we can consider the complex technology that will underlie video-on-demand. This is expected to become a main revenue-generator of information superhighways. The concept is that users can watch anything in the video library, any time, anywhere – whether for business reasons or for entertainment:

- The computerized television, or *telecomputer*, will permit the user to scroll through a menu of programs, making a choice, and sending an order upstream.
- At the regional centre (or the corporate office), a robotic arm will pull the correct digital videotape from a library and empty the contents, probably onto a magnetic platter.

The multimedia digital streams will be sent in bursts to memory chips. Then, they will be downloaded off those chips towards the intended destination in a customized response:

- Transmission will be directed through a high-capacity switch to fibre-optics lines that extend to a storage device at the user's premises (for companies) or neighbourhood (for consumers).
- This storage media will take the light pulses from the fibres and convert them into electromagnetic pulses, which go over a coaxial cable to the box at the user's workstation or smart telephone set, and then to the screen.

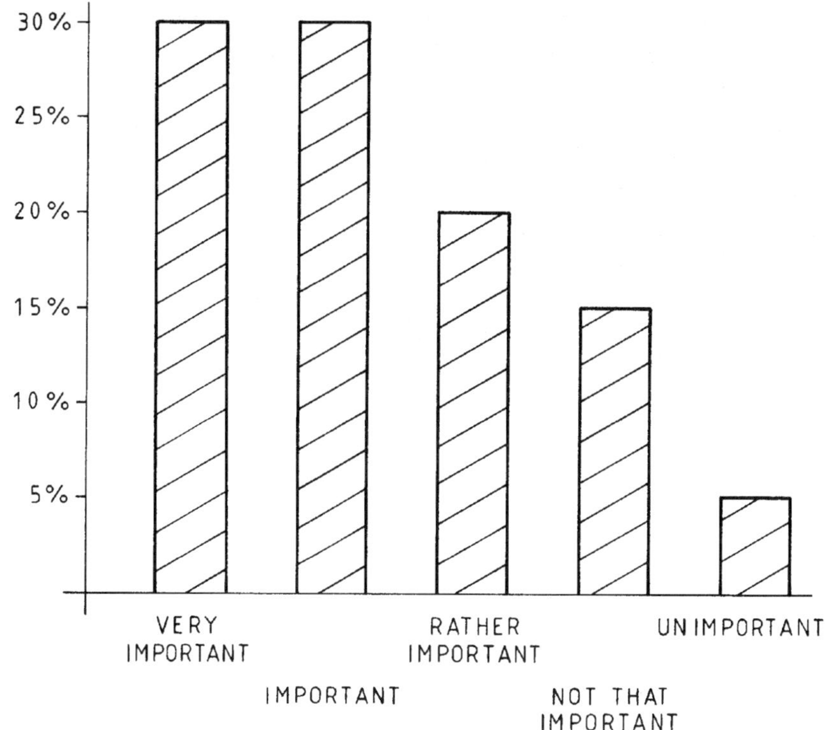

Figure 4.4 The importance of linking email, voice mail and facsimile, as seen by users

Such a sequence has been projected to keep costs as low as possible while satisfying customer's demands with minimal delay. In terms of storage, most multimedia information – from compound electronic documents to entertainment programs – can be archived on optical disks or digital tapes. Both are cheaper media than magnetic platters.

How much this may appeal to corporate users can be attested through the statistics compiled in the course of the research which we carried out in 1993 and 1994 in the USA, the UK, Germany and Japan. This research involved 89 companies and 244 executives.

Our research query concerned the importance of linking email, voice mail and facsimile. Hence, it was of a more limited breadth than that regarding compound electronic document – though it points in the same direction. Shown in Figure 4.4, the results are interesting because they may characterize future trends.

7. Seed Money, Pork Barrel and Brainpower

To enhance the financing of big projects like NII without overcommitting public money, some governments aim – particularly in America and the UK – to create a proper environment for investors by setting long-term goals as well as incentives. This is the right strategy. The only problem is that the seed money tends to be often treated as a pork barrel.

In an article entitled 'Hitting the Brakes on the Data Highway', published in *Business Week*,* the point was made that on the campaign trail, Bill Clinton and Al Gore talked of a 'data superhighway' that would be everything for everyone. But a year down the line reality has set in and things looked complicated.

But there is precedence on which one can capitalize. Particularly in America, vast and powerful networks have already been built by many universities, industrial and financial institutions, as well as federal agencies. But the most important issue is that attached to this complex system is a web of entrenched interests.

As a result of these realities, the US Government came to realize that the initial expectations and pronouncements may be out of control. This is true even if, since its inception, the projected NII seems to be based on a phasing-in process which will be gradual. A similarity could be drawn with the High Performance Computing Act** which does not call for massive federal funding but:

- aims to allocate $2 billion in federal funds over five years
- hopes to catalyse a much larger investment by a wide variety of private companies.

The underlying concept is that, provided this effort is indeed successful, it can attract risk capital. The initial money of the Gore Act would go mainly for research on ways to use and interconnect the high-performance computers, databases and networks. About 20 per cent of the money would be allocated to upgrade existing networks into the National Research and Education Network. But will small, dynamic companies be the favoured recipients of the rest of the budget, or will it mainly be seed projects conducted by the larger firms?

Since the dust on what NII will and will not be has not yet settled, the telephone companies in America fear competition from partly subsidized networks. These often allow users to bypass local telephone companies for services such as email. At the same time, the prospect that households will be able to get entertainment on demand worries cable companies. They see competition for their systems and loss of revenue.

- The competitive moves during the coming ten years are vague because the technology is moving very rapidly, and

* 27 September 1993.

** Part of the High Performance Communications and Computing (HPCC) program, which we examine in Part 2.

government is so far behind that legislators have not yet begun to tackle the bigger issues.

- This does not happen only in the USA but all over the world. Yet, the need for clarity in setting policy is there and pressing – particularly so in First World countries.

The challenges are compounded by the fact that many of the different government initiatives mainly throw money at the problem. But the technological challenge of blanketing a whole nation with gigastream information superhighways are taxing the best managerial talent currently available – and those with engineering know-how.

Many of the thinking people in the telecommunications field believe that a synergy of competition and government prodding can speed progress, and some cases suggest that this may be true. The crucial issue, however, is *brainpower*, not dollars – and brainpower suggests that only very flexible information highways will be worthwhile.

8. Flexibility Will Be the Keyword of Competitive Solutions

The information superhighway would carry wideband multimedia streams to and from offices, homes, schools and hospitals changing the way we live. It will also create many new businesses. Therefore, during the late 1990s industry will be racing to build it.

At current loop level, the plant of telephone companies is a shambles, but the cable TV network is another story. Since their original inception, the cable companies' coaxial lines have had a large carrying capacity, though not as large as optical fibres. The cable companies' problem is with the quality of the signals.

At the same time, while still operating with low capacity, noisy and unreliable copper telephone wires, telephone companies are masters of the other parts of the new business perspectives in telecommunications: from switching signals down the fibre pipelines, to measuring customers' usage, so that detailed bills can be established and sent. To date, limited pay-per-view revenue is the cable industry's only experience with on-line transactions. By contrast, transactions based on telephone calls represent the entire telephone business of telcos.

Telephone companies also have experience with network control centres which they need for higher telephone network reliability. With this and with the products currently in their laboratories,* they can

* As we will see through detailed examples at the best projects currently at the NYNEX Laboratories.

significantly contribute in bolstering the cabled TV companies' fibre and coaxial network with telephone and video switches.

Systems expertise is absolutely necessary to develop *multimedia server* systems even if many details, such as whether the home communication unit is served by coaxial or fibre and whether it is inside or outside the house, will depend on economics.

- The exact architecture and its component parts have to be flexible.
- The goal is cost-effectiveness at take-off, and after the system reaches cruising speed.

For these reasons, in terms of the strategic moves which count, business and industry seem to be by now well ahead of governments. Therefore, unless the different legislators and regulators get their regulatory act together before major deals are cut, the various First World governments will not have an opportunity to affect the future of the communications industry in any significant way.

Whether in America, in Europe, in Japan or elsewhere, the real question today is: What is the government's role in the long-term telecommunications policy? Is it a promoter, an inhibitor, or a powerless spectator?

- Like the current telephone system, the intelligent network of the mid- to late 1990s must be accessible to everyone, even if hook-ups to individuals prove to be money-losers.
- But since the new networks will be built and run by industry, which is naturally more interested in profits than social policy, there may develop a hub-and-spoke network rather than a grand design.

The notion underpinning a grand design is that of a network like a market-place where every participant – company or private citizen – has equal opportunity to buy, sell and exchange information. By contrast, hub-and-spoke approaches are feeders of data streams, reducing both flexibility and choice.

Realizing that this is a background thought of many regulators, the foremost network operators in America insist that *globality* and *interactivity* are part of their vision. The same is true about the contemplated network's flexibility.

Most operators realize that there is a significant requirement for internetworking facilities, in order to ensure that all customers will be able to access all available multimedia sources. This includes:

- image standards conversion
- the associated access control systems

- ways and means for facilitating commercial and cultural integration.

The key issues remain those of reviewing and reforming government regulations that impede development of interactive services and applications, and funding research and development of new technology in a partnership between government and private industry.

One of the subjects which is yet far from being settled regards universal access. Washington wants networks to be linked in such a way that information can flow seamlessly from one to another, creating a true national highway rather than a mesh of private roads. That means, among other things, mutually compatible equipment and software at the exchanges – and those who have read the history of computers and software know that this is simply not achievable.

9. The Quest for Universal Access

The practical value of an information superhighway will be so much greater if it assures universal access. Everyone seems to favour it. But exactly what does this term mean in the multimedia age? Who pays for it? These questions cannot be answered as in the 'good old days'.

In the past, for universal access reasons, regulators required long-distance and business customers to subsidize money-losing voice services to rural and poor customers. But an information superhighway is not plain old telephony, and rate subsidies will not work if local calling is opened to competition.

It is a foregone conclusion that in a free market new players would skim off the most profitable customers, who will get the bulk of attention. Therefore, consumer groups fear that equating universal access with a digital line into every home misses the point:

- As ISDN has shown, nearly every existing telephone wire can carry digital signals – but at a high bit error rate.
- What counts is whether the line can support high reliability with interactive video, and what services it brings in.

A different way of making this statement is that unless every user gets high-capacity links, the information superhighway could end up with islands of multimedia digital supports and many bottlenecks – which nobody wants.

The aim, at least the one generally stated, is that of shaping the future of telecommunications in a way which is satisfactory to every party. But is this a realistic objective? As with banking and other service industries, two main trends are shaping the future of communications

– deregulation and technology. Their synergy brings into perspective a third crucial factor: the increasing dependency of every business on the communications infrastructure on which future profits largely depend.

Deregulation lowers costs and improves quality due to tougher competition. Improvements in technology allow powerful networks using diverse facilities and media to be established and operated in an effective manner.

The real challenge is focused on the ability to exploit the new business opportunity horizons, taking into account the fast-growing user requirements – starting with those of the most sophisticated customers for income reasons. Among the issues of competitiveness we distinguish:

- the achievement of the polyvalence and quality of connection promised by the service provider
- the ease of accessibility, low cost and high performance of the facilities assured by the network provider
- an objective way to determine the responsibilities in the chain of service provision, when something goes wrong.

These challenges can best be faced when networks and terminals are intelligent; particularly, when they are enriched with knowledge artefacts. Hence, R&D has to focus in that direction, particularly given the expanding multivendor environments and the geographical dispersion of users.

The networks of the second half of the 1990s and beyond must provide the flexibility required to meet a mixture of regulated and unregulated environments, containing both new and old technologies. This must be achieved without interruption of service, while assuring a multiplicity of functions.

10. Information Infrastructure and Gigabit Network Projects

If we think of the network as a layered structure, we will find at the bottom the raw carrying capacity and in the upper layers the knowledge artefacts supporting user services. Both are necessary aspects of the information superhighway and the facilities which it plans to offer to the user community.

But the grand vision is still the exception. All over the First World, current telecommunications policies are still a reflection of those developed for copper wire telephony. The so-called POTS mentality is still alive and well.

In most countries, old concepts and rusty policies are hindering the development and deployment of the new fibre-optic technology, but things start changing. A new landscape opens up, even if the powerful entrenched administrations that built and run the existing POTS resist new policies that might lead to competition.

A fact of business life is that, built to handle the low capacity required for human voice, today's telephone lines are greatly underpowered for computer-based communications involving text, data, graphics, moving image and video. Yet, our service economy has an insatiable appetite for telecommunications bandwidth.

We need wideband channels and network intelligence for processing financial and other transactions, handling distributed information services, conducting video teleconferencing, and moving multimedia information from database to database. Few governments appreciate that an inferior communications network can:

- hamper business transactions
- increase the cost of production and distribution of services
- drive banking and stock trading offshore.

It is precisely in appreciation of this challenge, which is becoming increasingly felt in the more advanced economies, that many First World nations start investing heavily in digital switches and optical-fibre links.

Japan's Nippon Telegraph and Telephone (NTT), still more or less a regulated monopoly, plans to lay fibre-optic cables to every Japanese home, school, and business by the year 2015. But Singapore has already installed a state-of-the-art network to attract global investment and even some Eastern European countries have tried to move in that direction.

Telecommunications technology has leapfrogged computer installations in terms of channel capacity. Some 25 years ago we had very slow 300 and 600 bauds lines. Then, in the early 1970s we started counting transmission in kilobits per second (KBPS). As Figure 4.5 demonstrates:

- in 1970 the telecommunications channels featured 1.2 KBPS while computer interconnection operated at 9 MBPS
- in 1994, digital circuits in broadband telecommunications had overtaken computer cabling to reach 2 GBPS, while computer channels still worked at 90 MBPS.

The drive towards high-capacity and high-quality networks is motivated by the fact that towards the end of this decade telecommunications will radically transform the world's most advanced economies. New kinds of switches, transmission lines and software will make it possible to send *virtual reality* images just by dialling a telephone number. But, as we saw in the preceding sections, information superhighways won't appear by themselves – they need a great deal of preparation, major investments and great care in implementation.

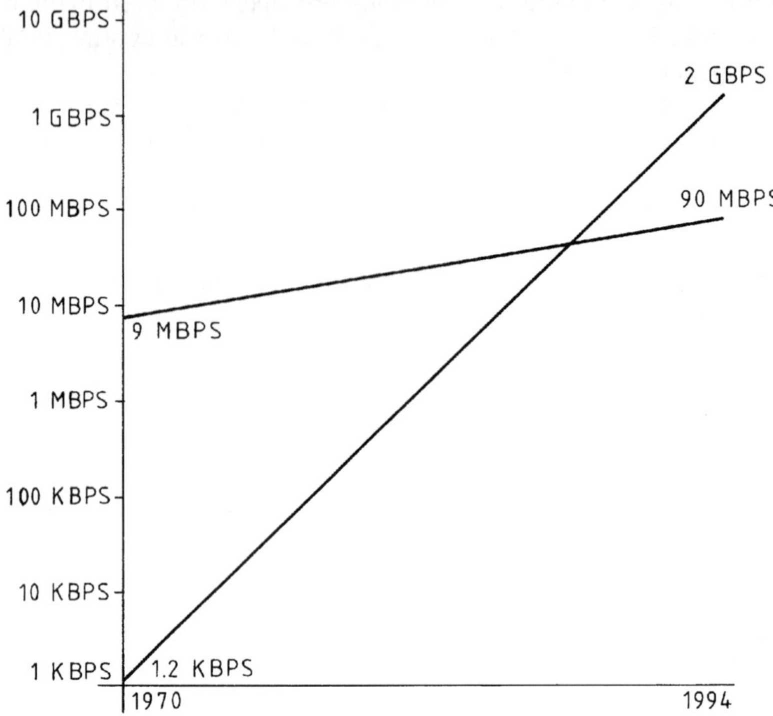

Figure 4.5 Twenty-five years of change in transmission capabilities (logarithmic scale)

In the more advanced cases, implementation takes advantage of emerging *visualization* technologies to explore the formation and dynamics of underlying systems factors. These affect information transmission, processing and presentation. The able execution of advanced applications:

- requires metasystem layers able of interconnecting heterogeneous computers
- calls for networks permitting wide-scattered researchers to work on a single problem at the same time
- makes available on-line realtime search through processes which seamlessly access a golden horde of distributed databases.

The principle is that all computers, databases and existing networks must be interconnected long haul, including the capability of interoperating heterogeneous engines.

This is a different view of universal access than the one we considered in section 8, which was by and large consumer oriented. Internetworking should not only include new resources but also old ones, whether *as is* or expanded and upgraded – the whole structure becoming an open but secure system.

11. Interconnecting Workstations and Multimedia Services

Multimedia applications of advanced networked systems require a wide range of combinations of hardware and software. Design considerations include not only links and nodes but also business functions whose requirements are not always easy to identify.

Experts with experience in the design and implementation of flexible and evolving network structures underline that, in their judgement, three levels of reference must be addressed in the design of telecommunications systems:

- the network proper
- its server modules
- user level workstations.

At network design level, the flexibility offered by new technology has to meet differentiated and customized user needs. It must also provide for a seamless cross-network service, including a range of different infrastructures: terrestrial, satellite, broadcast and mobile; local area networks, metropolitan area networks and wide area networks.

As we have seen in the preceding sections, any valid solution must pay due attention to customer access equipment and terminals for voice, text, data and video – whether individually or integrated. Eventually, differentiated control options for network operators, service providers and users should be universally offered. This includes the ability to:

- configure or reconfigure the offered services
- provide for integration of different network management and operations characteristics.

One approach suggested for addressing the stated problems is modular standardization, which has been a cornerstone of the success of the electronics industry, as well as of computer-integrated manufacturing. The goal would be an open system architecture in which standard components can be combined to achieve flexible solutions and provide for service integration.

Network planning, network design and network operation are complementary functions. They have in common the objective of optimizing the allocation of resources but their time-scale is different:

- Planning is medium and long term.
- Design is short to medium term.
- Operations and maintenance is realtime.

How successful these tasks will be, as well as the quality of their integration depends on the degree of automation and the knowledge engineering artefacts being used.

Whether we talk of an information superhighway or any other network, many advanced applications raise issues of integrity, security and privacy. All future network offerings must also have an acceptable level of protection against fraud.

Verification of the operational aspects of services cannot be covered by laboratory integration alone and will, therefore, require the availability of an appropriate network infrastructure for experimentation. The leading thinking is that the solution to be adopted must make possible to test many network features. For instance:

- mobile network systems and services against expectations and needs of network operators, service providers and user organizations
- different service characteristics and geographical coverage, which may vary according to the type of applications, technology used and actors involved.

A different way of looking at this subject is that to maintain business vitality and stable growth, we must continue to expand R&D, as the foundation of technical innovation. But we also need test beds to evaluate our designs and policies to serve as guidelines for the tests.

For reasons of functionality and costs, it is quite likely that there will be requirements for flexible configurations able to assure a mixture of different media and of realtime versus non-realtime response. Under this perspective should be seen some of the most interesting projects currently in the laboratories of NYNEX (Chapter 11). They are the type of communications solutions that are necessary to face in an able manner the challenges of the 1990s.

Part 2

The Challenge of a Business Systems Architecture

5

Principles Characterizing a Business Systems Architecture

1. Introduction

The concept underlying an architecture has been introduced in Chapter 2, along with the notion of what constitutes an open architectural solution. In the same chapter we discussed the sense of an open vendor policy, gave examples of implementations but underlined that technology is only half of the job. The other half is the organizational infrastructure.

Typically, we create architectural models to map system designs and experiment with them. This study ranges from the overall network (or grand design), to the configuration of its physical and logical modules; selected details of each component part; hardware and software characteristics; and the way the different system modules interconnect. A sound architectural model must take into account:

- the overall objectives of the investment, and the functions we expect to perform
- the way in which each software and hardware component is embedded in the larger framework of a network.

In every study, attention should be paid to to the fact that, due to their size and complexity, many computers and communications aggregates involve concurrency of operations as well as overlapping functions. Therefore, architectural models must be capable of providing a platform for experimentation and optimization.

Many different systems modelling methodologies have been adopted in everyday practice. Typically, they map logical processes to physical resources, but several technical plans have the disadvantage that they are single layer diagrams representing in 2-D largely 3-D structures. Hence, they are:

- incapable of accommodating large and complex networks
- failing to provide the necessary flexibility for future expansion.

Capitalizing on the ability to model through simulation and knowledge engineering, and therefore to experiment and optimize, the foremost network designers today practise sophisticated approaches. These include a rigorous analysis of logical and physical characteristics, the study of structural requirements, and so on. Any serious study requires a valid description methodology.

In general, in order to create a sound architectural model we must know the tasks performed and to be performed by the system, as well as appreciate that variations of given tasks may appear in more than one architectural component. Furthermore, we must appreciate that many of the assigned tasks may be reassigned in a dynamic manner. Hence, the solution which we adopt must have checks and balances.

2. Principles of a Modern Systems Architecture

It has taken a surprising long time to take account of architecture principles which are governing the development of information technology systems and, particularly, complex networks. These principles concern both the logical and physical aspects and the structure of the whole aggregate – leading to a progression from business elements to their implementation through software.

The functionality we support defines the *logical* characteristics. Overall design provides the *structure*. Systems analysis targets the identification of *business elements*. System design specifies the principles by which software and hardware will serve these business elements. Then comes the task of a flexible integration:

- Implementation outlines the principles needed to join trunks and nodes – or client and server software running on diverse computer platforms.
- Deployment identifies the ways and means for placing the hardware and software in operation, in a manner satisfactory to the user.
- Maintenance addresses uptime, dependability, reliability and the expert systems required for diagnostics – as well as system improvements.

These three phases of a policy which goes beyond R&D focus on *deliverables* (Figure 5.1). In all applications involving communications, computers or software, they constitute a frame of reference which enables the user organization at large, and each user in particular, to gauge how successful is the solution offered.

Because technology has broken down the former divisions between system specialists and users, end-users have an unusual opportunity to

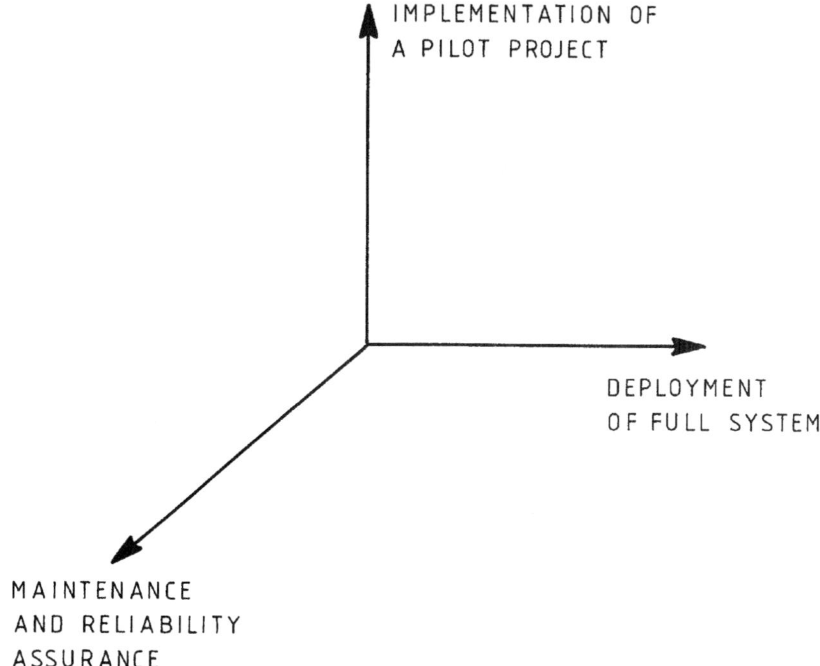

Figure 5.1 Beyond hardware and software design: a frame of reference for deliverables

shape the next generation of systems specification by aggressively applying pressure on deliverables. This enables immediate realization of significant benefits through tactical decisions about technology standards and products.

With an open, flexible and integrated network architecture, it is possible to produce systems that are significantly better able to support changing business requirements. At the same time an open vendor policy sees to it that these solutions are more flexible and less costly. Modern designs are based on:

- the use of a distributed technology across a global network
- an interactive use of business elements to specify the functions to be performed at the nodes.

Software modules need to be built according to business element templates, developed by means of rapid prototyping. Such modules will be interoperating through knowledge-enriched interfaces, producing better business results than those offered today by centralized or semi-distributed networks and production systems.

Whether we talk of communications networks, computing processes or databases, today the most effective way to manage corporate resources – in finance, manufacturing or merchandising – is *through* federated independent solutions which address local conditions but come under an integrative architecture.

An example is provided by the practice of *federated databases*. Prior to going into the details of a federated solution, it is appropriate to define what is meant by federalism, as well as to make explicit that federalism is not just another form of decentralization. The conceptal differences are important:

- *Decentralization* implies that the centre *delegates* certain tasks or duties to the outlying units, while the centre remains in overall control.

In this sense, the centre does the delegating, the initiating and the directing.

- *Federalism* is different. The centre's powers are given to it by the outlying groups, in a sort of *reverse delegation.*

The centre, therefore, co-ordinates, advises, influences, suggests – but it does not order. There is a major difference between federalism and decentralization, with the former having the upper ground in terms of flexibility and efficiency.

The evolution towards federalism has been necessary because both in an organizational and in a technological sense we deal with big systems. Big systems are not small systems which have grown up. Their study poses totally different requirements in terms of clearly set goals, technical detail and design know-how.

The cost of R&D connected to big systems is so huge that, as we have seen in the preceding chapters, countries set up national programs to build advanced networks. And there is often close co-ordination between the government and the leading national telephone companies as well as hardware/software suppliers in order to reach better focused results.

3. Design Characteristics for a Federated Solution

The point was made in section 2 that new architectural solutions are evolving in business and they have a significant impact on communications, computers and software. This evolution has been gradual. Neither in an organizational sense nor in terms of technology has the federalist approach developed overnight.

Rapid product development, intensive marketing and the globalization of business saw to it that the first alternative to be rejected has been the highly centralized, hierarchical organization. It fell out of favour because it proved to be ineffectual and has been replaced by a decentralized or divisionalized approach.

This divisionalized solution distributed the information technology support to the divisions, but also kept a forward-looking co-ordinating authority through the institution of Chief Technology Officer (CTO) functions. In some large organizations, the CTO retained the responsibility of the company's global network.

- With time, the range of duties assigned to the autonomous business units increased.
- Many of these units had to develop their own technology to remain competitive.
- Federated solutions became structured because of a need for co-ordination and for cost-sharing.

Within a business organization perspective, in a federated solution each local unit works autonomously but at the same time it is part of the larger aggregate of business units. In this manner, for example, a local network and a local database handles transactions and queries of interest to it locally; but it is always ready to collaborate in global events. This concept of 'less than 100 per cent control' has become 'bread and butter' in business. But it is fairly alien to many technologists and most particularly data processors. Yet, it is a powerful approach which merits a great deal of rapid and punctual developments.

In a way, federalism is how the Board of Management works in central European companies. The members of the Board are equal or semi-equal. The chairman practically acts as the speaker of the Board, reigning by consensus. There is no president or chief executive officer with 100 per cent control.

Even when control is centralized at headquarters, local conditions, and less than 100 per cent reliable management controls, ensure that many units work practically autonomously. This is written in a business sense, but it applies as well in technology.

Both federation and decentralization evidently bring up the need for *system integration*. System integration is a most vital function as the pace of technological change, that has taken place during the last 20 years, is expected to be duplicated over the next six to seven years; and duplicated again during the following three years.

At the same time, the proliferation of communications and computers as well as software modules makes mandatory the use of knowledge and skill in tying all of them together. The higher the level of technology we employ, the more the CTO and his or her immediate assistants must be integration specialists able to develop federated strategies and bundle together all communications and computing devices into an efficient system.

- In an architecture of this kind, all business element servers are peers.
- There are no controlling components in a truly federated computing, databasing and communications network.

Integrated federated solutions are the opposite of centralized approaches. But they are not the equivalent to today's semi-distributed systems and subsystems. They result from the flexible re-engineering of software according to global business requirements and must come together in product-oriented solutions physically located where business requirement and opportunities are found.

Contrary to the practices which dominated 40 years of computer applications, this coming together in a federated sense has to be governed by fast-evolving business needs. Both the definition of business elements and the implementation principles have to abide by this concept.

Architectural principles are necessary to reduce the complexity of the transition presented by *legacy** software. In communications and computer systems, legacy software will continue to coexist over a number of years. Citibank, for example, proposes *wrapping* these legacy systems and subsystems in software hiding them from the world of clients and servers:

- The wrapper acts like a business element server.
- An encapsulation interface makes it feasible to deal directly server to server.

In this manner, legacy systems can continue to perform their business functions without major code rewriting. The existing bilateral relationships among legacy modules and links can remain unchanged until replaced by modern servers.

Figure 5.2 shows this approach which now finds favour among many business firms. One of the better-known money centre banks gave itself five years to hide its remaining legacy applications through encapsulation. The goal is to handle them by means of fully peer-to-peer networks, while all new competitive applications are cast into client-server solutions.

4. An Example from the Banking Industry: the Global Assets Architecture

One of the challenges with the strategy outlined in section 3 is to avoid discontinuities in service. Another crucial issue is to ensure that the

* Typically mainframe-based applications programs and communications solutions.

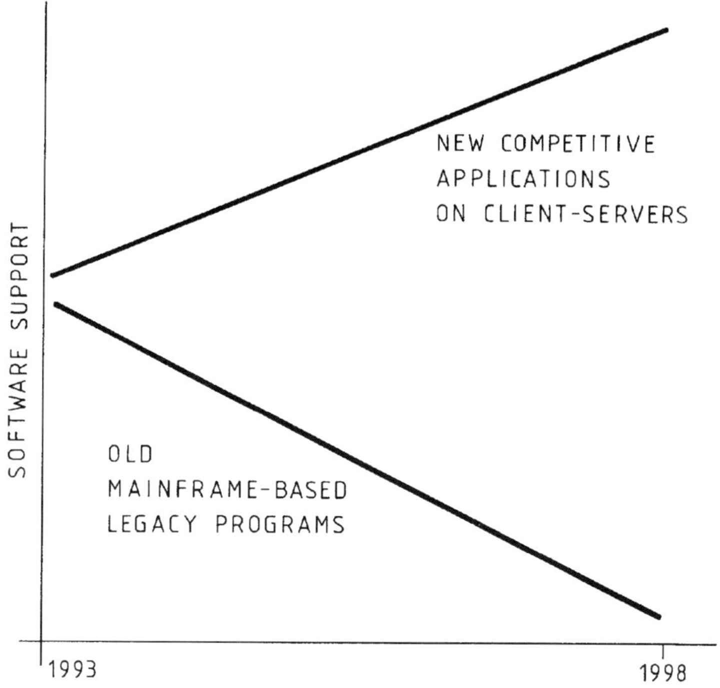

Figure 5.2 Downsizing the current inventory of mainframe-based programs

transition to a peer-to-peer network does not consume an inordinate amount of resources.

Every company today finds itself obliged to attend to a number of sophisticated but pressing needs. Typically, these are setting the stage for tomorrow's environment. The approach is to balance:

- the remains of legacy software
- today's growing requirements
- tomorrow's expanding needs.

System integration must take place in a context of formal architectural plans. The solution we adopt should be able to establish an overall computing, databasing and communication framework.

While different companies adopt different strategies and there is little in terms of common ground in their design or timetables, the following issues tend to characterize major financial institutions and industrial companies in their evolving strategic approach to technology.

1. Each software component is designed to execute independently of any other, doing so in asynchronous mode.

Therefore each module can be removed and upgraded independently of any other – a policy which fits well with the federated concept we have discussed.

2. Each component is reusable and may be shared across business products, in a local, regional and transnational sense.

This is particularly important as all client and server modules work co-operatively to perform a business service or function. The same is true of the nodes of a network.

3. There are practically no limits on the number of services or functions performed by an intelligent network.

Solutions are studied in a way providing a polyvalent any-to-any connectivity. There are no geographic or time zone limitations.

4. Knowledge-enriched software helps in establishing a technical infrastructure able to support any product or service, at any time, anywhere in the world.

Using this global infrastructure as a base, it is possible to develop applications tailored to the very different business environments in which a multinational industrial company or financial institution operates. An example from Bankers Trust helps to better explain this strategy.

The *Global Assets Architecture* addresses the customer-oriented side of the bank, which deals with transactions processing, trust management and other activities conducted in direct support to customers. Such services include cash management, payment orders, securities and custody as well as pension plans, savings plans and profit sharing plans which are administered on behalf of large corporations and their employees.

- The objective is to create a fully automated service environment, which becomes more sophisticated as its functionality evolves.
- The customer is able to access these services directly with an absolute minimum of human intervention on the bank's part.

Authorized direct access to network databases helps to automate both ends: the bank's and the client's. The system pays personalized attention not only to the level of each corporate treasurer, but also to each individual customer.

If a client company's employee is planning to buy a new house or a new car and would like to borrow money from his or her savings plan for the down payment, he or she can interactively find out how much money may be borrowed, what the interest rate will be and what terms are available. All this is not just automated but also *customized*, self-actuated and can be actioned on-line.

What an individual client needs to do is to go to one of the employee service workstations in his or her office, sign on, identify himself or herself, explore the available options, then select an appropriate loan amount and term structure. Having decided to enter into a transaction, the client requests a certified check which is printed out on the spot. In one sitting:

- all the information the end-user needs is available
- execution is immediate through smart software.

Using client-server technology, the customized service integration developed by Bankers Trust repackages the appropriate processes in the form needed for a particular customer interaction – without intervention by the banking staff. Should a problem arise, however, the bank's customer service staff is ready to join in the interactive session providing direct and personal assistance.

The presence of a flexible architectural framework, such as the Global Assets Architecture, ensures that the individual function processing and service integration modules can be developed independently with a minimum of classical type co-ordination. This:

- speeds development
- maximizes flexibility.

Knowledge-enriched, hence flexible, architectural standards ensure that all modules will work together in a coherent structure creating a transaction processing model. The latter is kept in full evolution while serving the company's day-to-day business.

This is not an exceptional example, but it is one of the better today available in industry. The bottom line is that communications networks have evolved tremendously in terms of supported functions. They have also integrated with what used to be the computer applications domain – which is reasonable since they share the same software.

5. The Integration of Networks and Computer Applications

Section 4 made reference to the fact that what used to be distinct networking and computing functions have now integrated into one system. Figure 5.3 explains this and also introduces a third component: the networked databases each with its database management system (DBMS). Layer by layer, whether local or remote, the user applications and

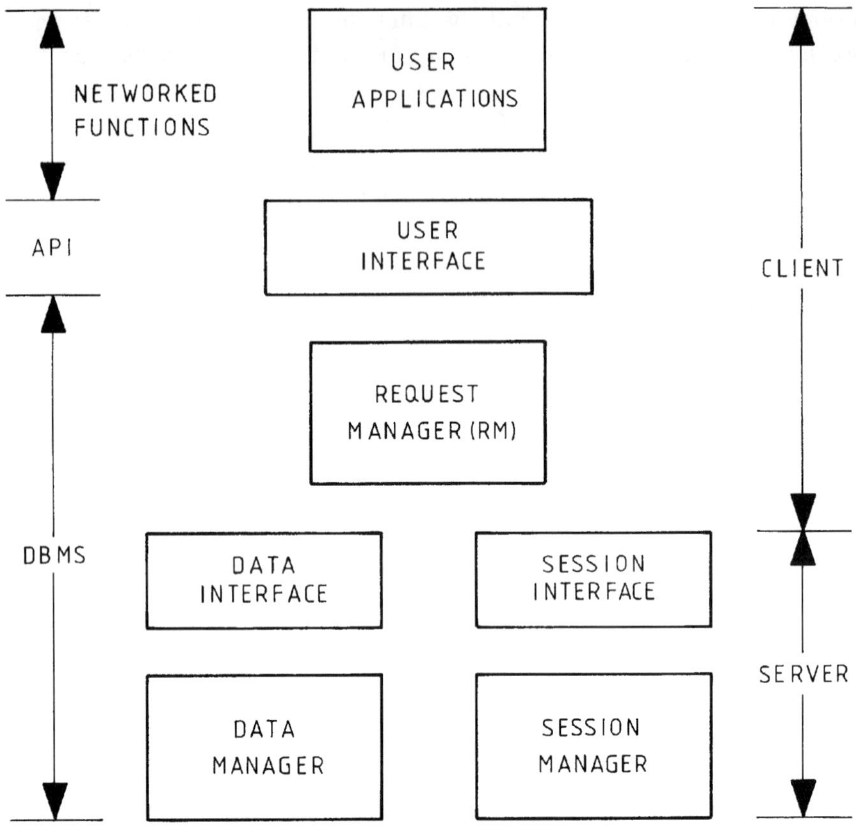

Figure 5.3 Modular components of a client-server architecture

databases are networked, but user interfaces are of two kinds: general and dedicated. Notice that the top three layers in Figure 5.3 are resident at the client; the clients are networked. The two layers at the bottom are resident at the server. The servers are networked. All this indicates a great deal about communications requirements.

The example on the Global Assets Architecture, which we have seen in section 4, is based on this concept of networked clients and servers – hence the integration of computers and communications. At Bankers Trust, a still more sophisticated solution is the *Financial Services Architecture* which deals with:

- trading
- positioning
- risk management.

The bank carries out these activities primarily on its own behalf, and only secondarily sells the services (to be described) to its clients. However, the network has been designed to effectively handle both types of usage.

- The client sees these functions primarily in the form of financial advice based on expertise and data access.
- Hence there is a great need to support highly volatile trading activities connected to complex financial instruments.

A good way of looking at what the financial services architecture provides is from the viewpoint of a trader who operates in several markets and handles a variety of specialized financial vehicles which typically work cross-border.

Each trader works in the context of a portfolio and is constantly looking for business opportunities. His or her activity, in essence the profit and loss (P&L), is treated as an independent profit centre with its own P&L scenarios. Hence the financial services architecture must be tailored to each trader.

This requirement makes it necessary not only to provide network support but also personalized portfolio managements. Applications are customized to meet each trader's unique profile and profit strategy. Such a financial services environment must provide, in realtime, market analysis to help in:

- identifying developing business opportunities
- assisting in the execution of multiproduct trades
- being able to monitor profit and risk parameters, as well as open exposure.

Behind the portfolio management applications are a series of product control modules. Each provides the processing software for a specific class of financial instruments. Many of these products, such as exotic derivatives, are very complex. Hence by having each module deal with only a single product, no one application becomes overburdened or slows down.

Written for risk management, sophisticated knowledge artefacts oversee the trading activity of all traders in all products. They assure an overall balance of risk and reward through a flexible and highly tailored approach to meeting the needs of trading – while keeping derivatives risk under close supervision.

This evolving flexible applications environment uses atomic business elements such as: interest terms, payment orders, commodity options, currency futures, general ledgers. These are combined to form the products the bank sells – from account handling to mortgage securitizations and controlled disbursements. Business functions are networked and they are defined in terms of:

- the attributes they have
- the information elements they need
- the behaviours they exhibit in market terms.

Business elements are networked and serviced through resources, but to start with they have to be defined as the smallest or atomic components of banking activity which can be reasonably stable and persistent. Once this is done, the development of smart software modules can be fairly simple, flexible, and cost-effective.

The use of an object-oriented approach in system analysis and design permits considerable flexibility in handling business elements. Available methodology and tools can manage attributes, functions, instances of business elements as well as a collection of instances.

Citibank, for example, has used a variety of techniques to reach this attributes-and-functions redefinition, and recently focused on object-oriented methods.* Object orientation served to analyse the business, identify business elements, study their attributes and behaviour and provide the needed links.

6. Networked Artefacts to Oversee the Business Activity

Expert systems have been the first practical implementation of artificial intelligence. Their application range from the manufacturing industry to banking.** Telephone companies have extensively used knowledge artefacts for diagnostics and maintenance purposes. Now agents are graduating into self-actuating operational components, regarding system management functions and acting as supervisory processes at the network's nodes.

One of the implementations of knowledge artefacts in connection to a business systems architecture is in the development and actuation of flexibly structured templates of attributes and behaviours. A business element instance has values for those attributes and behaviours that fit the template, and it is implemented in knowledge-enriched software:

- Each kind of networked business element defines a separate server that will manage the collection of instances.
- Business element instances interact with each other when they exhibit their behaviours, usually through message passing.

* See also D.N. Chorafas, *Intelligent Multimedia Databases* (Prentice-Hall, Englewood Cliffs, NJ, 1994).

** See also D.N. Chorafas and H. Steinmann, *Expert Systems in Banking* (Macmillan, London, 1990).

- Each element triggers another in a domino-like way, following a path that consitutes a business transaction.

This process can be viewed in terms of network design since it is influenced by actual and potential paths, or in terms of processing history which follows actual paths similar to audit trails in connection to business elements.

The way they have been projected and are manipulated, the potential paths of networked business elements show the systems designer the features that can be offered to traders, relationship bankers and customers.

- An actual path contains records of events in the processing of a transaction.
- Product processing typically involves a particular set of business element instances working together.

In this sense, an individual transaction within a networked business environment stimulates the behaviour of business elements until the transaction is complete. The path through these business elements is dependent on the application and is purposely kept very flexible as it may vary from application to application, according to customer or management requests.

This approach to networked services can become quite sophisticated in its planning and execution, and it constitutes a first-class example of goals targeted through modern network design. In the background of message passing and communications are agents that are proactive – a concept equally well applicable in:

- *product design*, whether in engineering or banking
- *manufacturing activities*, whether in the plant or the back office
- *marketing* and *sales*, of industrial products or financial vehicles
- *control functions*, from risk management to quality assurance.

In an interactive networked environment, the behaviours and attributes of business element instances are implemented in software and constitute programming artefacts. These are agents, which may be perishable or permanent objects.

Seen from a systems perspective, administrative services manage the collection of instances but each server in the network has the software and data needed to implement one kind, and only one kind, of business element. The network has the necessary smart software to manage the collection as a whole.

Each server has a service interface through which it offers publicly defined services, but the commanding authority is the network. Within this framework, business element servers act only in response to appropriate messages, as members of the client-server architecture. They do so through message-passing interfaces. Here are some examples:

- private services to clients using local workstations and accessing the system through external interfaces
- business support services, derived from the behaviours of element instances
- administrative services to manage software instances and for housekeeping reasons.

Examples of business support services are post, advise, validate. These are offered to all members of the global network. By contrast, administrative services are create, find, select – needed by the architecture to assure consistency across servers.

All these are transaction characteristics and the reader will observe that they constitute a more sophisticated version of transaction management process we see in Chapter 8. Within a modern transaction environment, knowledge-enriched software is responsible for validating a client software instance's right to request the service. Agents have access to information needed to perform this validation.

When a server executes an administrative function at the request of a software instance, it also confirms the entitlement which goes together with a valid identity. Let's recall that a server might simply be a shell or wrapper around an existing interface, a module, a workstation or the whole network. Such a wrapper would appear as:

- a server offering functions defined by the architecture
- software that translates from system services to customized private services.

In an aggregate sense, the global network is responsible for identifying a requester of services and for validating the client's right to call for that business service. In practical banking applications, for instance, this responsibility authentication and authorization function enhance the system's privacy and security.

7. Sophisticated Software for Telecommunications

The concepts and practical implementations we have seen in sections 4 to 6 identify the level of sophistication which has been reached currently in the development and deployment of communications software. The technology underpinning the solutions we have is object-oriented* –

* See also D.N. Chorafas and H. Steinmann, *Object-Oriented Databases* (Prentice-Hall, Englewood Cliffs, NJ, 1993).

from system analysis to software development, including databasing and programming.

We discuss object-oriented solutions in Chapter 7. In the present chapter the emphasis is on the business architecture as a whole, its global nature and the technical characteristics which distinguish it from older solutions. Notice that in this networked environment attention is paid to both clients and servers.

All servers are members of the global network. Requests for private or administrative services and the responses to those requests must be conveyed by the network. From a server's perspective, the global network is a message interface defined by the architecture from interactive workstations, databases, number crunchers, communication devices and network software.

- A networked application is seen as a set of servers that satisfies product needs.
- Only servers defined by the architecture can be used in the construction of applications.

Each application is managed as a single organizational unit. However, at atomic level, that unit may have many component parts. In a banking environment, for instance, applications such as demand deposit, funds transfer, currency swap, forward rate agreement, custody and so on are created to serve particular products and clients.

As a product system, the business architecture defines applications and their platform. Both knowledge-enriched application software and an advanced platform technology are necessary to have a properly deployed, competitive working system. In its deployed form the product system is managed as an independent operating unit, but in its networked form it may be part of a larger operating unit. This duality makes possible considerable deployment flexibility as well as systems changes without interruptions in steady functioning. We have spoken of the wisdom of this strategy in sections 2 and 3.

Applications are assembled by *application integrators* from the server kits produced by developers. Application integrators work closely with managers and professionals to understand exactly how the servers should be assembled and configured. They are responsible for:

- the viability of the application in addressing business needs
- the realtime response which has to be provided
- the functions supported by individual business element servers.

Bank clients, traders, managers and professionals are the customers of application integrators and application integrators are the customers of server developers. A similar statement is valid in the manufacturing industry, in marketing, in merchandising, in government work and any other type of activity.

The central point of this discussion is the role played by telecommunications software. The strategy of a business unit approach and of object orientation rests on the fact that the aggregates which constitute a telecommunications system tend to be large and fairly complex, exhibiting a dynamic behaviour. They usually have distributed features, and these features require intensive on-line services.

For both customer service and administrative reasons, computer-based solutions in telecommunications need sophisticated software whose development involves several levels of abstraction. Therefore, software development methodologies should be able to model communicating processes that might not be in a 1:1 relationship with one another.

One of the characteristics of modern networks, and of the business architecture on which they rest, is their capillarity. Emulating the behaviour of telephone systems gets easier, thanks to new optimization capabilities offered by realtime simulation procedures. In fact, several telco laboratories are actively working on:

- virtual prototypes which enable studying a network's behaviour,
- experimental models enabling perfect designs before new lines and new switching centres are built.

Knowledge artefacts make feasible the emulation of network capabilities and studying their optimization. They enable refining of design objectives, elaborating operating constraints and identifying the variables to be modified during operation.

Genetic algorithms* start being used iteratively to assist in the optimization of components and configurations. Both at user organizations and in telecoms, engineers can define interactive bounded design variables that are either continuous or discrete. They can analyse two types of functions:

- standard, classically expressed in studies of networks
- mathematical referencing models with inputs and outputs.

The optimization process is capable of referencing single or multiple objectives. This is one of the domains where quite significant strides have recently been taken. Advanced realtime simulators include powerful statistical prediction techniques for prototyping and planning – radically altering the way of looking at network software and its functionality.

* See D.N. Chorafas, *Chaos Theory in the Financial Markets* (Probus/Irwin, Chicago, 1994).

8. Assuring Critical Software-Supported Communications Functions

If one asks which has been the most significant common characteristic of communications software functions during the last five years, the answer is: the wider implementation of artificial intelligence in communications. *Knowledge-enriched* features enable to develop a more thorough understanding of the solution space, leading to greater robustness of the network and accounting for functional sensitivities and trade-offs.

The second most important contribution to telecommunications software has been by *simulation*. Through simulation, users can define design variables with specific value ranges or tolerances, and produce an array of permutations required for a complete implementation experiment.

The third most significant contribution is by *object orientation*, both in programming and in database management. We have already spoken of the contribution of software instances to network functions, and we will look much more carefully into the subject of object solutions in Chapter 7.

The three main issues discussed in the preceding paragraphs are not distinct from one another. They work in synergy. Knowledge engineering and simulation procedures are greatly helped by means of object-oriented approaches. First-class results prove this statement, particularly in the way it applies in the telecommunications industry. A modern telephone service consists of:

- an object orientation providing necessary features for increasing the internal consistency of analytical results
- software objects that are running on hardware objects which constitute the main component of the network.

The synergy of knowledge engineering, simulation and object orientation makes it possible to support novel development approaches that have polyvalent perspectives. It also helps in emphasizing different system features within the architectural layout and the task distribution of the telecommunications system.

In terms of critical software-supported communications functions, the three issues we just saw are joined by *intelligent diagnostics* and maintenance agents. These apply to lines, trunks and nodes. Agents perform tests, do loopbacks, analyse the contents of quality databases and produce quality reports which are proactively brought to the attention of appropriate users – or are interactively accessible by telecommunications engineers, whether regular or on an *ad hoc* basis.

A fifth major software-supported communications function is *filtering*.

Experience exists from numerous applications in engineering and physics which require the use of filters to selectively pass, accept or reject various features of an incoming signal. But in communications filters invariably suffer from one main problem connected to the passband they feature and its centre frequency and width. The centre frequency and width of the filter's passband is difficult to control precisely. This is especially true in the case of filters that are intended to be very selective; a term practically synonymous to filters having extremely narrow passbands.

In contrast to filters used in physics and in engineering, which are job-specific, filters in telecommunications have to do with noise,* in a large number of cases. This calls for sophisticated software approaches, where knowledge engineering, simulation and object orientation offer significant assistance.

The sixth major reference in connection to software-supported communications functions is *on-line database access*. These databases may be for store and forward, for diagnostics, quality histories or other network functions.

Since the advent of computer-based switching centres in the 1970s, it has become increasingly clear that established patterns of work and study in connection with telecommunications networks have been breaking down. Many communications professionals today require continuing access to database information.

- Database access requirements start with computer-aided design (CAD), whether for original projects, re-engineering or maintenance.
- All these issues call for on-line handling of information resources in an effort to be more creative and much more flexible than in the past.

From CAD to any other functions and from original design to plain daily usage, the key phrase is *database mining*** which has by now become a well-established technology – even if practised only by pioneering telephone companies, manufacturing organizations and financial institutions. For these companies, database mining is currently a principal area of investment in new information technology.

Whatever an organization's field of activity, it is now almost certain that top-flight competitors are building database mining operations.

* Noise is any unwanted input. Even chamber music is noise if one wants to sleep.

** See D.N. Chorafas and H. Steinmann, *Database Mining* (Lafferty Publications, London and Dublin, 1994).

Some of those applications have already been identified by their owners as major new sources of profitability, including new design issues, opportunities for sales revenue and large cost savings.

Results from the able exploitation of databases through mining operations have enabled recovery of investments within months, rather than the many years that legacy systems require. The incentivies in adopting database mining strategies are evident on many occasions, but so too are the problems derived from lack of skill in this domain:

- Effective data mining tools have been slow to emerge from vendors and therefore commodity software is inadequate.
- As a result, whether in telecommunications or in other domains, foremost organizations have developed their own solutions, particularly in connection with database computers, disk farms or client-servers.

One of the handicaps with old approaches is that mainframes have great difficulties in overcoming performance problems, and their software is not adept in providing the levels of data integrity required. Also, lack of generally available database mining skills introduces problems in meta-data management. Added to this is political and cultural resistance to change.

The radar chart in Figure 5.4 summarizes the six major issues raised in this section in connection with critical software-supported communications functions. These issues are interrelated; the combinations and

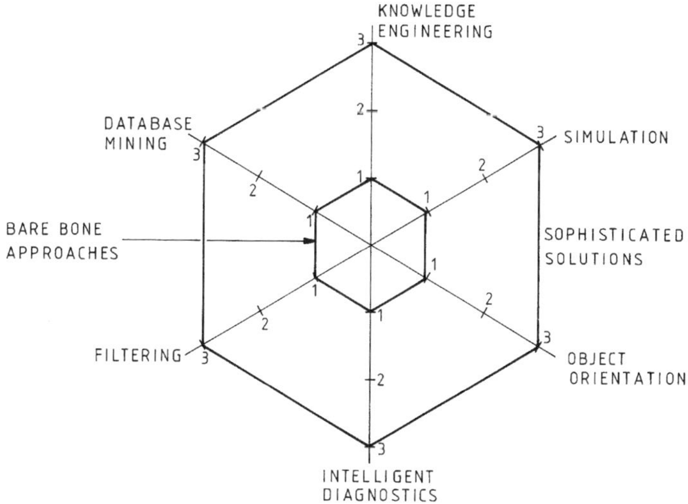

Figure 5.4 The top six functions to be supported by sophisticated communications software

permutations they present lead to other challenges, but by and large a telecommunications company or user organization that masters them has little to fear from the complexities modern networks present.

9. Establishing and Maintaining Technology Supply Chains

There are no miracle solutions to the telecommunications challenges this chapter has identified. Neither is it possible that one organization – whether telco, equipment vendor or user entity – solves all problems single-handed. The cosy relationship which, depending on the country, used to exist 20 years ago, or even five years ago, between the national and local telephony company and its preferred vendors has now been replaced by *dynamic partnerships*, which can best be described as technology supply chains.

- No organization, no matter how potent, can keep all technology developments in-house.
- Hence, the trend toward farming out technology development to suppliers all the way down the food chain.

While this practice is today on the increase, many companies are concerned about losing control of their business by giving away control of key technologies. Therefore, they prefer to keep them in-house. The downside however is that this approach keeps the company in a backwater; this is as bad as having only one main supplier.

The upside of an open architecture, which is the enabling mechanism for technology supply chains, is that it permits a company to hedge its bets, and do a better job of maximizing profits when it comes to choosing and implementing high-profile software and hardware.

- In the coming decade, failure to develop technology supply chains probably will prove economically and technologically disastrous.
- The more complex are technology developments, the greater the need to support sensible collaborative efforts that will benefit all participating companies.

Such strategy calls for a thorough rethinking and re-evaluation of technology procurement all the way to the roles likely to be played in technology supply. This includes operational issues as well as technology management – both being basic ingredients in building a network of supply chain relationships.

More than ever a company's success depends not only on its products' features, price and performance, but on its flexibility in meeting changing demand. If the firm does not have timely access to state-of-the-art technology, it will face major competitive barriers. The crucial question then becomes: How can you ensure that access?

- Should one downsize internal capabilities and give preference to key technology partners?
- Which technologies and functions are so critical that they must be maintained in-house?
- What is the strategy one should follow in building a technology supply chain to support future growth and competitiveness?

These queries pose a host of new strategic and operational issues to technology management. The necessary answers range from critical in-depth evaluations, to field studies on how telecommunications, computers and software manufacturers are slashing product development expenses by farming out some of the work to suppliers.

After the decision is made to establish polyvalent technology supply chains, the critical question becomes what one gives up and what one retains. Which are the trade-offs when outsourcing core technologies? The answer divides into two parts:

- how to co-operate and compete by developing and maintaining a technology infrastructure at state-of-the-art level
- how to identify viable supply chain partners, keeping proprietary technologies out of the hands of competitors.

Entering into the wrong partnerships could be equally harmful as trying to go all alone. But which factors should be weighted in terms of corporate culture and complementary technological capability before a deal is made?

Should we source from competitors? What should the policy be on joint developments? How long should the commitment be? What are the trade-offs between long-term partnerships and keeping the options open? What sort of balance should exist between the financing of new developments and the sharing of pay-offs?

Other queries relate to human capital: what new human resource issues will emerge as a result of technology partnerships? What level of investments in human capital should we be prepared to make? How can technology assist in making the internal lifelong learning programmes more effective?

Still other issues are market oriented. For instance, what's the price we must be willing to pay for faster time to market and lower unit costs? Will a dynamic partnership strategy result in loss of control over sensitive information involving profit margins? What may be the longer-term effect on market share?

Some queries are structural: how to downsize internal capabilities and invest in outside suppliers? Will there be organizational complications by integrating outside suppliers into our company's internal development and manufacturing processes? Should we, as counterweight, strengthen selected internal technological capabilities?

As a guide, a range of corporate technology strategies are now employed by American and Japanese firms in the automotive, electronics, machine tool and other industries. The foremost companies in these industries have gone through soul-searching 'make versus buy' decisions; equipment development practices; and supplier relations. Telecommunications organizations and projects can learn a great deal from this precedence in terms of establishing and maintaining a competitive technology supply chain.

6

The Network is the Bank: Realspace and Virtual Reality Applications

1. Introduction

The statement that *the network is the bank* may sound like long-range planning. But, as Dr Peter Drucker aptly suggests, 'Long range planning does not deal with future decisions, but with the futurity of *present decisions*'. The decisions which we are making now will weigh heavily on the fate of a bank in the years ahead – and the network is the kernel of the financial industry's future.

By radically rethinking and redesigning business processes, with assistance from advanced information technology, banks can produce quantum improvements in quality, speed of service, and costs. They can:

- serve their clients better than ever before in spite of the multiplicity of products
- control their exposure at any time anywhere in the world.

This evidently requires a radical change in culture, but let us never forget that a stubborn, inflexible attitude is a sign of weakness not of strength. Stubbornness is the typical response of average bankers and mediocre technologists.

Virtual reality, several experts believe, is the next generation in man–machine communications, currently evaluated in prototypes addressed to different applications areas. In terms of execution, virtual reality is synonymous to *realtime simulation*, which can be defined as:

- the interactive presentation of the computational model
- able to support continuity in terms of human perception.

Beyond realtime, the banker, the trader and the investor must be able to see market patterns in realspace, mapping market behaviour through mathematical models run on supercomputers. These models will be fed with instantaneous information through networks.

- Realspace is realtime but executed as if it were in one geographic location.
- This one virtual location reflects the pattern and the details of financial markets in the four corners of the world.

The existence of realspace facilities leads to *value differentiation* in financial services and provides a competitive edge to a bank. While realtime and realspace are not the only factors promoting relationship banking, their role is vital. This is particularly true when the use of networks is enriched with knowledge engineering as well as with sophisticated visualization functions.

2. The New Role of Telecommunications in Banking

The relationship between the virtual bank and its customers is promoted by the way electronic communication technologies have changed the nature of finance. This has happened at a fundamental level almost without anyone noticing. Suddenly, traders, portfolio managers and financial analysts find themselves in a *cyberspace*.*

The notion of cyberspace is indivisible from that of the global information economy which is now a plausible scenario. The basis for wealth has changed subtly but profoundly over the past three decades, due to the increasing linkages between:

- financial transactions
- global communication
- computer systems.

Transaction execution and the representation of financial flows are interlinked through mathematical models and databases. No sophisticated financial activity, and particularly no derivative financial instruments, can be handled without this infrastructure.

Rocket scientists and their management should appreciate that realspace and cyberspace are milestones in the evolution of realtime which is in itself a concept in full evolution. Since the mid-1960s the use of realtime made possible speedy handling of local markets and customer requirements. But as the latter grew in complexity, and 24-hour banking came about, though necessary, classical realtime is no longer enough. Global networks are needed since a leading financial institution has to operate:

- at any time
- in any market

* See also D.N. Chorafas and H. Steinmann, *Virtual Reality. Practical Applications in Business and Industry* (Prentice-Hall, Englewood Cliffs, NJ, 1995).

- or any product
- on behalf of any major customer.

The movement of novel financial instruments through global communication systems has irrevocably changed the nature of banking. The value of currencies is no longer determined by international trade volumes or any of the physical activities normally associated with industrial economies. Trade in physical commodities is now less than 10 per cent and in some cases less than 5 per cent of daily financial swings over the exchanges.

- Want it or not, this pace is increasing. In 1986, international foreign exchange transactions reached \$87 trillion in one year. That was 23 times the American GNP.
- Currently, the foreign exchange transactions alone exceed \$1.2 trillion per day. With all other money movements included, the sum reaches up to half the American GNP per day.

All this is generated by electronic transactions executed through networks. Money is now a kind of message, and the message it carries would soon create a new sort of wealth based on *virtual assets* – that we have barely begun to understand.

This new kind of wealth will be characterized by huge amounts of fluid, rapidly moving financial assets based on communications rather than gold convertibility or legal tender in the form of paper money. All this evolved over the past 20 years because of several interrelated factors, as we will see in the following sections.

For instance, the virtual merger of widely scattered financial markets ensured that exchange rates which determined the relative values of various currencies were cut loose when the Bretton Woods agreement fell apart in 1971. For the first time in history *a networked market-place* was created.

The Bretton Woods agreement that had been established in the 1940s, as World War II came to a close, provided a relatively slow-moving mechanism for adjusting the exchange rates of currency. Thirty years later it disintegrated.

- The old rules for determining the values of currencies from day to day were no longer valid.
- The new rules were fathered by the networked markets rather than by governments and regulators.

At the same time, as exchanges started trading in options and futures, computer-based financial models became available for pricing purposes.

In the 1980s with off-balance sheet (OBS) financing, it became possible to make huge amounts of money by moving even greater amounts of money from one currency to another, not on the spot but sometime in the future.

Many off-balance sheet deals are bilateral agreements. They are generated in the minds of people versatile with banking, and who obey regulations only marginally but are very sensitive to market values. The way in which transactions are consumated is via communication technology which is fast evolving.

All this provides plenty of evidence that *the network is the bank*, and vice versa. Advanced technology and financial markets also have this in common: they are never static. Hence the snapshot of today is practically irrelevant. According to Dr Drucker's dictum, we need to look far out into the future in order to appreciate what we should be doing at the present time.

3. Appreciating the Intrinsic Aspects of Realtime and Realspace

Realtime is a development of the mid-1960s. The term was coined to differentiate between batch operations, whose output took ages to reach the end-user, and the possibility to access on-line information stored in the machine.

- The results of the computation can be recorded or used to guide a physical process, which is important in a realtime concept.
- Early examples have been computers that guide weapons systems, refinery operations or airplane landings.
- On-line access compressed the time necessary to obtain data from the database and manipulate these information elements.

Database interactivity ensures that, by extension, realtime also refers to direct access to computer storage for fast updating of a field, file or record. Both the retrieval of information elements and their manipulation was originally achieved through *time-sharing* of computer resources.

The process of time-sharing a central processor preceded that of realtime for a few years. It resulted from the seminal work that Dr Myron Tribus, of Dartmouth College, had carried out for General Electric, with the goal of providing on-line services to many users by running each one's task part of the time on the central processor – a process later labelled cycle-stealing.

Since response time has to be shorter and shorter for guiding physical processes, time-sharing reached its limits. Subsecond response requires very fast computers and software that perform during the actual time of the physical process under control – and by extension dedicated resources.*

Even better, if the control software responds faster than the physical process, it is possible to provide *feedforward* capabilities, projecting the deviations that might take place in the controlled process and making feasible corrective action before these deviations occur.

- Line by line, what the preceding paragraphs have stated is applicable to banking.
- In finance, too, there exist processes which under certain conditions tend to run out of control.
- Therefore, we are interested in correcting deviations before they take place, using the power of prognosis.

There exist however two major differences between the mid-1960s when the concept of realtime came to life and today. One lies in the fact that three decades ago realtime meant immediate access to central computer resources by non-intelligent terminals.

With intelligent terminals and communicating databases, there has been a bifurcation in classical realtime. For several applications, *real enough time*** will do. For instance, full, comprehensive, consistent update of a distributed database can be actioned every 'x' minutes or an hour – to reduce the costs. This may be an acceptable practice for management accounting and other data – provided a number of system prerogatives are observed.

On the other hand, as Figure 6.1 suggests, mission-critical applications can be satisfied neither by classical realtime nor by real enough time. The computational results must be available instantaneously at subsecond speed – a job which can never be done through cycle-stealing, hence the Stonebraker rule which we discuss in sections 9 and 10.

The second major difference between the mid-1960s and the mid-1990s, in terms of the implementation of realtime systems, is that in the 1960s the controlled processes were local. By contrast, in the 1990s the most competitive systems must address global operations spanning countries, continents or the whole world.

This globality of operations creates the need for realspace applications, which as defined in section 1, bring to one focal point – which may be virtual – scattered activities making feasible command and control.

* See also the discussion on shared-nothing solutions in section 10.

** This is deferred transmission to capitalize on the systems economics and reduce costs.

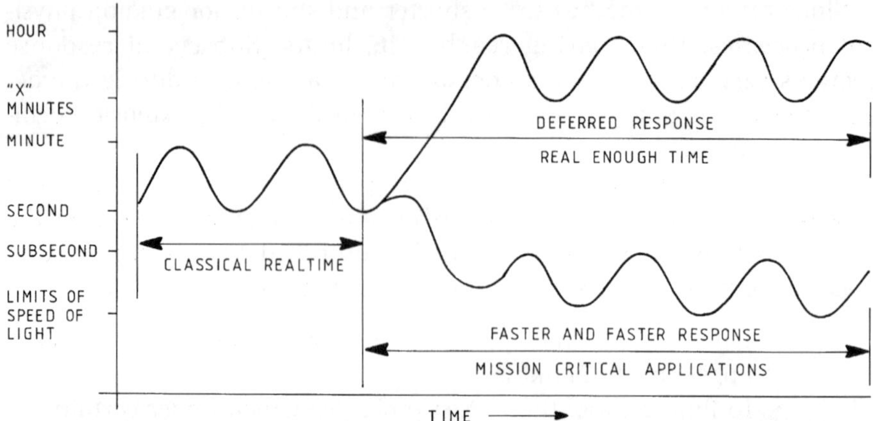

Figure 6.1 Old and new realtime perspectives differ in many ways as the characteristics of the process being controlled have changed

- Such organization is far from being centralized and it is more than distributed. It is a *federated* solution.
- The focal point where realspace functionality is exercised may be anywhere in the network at 'this' moment, and somewhere else in the next moment.
- This flexible, *virtual centralization* can be exercised from different nodes in the network simultaneously, as required by operational characteristics.

Realspace solutions are therefore at the core of interactive computational finance, which has become an essential element of competitiveness at Wall Street, as well as elsewhere in the First World.

Virtual centralization is an intensive process in terms of networking, databasing and computation. It requires sophisticated mathematical models for the global exploitation of business opportunity, but it can serve in an able manner relationship banking with transnational corporations. It also enables an effective control of risk.

4. Business Opportunities Opening Up with the Implementation of Realspace

As new financial products evolve and their market grows, it is necessary to work in realspace in order to evaluate windows of opportunity, assess the effects of market changes on client portfolios and manage exposure in compressed time-scales. With tick-by-tick high-frequency financial data, solutions executed in realspace make the difference between profit and loss.

Money centre banks have learned by experience that they must provide themselves with the ability to rapidly evaluate business opportunities and exposure, amending positions or adding new ones as required in a global sense. This will not necessarily be required every minute, but when it is needed everything has to be in place for subsecond response. The reasons for rigorous financial evaluations may be a political upheaval, a local war of significance like the Iraqi invasion of Kuwait in August 1990, a stock market crash like that in October 1987, a bond panic as in March 1994, or any other.

- There are intriguing possibilities in bringing together in realtime different financial markets and analysing their behaviour in a split second.

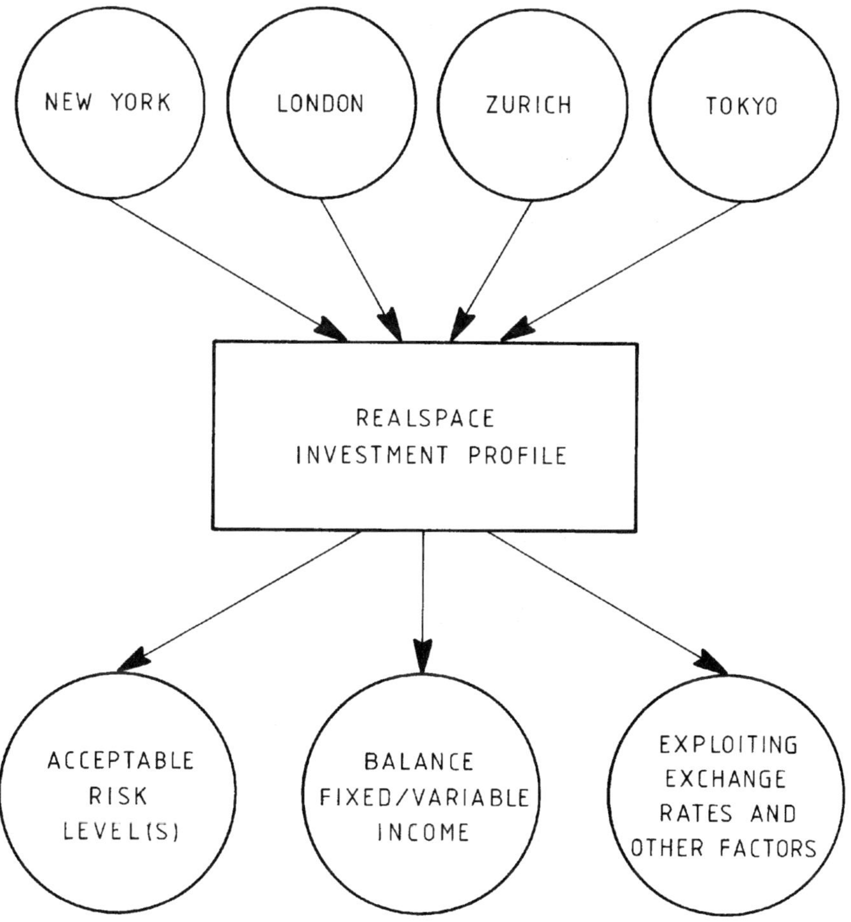

Figure 6.2 The focus must be worldwide at the same moment based on market conditions and investment goals

There may be many more than Figure 6.2 presents as an example. During meetings some banks suggested up to a dozen different reasons. Each has its specific characteristics, its mode of responding to market challenges, its sensitivities, its lust and greed, its reaction time and the depth this reaction can reach.

- A valid way to exploit opportunity and to manage exposure is to work simultaneously worldwide, based on market conditions and/or investment goals, as shown in Figure 6.2.

Experimentation is another goal served by the implementation of realspace. For instance, evaluating the observance of defined limits by customer, no matter how the portfolio is structured in terms of currencies, countries, credit types, financial instruments, or other categories.

For multinational clients the bank must be able to test in realspace world-wide credit lines, limits and associated rules. This must often be done at transaction entry to determine current availability of funds and credit lines in any place, at any time. Solutions should also feature an on-line, perpetual capability for risk management as interday exposures tend to mount.

The crux of the matter is that modern banking makes it necessary to support a wide range of information on a global basis: sharing, allocating, excluding and reserving limits and/or financial instruments between customer entities, credit/debit types, moneys involved and branches – and being able to see the position of corresponding banks with which accounts are shared.

By augmenting the existing facilities through the synergy which it provides, the realspace system should lead to a prognosis on oncoming defaults. Agents must help to automatically adjust interest for back-valued deals or changing interest rates; one agent per supported instrument, specific feature or customer relation.

- A change in the value of a floating rate automatically changes the rate of interest for adjustable loans and deposits.
- A change in the value of an underlier affects the value of the corresponding derivatives product.

Realspace information should provide a clear, consistent, steadily updated pattern on *total commitment* (the total sum of all contracts granted to the customer), *settlement limits* (the total amount that can be settled on any given value date) and other crucial variables. Balances outstanding should show individually and as an aggregate all customer contracts including deals:

- from past history
- to projected value dates in the future.

The more sophisticated the products the bank features, the more advanced must be the technology to support them. Treasury applications require on-line, perpetual deal capture with bank-specified verification. They call for support of foreign exchange trading operations including:

- spot deals
- forward outright
- forward rate agreements
- interest rate and other swaps
- option contracts
- covered interest arbitrage.

For operations with large notional principal as well as the more risky deals, realspace enquiry should take place at the time of deal clearance, and realspace updates at deal capture. This will help provide realistic responses to queries regarding foreign exchange positions as well as gaps; loans and deposits positions; nostro current and projected; forex contracts and so on.

Among the requirements are realtime updates of foreign exchange positions for non-dealing-room activity such as funds transfer, cross currency payments, and larger teller currency exchange. Increasingly the law requires reporting of deals exceeding a certain amount for money whitewashing and other reasons.

5. The Expanding Domain of Studies in Rocket Science*

As financial institutions and other companies divide their operations into independent business units and reform themselves into federations of autonomous firms, they restructure their command and control around their information networks. These are tying together country headquarters and branch offices, telecommuting employees, suppliers and customers.

- On the technical side, networks use coaxial, optical fibres and satellites to provide bridges among workstations, database servers, laptop computers and fax machines.
- On the organization side, the result is the removal of entire middle layers of management, thereby flattening the organization.

* See also D.N. Chorafas, *Rocket Scientists in Banking* (Lafferty, London and Dublin, 1995).

Classically, the job of middle management has been to collect, digest and disseminate information. This is done today better, faster and at lower cost through networks, algorithms and heuristics.

In this simple paragraph lies a vast amount of work for rocket scientists. Not only information filtering functions have to be expressed algorithmically and also programmed, but so do all the transactional chores which can be automated through agents, for instance:

- the flexible but precise observation of bank-defined rules for transaction verification and message release
- agents can action verification by customer, amount, transaction type and other operating parameters.

In terms of funds transfer applications, agents can assure on-line, perpetual, realtime entry generation and processing of payments and receipts. This may include foreign currency of payments using settlement instructions, customer advices, and links to other processing modules. Automatic releases must be based on bank-defined parameters, such as:

- account owner
- current level
- current and projected balances
- overdraft limit, and so on

including on-line maintenance of standing orders. The implementation of interactive expert systems sharply reduces manual costs. It also assures that the facility automatically formats and translates to a standard frame of reference incoming and outgoing messages via external communication networks including SWIFT, CHIPS, CHAPS and ZENGIN.

Another banking prerequisite to be handled through agents is reconciliation. This requires on-line, computer-based matching of actual to expected receipts, and reporting of failure-to-receive. Exception reporting should include:

- upcoming settlements
- received and not received
- advised and non-advised
- all exception conditions such as unverified items and failed payments.

These issues are not new to the banking industry. What is new is the need to execute them through algorithms and heuristics. Beyond this, realspace consolidation is critical to the bank's profitability and survival.

When we talk about advanced applications of information technology we must keep in mind that by the end of this decade, technology will enable three most fundamental advances which would have been impossible in the past, but now are becoming the spearhead of computing:

- The on-line gathering of inputs at point of origin.
- The on-line use of databases and of number crunching facilities.
- The creation of fully interactive animated output – also online.

That is where the contribution of virtual reality (VR) comes in. Generated by means of computers and software, VR lets users create entirely new worlds and provides ways to augment perceptions of the existing environment. Among the technical problems confronting such applications domain is feeding into the database generator. This may pose bandwidth problems connected to *generic visualization*:

- One of the challenges with generic visualization is the able generation of networked computer-supported collaborative work.
- All actions in one screen must be reflected on the others, but at the same time everybody may need to have their own 3-D view.

In conclusion, networked collaborative work has become most crucial in a number of projects with the goal of shortening the time to production and delivery. The new solutions which we are discussing aim at reducing time to market, cutting costs and assuring a better quality product. This is why financial institutions need this technology.

6. The Difference between MIS, EIS and Virtual Reality

Some people ask what is the difference between virtual reality and management information systems (MIS) or executive information systems (EIS) – as well as what is the difference between MIS and EIS. Starting with the second question, the difference between MIS and EIS is a gimmick, a sales trick. As for the first query, Table 6.1 provides the answer.

Beyond the better-known simulation and graphics aspects of advanced technology lies the problem of realtime data analysis which is not addressed by MIS, EIS and the mainframers supporting them. The cornerstone to this effort is the creation of distributed deductive databases which will be interactively rendered and presented in 3-D.

Because virtual reality is based on realtime simulation, its users must be aware of the notion underpinning hypothetical or simulated performance results. Unlike an actual performance record based on accounting and statistics – as is the case with MIS/EIS – simulated results are

Table 6.1 Old realities and new information technology

MIS/EIS	*Virtual reality*
1. Pre-processed data	1. Post-processed information
2. Executive level	2. All levels
3. End product	3. Enabling technology
4. Character user interface	4. Graphic user interface
5. Fixed data reports	5. Generic visualization
6. Heterogeneous presentation formats	6. Homogeneous presentation formats
7. Mainframe-based	7. Client-server based
8. Rather inflexible system	8. Flexible system
9. Mainly batch update	9. Realtime response
10. Closed environment	10. Open environment
11. High initial costs	11. Low initial costs
12. High operating costs	12. Low operating costs

projections. They do not represent actual trading or any other activities which have taken place.

Limitations exist, of course. Since the trades have not actually been executed, the results may have under- or overcompensated for the impact, if any, of certain market factors, such as lack of liquidity.

- Simulated trading programs in general are subject to the fact that they are designed with the benefit of hindsight.
- No assurance is being given that any account will or is likely to achieve profits or losses similar to those shown in a VR presentation.

On the other hand, MIS/EIS has significant shortcomings in terms of guiding the hand of the manager, the trader or the investor. Because it is based on statistics, it strictly shows past performance – but past performance results are not necessarily indicative of future performance.

The fact that realtime simulation enables looking into the future has ensured that over the years virtual reality technology has been put to good use in the fields of architecture, engineering science, education and, more recently, finance. New types of applications come on stream as VR emerges and matures, becoming one of the important computer-based tools.

The difference between MIS/EIS and virtual reality can also be seen in another way. Both MIS and EIS are very short bandwidth outputs. The real world is composed of an infinite number of spectra, frequencies and textures which MIS/EIS cannot possibly capture and they can transmit even less.

- Unassisted, human senses perceive some of these frequencies and spectra and simply ignore others.
- By contrast, computer-generated virtual reality allows users to perceive and sometimes to create entirely new worlds.

Advanced software lets a user interact with the generated virtual world forms, the heart of any VR system. The reality engine takes a stored set of objects and landscapes and manipulates them, such manipulation being interactive and user directed – employing a broadband in visualization.

Whether in finance, in engineering, in architecture, or other fields of business and science, broadband output is necessary in order to accommodate the goals virtual reality sets itself. Such goals revolve around the need to induce a realworld sensation in the application developer as well as the end-user:

- involving visual, audio, tactile, and olfactory input/output
- employing realistic backgrounds and animation
- meticulously reproducing immediate surroundings
- employing parallel processing for realtime response.

Current applications examples include deployment of weapons systems; tank battles; aircraft cockpit simulation; helicopter landing on high seas; automobile driving simulation; portfolio management involving equities, debt, real estate and other assets denominated in different currencies and traded in different markets.

Other implementation examples can be found in medicine. During the last five years a growing number of surgical operations are undertaken in virtual reality setting. Still other applications concern molecular structures, fluid flows and vehicular body contour design. Also financial flows can be effectively represented:

- reflecting market activity
- enabling analysis of the resulting patterns.

Virtual reality involves *rendering* – that is, direct display of physical phenomena whose characteristics may, or may not, have obvious visual representations as well as audio and being tactile. Animation may, or may not, be employed in connection to a virtual reality world.

This last remark brings up the subject of *immersion*. Widely used in engineering and science, immersion allows a direct, dynamic and intuitive manipulation of objects, through gestures and human body movement. It generates a direct and intuitive feedback, regarded as a significant step in advanced man–machine communication.

A VR study completed at the University of Tokyo for Tokyo Electric enabled the power engineer to walk with a helmet, dataglove and a data stick through a distribution network. The engineer can, for instance, handlift a 24,000-volt power line and immediately observe the power flows and bottlenecks.* But for the time being immersion is not necessary in a financial environment – though animation may be needed.

7. Three-Dimensional Modelling and the Study of the Virtual Environment

As financial information systems continue to grow, with an increasing need to establish relationships between widely spread points, existing interfaces such as windows, icons and menus fall short of assisting the end-user in an able manner. Just accessing the distributed databases through printouts or screen displays, is a limited bandwidth which gives very little in terms of relationships between sought-out information elements. This is especially true where many relationships and cross-references exist and need to be dynamically exploited.

What is necessary is an action/reaction animated presentation with information presented in a graphic form, with audio enhancements. The output stream must be updated continuously in an interactive manner. This is what VR offers.

The point has already been made in section 6 that an effective virtual reality application requires 3-D modelling presented in a world sustained by the use of two-way realtime data transfer.

- The channel will be fibre optic or radio links interconnecting workstations and servers.
- The software must be able to present motion data as well as modify the graphical presentation made by the model.

'A virtual environment,' said MIT's Dr David Zeltzer, 'is a better platform for computer applications in science, engineering and business than the alternatives we have had so far.' What is new in this implementation is that the workstation of the end-user is now so cost-effective that we don't need millions of dollars anymore to make realistic and interesting:

- realtime simulation
- computer graphics.

* See also D.N. Chorafas and H. Steinmann, *Virtual Reality. Practical Applications in Business and Industry* (Prentice-Hall, Englewood Cliffs, NJ, 1995).

Technology is now providing miniature stereo displays at an affordable cost. Therefore, the question posed to every bank is whether or not it is willing and able to capitalize on these modern advancements.

As the Santa Fe Institute was to underline, the whole issue of implementing virtual reality is one of need to significantly improve upon *presentation* of information – not its processing. Effective presentation can take many aspects, all of them having to do with different degrees of sophistication in visualization.

Let us put these issues into correct perspective. Virtual reality today may be an expanding field but we should not forget that it owes much of its background to simulation and 3-D graphics. Realtime simulation puts emphasis on *applications building* which poses a number of challenges in:

- rocket science
- systems engineering
- human interfaces
- applications development.

The more advanced the solution, the better able it is to cut inside the problem of emulating market behaviour through technology. At the same time, the more these issues are faced in an able manner, the more they enable the extension of human senses – as we saw in section 6.

The factors of success do not only lie in building simulators, using knowledge engineering and implementing 3-D graphics but also in collecting and filtering data to be used in providing effective visualizing solutions. The challenge comes by stages as practical examples help document:

- Designing an aircraft carrier or a financial system is a much larger problem than the better-known 'one product only' orientation.
- Systems complexity affects the *whole process*, and we must take this into account in the *solution* space.

Figure 6.3 presents an example from risk management focused on derivative financial products. It can be approached either way, depending on the chosen design and the availability, of detailed risk control components:

- If credit risk and market risk components already exist, it pays to build a *consolidated* exposure module in virtual reality.
- Otherwise, the sound approach is to develop first the peripheral VR modules (of which six are suggested in Figure 6.3), then integrate them in a consolidated exposure artefact.

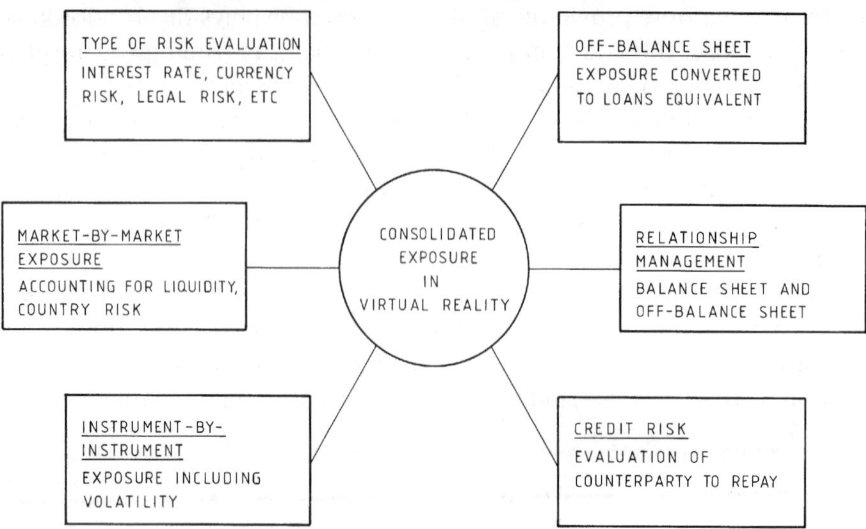

Figure 6.3 Component parts of a risk management structure designed for off balance-sheet operations

Either strategy will require high-level graphics tools with a set of libraries and primitive commands. An object-oriented database management system, interactive input/output (I/O) utilities, languages and high-performance hardware are vital component parts. Even more crucial is know-how. These are not subjects the technologists alone or the banker alone can solve. As we will see in section 8, the answer is *synergy*.

8. Why Technologists must become Bankers, and Bankers must be Technologists

One of the outstanding contributions Field Marshall Montgomery made before D-Day was his careful meshing of experienced veterans from the Eighth Army with the keen but green formations that had been training and languishing for so long in England. An old desert hand, Major-General G.P.B. 'Pip' Roberts, found his new headquarters at 11th Armoured Division still operating the routines and mess life of the peacetime British army.

Without loss of time General Roberts relieved them of such formalities, sacking his senior staff officer, a meticulous Guardsman, who had a red light over his office door to indicate that he did not wish to be disturbed. Rapidly, at the beginning of 1944, all the senior officers were abruptly removed and replaced by others from a quite different mould.

For hours and days at a stretch, officers and soldiers of the British

Army preparing for the invasion of Nazi-held Europe shivered in their tanks on the hills through endless mock attacks and deployments. They were preparing in earnest for what they had to do. That's a good example for bankers to follow if they wish to survive in the financial markets of the 1990s and beyond.

The Eighth Army versus the Guardsmen is a metaphor which should teach a lesson to the financial industry. A parallel metaphor is that of rocket scientists versus the leisurely vanilla-icecream data processors and the staff bankers who don't want to be disturbed about the great strides of technology, yet play their bank in the derivatives markets where exposure can build skyscrapers.

Quite likely, the gap is not only cultural but also of an investment nature. Classical bankers fail to appreciate the gigastreams, the terabytes, the billions of instructions per second and their affordable cost. 'What we obtain too cheap, we esteem too lightly,' said Thomas Paine in *The Age of Reason*.

Carrying information back and forth across cities, countries, continents or the globe, in large amounts and fairly quickly, is no longer a problem. But the financial implications of the transactions generated by such a system can be a problem in view of old concepts in banking and of substandard hardware and software used in the majority of cases.

The technological challenge grows not only with derivatives and other complex financial products but also with multimedia as well as with televirtual communications. These bring realtime networks technology and intelligent databases on a whole new references level, underlining the need to redefine *reality* and changing our notions of *time* and *space*.

Fortunes can be made by those who discern the new scenario early enough, and are able to capitalize on its potential while keeping the risks at bay. This task is by no means easy, but it is possible.

In the years to come, this and many other developments will be interdisciplinary. Just like technology impacts on banking, banking will greatly influence technological developments. Therefore, people with both backgrounds will be better able to face the developing challenges and to turn them into business opportunities worth talking about – that's the sense of synergy.

A serious research will extend beyond the financial issues into the social aspects. New communication technologies might bring new political regimes, new social institutions, new mental diseases, new concepts on how we live and work – and with them new economic opportunities.

- People, companies and nations too rigid to respond to the changes, and the challenges, will fracture.
- The survivors will be those flexible enough to adapt to the

transformed world view of the twenty-first century's new set of rules.

The workplace and the living room created by the act of computer-enriched communications will not necessarily be the same as those which exist today at either end of the communication link – and it is wise to appreciate the implications of this.

Currently, there is information at each end that is not transmitted or otherwise utilized. In a short time span interactive databases will take care of such storage, exploiting its contents through knowledge engineering artefacts, or agents. The net result will be to create a virtual world.

In this context, it will be wrong to think of communications as being only the transmission of information from one point to another – which seems simply a technical problem. While interactive broadband communications will involve an increasingly large amount of information generation, storage and *ad hoc* retrieval, the virtual world being created will have semantic content, and therefore will impact on the real world.

9. Networks of Computers or Computer Networks?

'Networks of computers are taking over from computer networks', said Ross Salinger, managing director of Credit Swiss Financial Products, during our meeting in London. 'The solutions which we are giving today will influence the way we do business in the late 1990s as well as the way we are organized and managed as a bank.' This statement is correct.

- The culture that we have defines the tasks that we undertake and the way in which we behave as professionals.
- It helps to facilitate or, alternatively, impede the products that we sell – and the way in which we do business.

'To be competitive, we will have multiprocessors at dealer desks', suggested Geoff J.R. Doubleday, chief information officer (CIO) of Credit Swiss First Boston (CSFB), and he provided some statistics on the computing equipment acquired off-the-shelf and now used in dealing at CSFB:

- 500 Unix boxes
- 250 personal computers.

In terms of installed power, at an average 40 MIPS per Unix workstation and 10 MIPS per PC, this represents an impressive 22,500 MIPS – plus the minis, maxis and mainframes still around.

'As everywhere else, most of this installed power is underutilized,' said Doubleday. 'If sufficient communications speed was available, we could use this computing capacity day and night to wire up and optimize processors.' I think in this particular instance the CIO is wrong.

This and similar concepts are born out of mainframe mentality and, as another senior British banker was to suggest, they essentially amount to the advice: 'Exploit to death the legacy system!' This is a very bad policy indeed – particularly for mission-critical applications.

- Building confidence in the programmer's ability to deliver advanced applications, is one thing.
- Sticking to old machines, obsolete languages and the tight coupling of mainframes, is another.
- Networking through tight coupling when the risk of system failure can be disruptive and destructive, is most inadvisable.

Dr Michael Stonebraker of the University of California, Berkeley, who in the 1970s led the effort which delivered Ingres – the first relational database management system – recently completed another milestone study on information technology. Its conclusions can be phrased in one powerful sentence: 'Every time you have more processes than processors, you are in trouble.'

- A computing bottleneck is bound to develop.
- Just as if there exist communications corks.

To break the communications bottleneck, CSFB looks towards optical-fibre linkages with FDDI II protocol and its 150 MIPS. But necessary channel capacity is not sufficient. No information technology plan should forget two important issues which, when taken into the picture, turn the whole idea of tightly coupling distributed computers on its head:

1. The software challenge.
2. Precedence from the power industry.

Currently, an estimated 95 per cent of all installed power in America (including electricity production plants) is under the bonnets of cars. These cars are used on average only an hour or two per day – but this does not stop people from buying them, because even at that low utilization rates they serve their purpose. The criterion is *utility* and *cost-effectiveness*.

The software challenge is, or at least should be, just as evident to everybody. Stated simply, today there does not exist any procedure anywhere in the world which can really optimize a complex installation of computing equipment – particularly when this equipment is tightly coupled, which is a typical case with mainframe installations.

But valid rules based on research findings do exist, which clear-eyed management will be wise to observe. One of the best comes from the aforementioned study at the University of California, Berkeley, and rests on work by Dr Michael Stonebraker and Dr Wei Hong:

- There is a dramatic drop in performance when there are more processes than processors in a network.
- The reason is contention, cycle-stealing, partitioning schemes, system overload, system overhead and lack of optimization.

To cure some of these 'illnesses', CSFB made reference to ISIS, a piece of software by Cornell University, but this approach is off target. ISIS is a simple optimizer written to satisfy sponsored graduate research, not the heavy duty of the information environment which today characterizes the foremost financial institutions.

Whether we like to think in terms of networks of computers or of computer networks, the principles guiding a sound systems design should be observed at all times. This is an issue which neither bankers nor technologists should forget. As the Magi advised Alexander the Great when he conquered Persia: 'He who is chosen the people's king, can choose little for himself thereafter.'

10. Computers, Networks and the Shared-Nothing Concept

The change in culture brought about through the new perspectives we have seen in this book rests on a number of financial and technological developments which progress in parallel, even if few people properly correlate them to develop a pattern. These developments revolutionize what we know so far in terms of the banking business – as well as in regard to computers, communications and software. The five top-most references are:

1. The virtual merger of widely scattered financial markets.
2. The availability of rocket scientists and of a new generation of computer literate users.
3. Massive infrastructural improvements and the fact that different technologies now converge.
4. The move towards realtime and realspace handling of information in a digital form.
5. The relatively low cost of billions of instructions per second, terabytes and gigastreams.

In section 2 we have spoken of the virtual merger of financial markets into a global networked environment, and how this has tremendously influenced banking. The need for rocket scientists has been an inescapable aftermath of this colossal change which altered the way business classically has been conducted.

The massive infrastructural improvements and the move towards the implementation of realspace, closely correlate to the new evolving aspects of global financial operations. Such investments, however, would not have been coming as fast as they did if it was not for

- large communications bandwidth
- significant database capacity
- high performance computing

becoming affordable propositions. But it proved to be much easier to radically cut down equipment costs than to alter the ways in which such equipment and its software are used. Some well-connected EDP bosses are incompetent but keep their jobs because top management cannot decide what to do with them so as not to offend their powerful backers.

This situation looks so much more ludicrous if we appreciate that in a large number of cases the fast-moving financial markets and the supports needed to sustain an ever greater sophistication of products and services, have been decoupled. Legacy systems are no longer able to meet the needs of:

- a tough financial environment operating in realtime under fluid conditions
- mission-critical requirements derived from trading 24 hours per day.

If the experience from mainframes is of any value, and no doubt such experience cannot be discarded, even if there was a universal technological optimizer it would have been a very dangerous tool indeed:

- Tightly coupled systems are failure-prone and slow to restabilize.*
- Any engine's failure can close down the whole aggregate killing mission-critical tasks.

In realtime operations, such situation would be catastrophic to the bank, as many references from real life help document. When the mainframes of the Bank of New York went out of business for one night, the

* For reliability studies and the stabilization of complex systems, see D.N. Chorafas, *Data Communications and Computer Networks* (TAB Books/ McGraw-Hill, New York, 1991).

institution had to borrow money from the Federal Reserve of New York to meet its obligations – and it paid the reserve bank, only for interest on that money, a cool $50 million.

One of the main benefits provided by a distributed client-server solution is their *shared-nothing* systems characteristic. Coined at the University of California, Berkeley, this term simply means that while the resources are shared in a system-wide sense, they are not multiplexed on the same piece of equipment.

The cycles of the processor, central memory and disk storage are not shared between processes competing with one another for these resources. Simply stated, there is no tight coupling. Therefore, while the system is networked, the shared-nothing architecture contributes a significant improvement in overall reliability and availability.

Negating such vital advantage through tight coupling is no act of wise men. Rather, it is a show of mainframe mentality – therefore of near-sightedness and obsolescence of skills. Why throw away reliability? For whose sake?

7

Re-engineering the Business Network Architecture Through Object Solutions

1. Introduction

In chapter 5 we explained the reason why object-oriented software may provide the best approach to the solution of networking problems, particularly when enriched with knowledge engineering. One of the basic goals in developing modern communications systems is to endow their implementation and maintenance with *software tool integration* – which should be done in a factual and documented manner without the hype which usually goes with practically all software jobs.

Practitioners in the communications and computers field would appreciate that too often there are claims and counterclaims about facilities which integrate software tools. Such claims are nothing new in the computer business, and the first challenge is to properly define the meaning of the word *integration*. As shown in Figure 7.1, in a telecommunications environment integration can be seen as having three dimensions:

1. Intelligence-enriched control of communications lines and nodes.
2. Seamless, universal database access with database mining capabilities.
3. Interactive user interfaces for presentation and visualization.

In communications, these dimensions of integration cover the main logical and structural characteristics of any efficient solution. This is true all the way from computer-aided design to shell scripts and other means for high-level programming, and intertool messaging using various notifiers, standard calls, broadcasts and the like.

Software process modelling and enactment can be effectively assisted by object-oriented approaches. The goals to be served by a dynamic, flexible networking solution should include access to interactive databases providing the capability for:

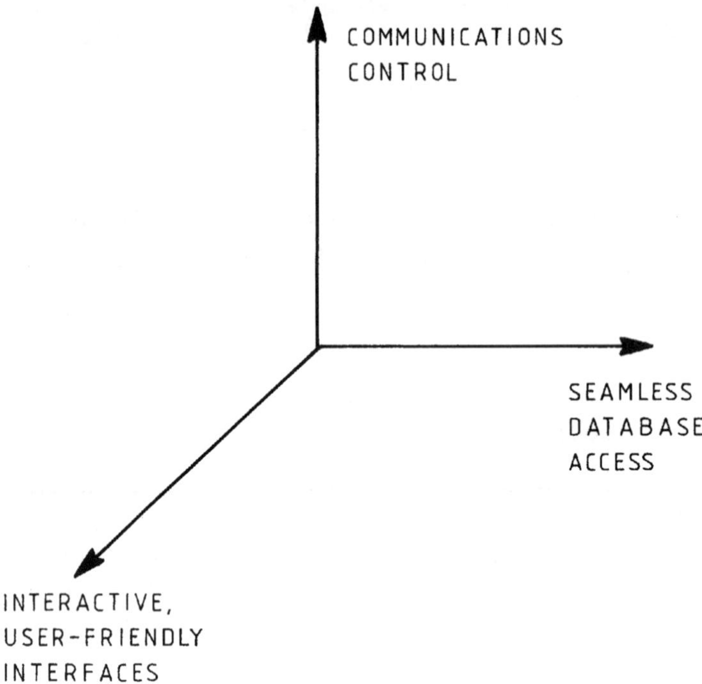

Figure 7.1 A frame of reference to help in visualizing what lies behind the concept of integration

- steady system evolution in a communications and computing sense, including agile human interfaces
- seamless interoperability and increased intelligibility by end-users endowed with comprehensive tools.

Besides the emphasis placed on end-users, there should be intelligent computer-based supports to co-ordinate the efforts of a team of developers and implementors. Interactive tools must use object-oriented approaches to permit the distribution and sharing of multimedia information as well as infrastructural facilities such as dictionaries, libraries and servers.

The emphasis on *multimedia* should be particularly appreciated as in this domain, more than in any other, kernel solutions need to be object oriented. Object concepts are most suitable as multimedia handling requirements require that system integration has to be achieved in a distributed sense – a goal which is not attainable through brute force.

2. Principles Underpinning Object-Oriented Solutions

The application of object-oriented principles has been successfully used in the design of specifications for computers and communications systems. Numerous projects exploited these principles in high-level design and the analysis of requirements at both the global level and with reference to the services provided to each end-user.

Objects can be *active*, including data and commands, or *passive*. The latter have only data. An object-oriented paradigm describes a communications system in terms of independently and simultaneously executing processes which co-operate to perform a business function.

- This approach permits the linking of business elements together as a means of defining products and managing business transactions.
- The process can emulate how a product planner might define a product from a set of existing business elements and a control function.

The product planner, and subsequently the product manager, specialize and recombine existing business elements. In a banking environment, for example, these may involve financial asset types, quotas, contracts and confirmations, identifying each as an object and its specific value as an *object instance*.

Major benefits derived from this approach come from three main notions underpinning an object approach: *inheritance, metaknowledge* and *polymorphism*. Taken together, they help in developing combinations which define flexible and adaptable templates for products and processes.

- *Inheritance* enables the construction of ephemeral hierarchies, whose elements can be recombined as the situation demands.

This makes feasible handling information elements and commands which have semantic meaning, a faculty which existed with the old hierarchical models, but has been lost with relational solutions. Figure 7.2 exemplifies this evolution in terms of semantics and flexibility.

- *Metaknowledge* is knowledge about knowledge, or a higher-up level of knowledge.

This characteristic is very important in communications and computing because it constitutes an elegant way of establishing specifications and setting constraints. In a business situation, for example, the product manager must specify the process which will be used to control delivery or level of risk.

The product's process control mechanism delivers the service by interacting with other pre-existing business elements, using the definition found in the template which has embedded metaknowledge. This enables the actuation of the third basic faculty.

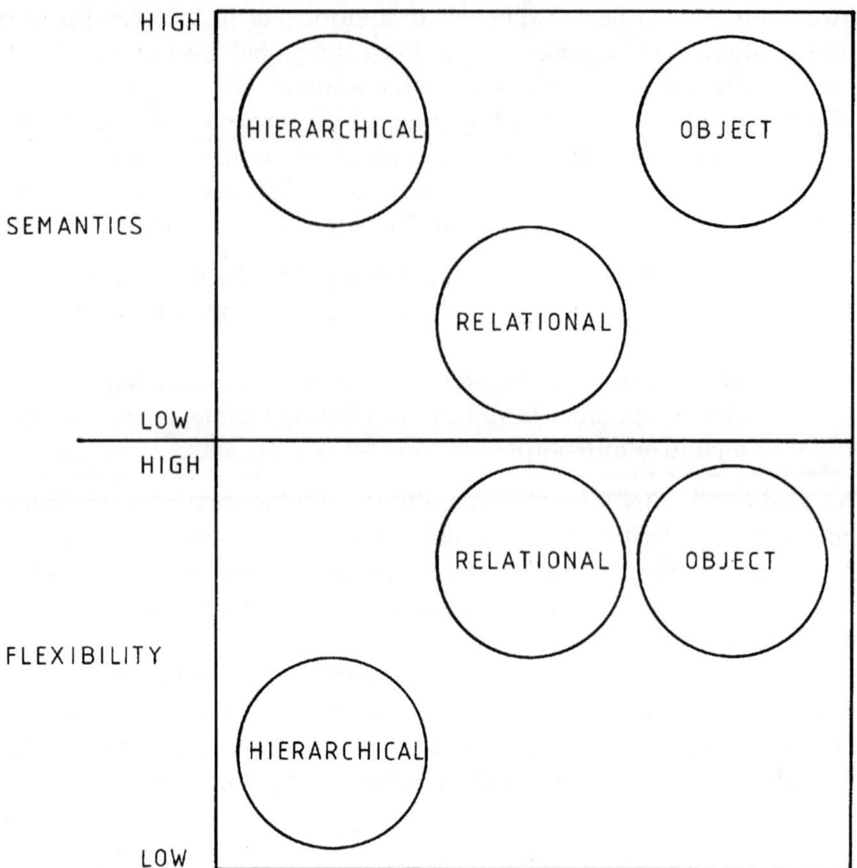

Figure 7.2 Semantics and flexibility underpin the object-oriented approach

- *Polymorphism* is a characteristic of flexible systems, supported by object orientation and conductive to rapid change.*

Polymorphism is a basic ingredient to a process of adaptation and, therefore, changeability. Since communications software is an embodiment of functions, it is subject to constant and continued pressures to adapt and modify. When this is effectively done, it enables innovations and imaginative extensions of functions and configurations.

There are other characteristics of object orientation such as *abstract data types*, but we don't need to dwell on these issues in this book since the goal here is to explain not the theory but the way an existing facility can be put to practical use.** Suffice to say that, in mathematics,

* See also a practical example in section 5.

** For details, see D.N. Chorafas and H. Steinmann, *Object-Oriented Databases* (Prentice-Hall, Englewood Cliffs, NJ, 1993).

abstraction is a widely used process of focusing upon the essential characteristics of an object, and therefore a basic aspect of any modelling activity.

Another feature of object orientation is *encapsulation*, or the process of hiding all of the details of an object that do not contribute to its essential characteristics. Encapsulation permits the creation of callable entities which may be atomic or more complex.*

Still another vital issue is *modularity*, a term identifying the properties of a system that has been decomposed into a set of cohesive and loosely coupled modules. Modularity is workable because, in a system sense we capitalize on the concept of inheritance.

These are the fundamental principles benefiting an object approach, distinguishing it from other methods. As we see through a practical example in section 3, there are undeniable benefits to be derived from object orientation in a networked environment, where processes compete for finite resources.

3. A Practical Example in a Networked Business Environment

Let us start with the fundamentals. The purpose of a business architecture, and therefore of a systems architecture, is to define a consistent means of implementating the business model of the enterprise. By combining these two paradigms; the commercial and the technical, we aim to develop an environment of independently executing objects which can be distributed on the global network.

The goal to be served in an architectural sense is a distributed object solution. One of the foremost projects in this domain, which for identification purposes we will call 'X', support intra-object distribution with each object implemented in four levels of reference:

- networking
- presentation and dialogue
- processing proper
- data management.

A good paradigm for the total engine is that of the familiar client-server model, extended in a global sense through internetworking. Each one of these four reference levels may operate on different platforms and in different locations while co-operating to produce the necessary business functions.

* As we saw in Chapter 5, leading organizations today use encapsulation to handle the remnants of their legacy systems.

As project 'X' demonstrated by means of practical results, in addition to a peer-to-peer distribution of objects into reference levels, the latter themselves should be internally distributed in a variety of ways. In a financial environment, for example, the objects associated with derivatives contracts must be distributed among a number of regional centres around the world.

- These processes are executed in a distributed manner in each trading room within each region.
- The presentations are customized and made available to each trader's workstation, upon request.
- The networking level provides the link among all the others, at the local, metropolitan, regional and global levels.

This structure is modular and flexible, but at the same time it effectively supports a variety of platforms by means of which business elements communicate. It also capitalizes on an interobject distribution isolating, for security reasons, both the network and the internal implementation of applications – while allowing both to evolve.

Project 'X' has placed significant emphasis on security. Information flows are controlled by assigning every object a *security class*, or security label. Whenever information flows from object A to object B, there is an accompanying information flow from the security class of A to the security class of B.

Objects are interconnected with relationships. A dependency relation relates objects that depend on one another – and this is done in a dynamic form. For example, there are dependency relationships among the:

- types of derivatives
- market in which each is traded
- client on whose behalf it is traded.

Constrained by the relationship, whenever a crucial factor is changed, the object identification is modified to maintain the dependency. At the same time, a sibling relationship denotes the encapsulation of objects in a module, and identifies their security class.

Changes made to an object are likely to propagate to its sibling objects, by using the inheritance mechanism which is well-described by the business system architecture.

Figure 7.3 gives a comprehensive view of this object-oriented architecture, its business elements, active applications objects, security supervisory processes (demons), and the global communications network on which they run.

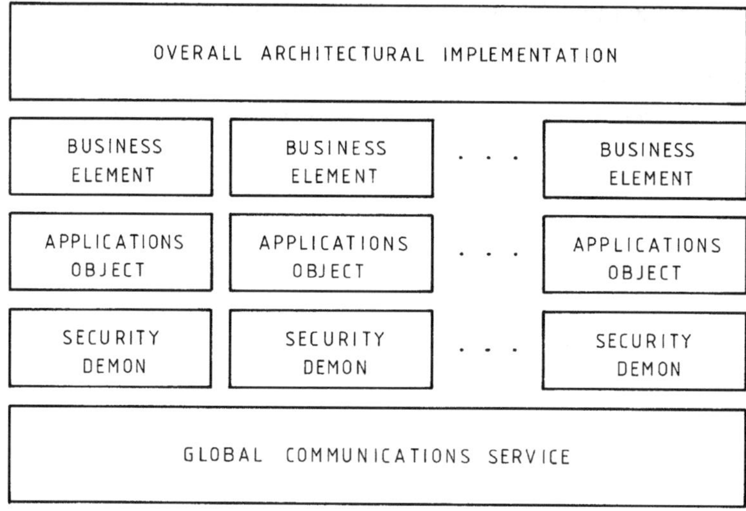

Figure 7.3 Accounting for security considerations in an object-oriented business architecture

- At project 'X' system architects have been led by users to pay significant attention to a number of critical issues.
- Interestingly, one of the most consistent user requests has been information security in a multi-user environment.

The solution which has been adopted has three separate but interrelated objectives: *confidentiality* related to disclosure of information; *availability*, that is denial of access to information; and *integrity* in connection to modification of information.

- Confidentiality concerns preventing a third party from determining the contents of messages and database elements.
- Availability involves ensuring that a transaction and its aftermaths are disclosed only to authorized parties.
- Integrity aims to assure that authorized operations are properly executed, but an outsider is denied interference with messages or databased objects.

A properly controlled information flow is clearly central to confidentiality and also helps integrity. But its relationship to availability is tenuous at best. Hence, more sophisticated security models are necessary, as the project leader of 'X' was to comment.

Within this perspective the project has attained a distributed implementation of business elements based on networked objects, whose services are made available over the communications links, nodes and distributed databases. One of the goals of the chosen approach has been to reuse existing technology as a better alternative to rebuilding from scratch – which is untenable.

The chosen business architecture provides for continuous evolution from the *status quo* and encompasses multiple overlapping generations of technology. For this purpose, it makes sure that legacy systems interact in a secure and dependable manner with the new architectural environment, which is fully object oriented.

4. From Realtime to Realspace Networks

As a number of examples in this and the preceding chapters demonstrated, both technology and the sophistication of implementations evolve very quickly. Therefore, one of the duties both of a company and of a professional person is to avoid falling behind. Personal skills and organizational skills are interrelated, since organizations are made of people. To succeed, technology officers ought to:

- make themselves better informed of the advancements of technology, and the achievements by competition
- steadily control the new advances to make sure the organization does not fall behind
- take advantage of these advancements as they happen, inducing their subordinates to do the same, training them and leading them.

One of the technological advancements on which it is wise to capitalize is *realspace*. The transition from realtime to realspace has been characterized by the ability to map into one point, typically by realtime simulation executed on a high-performance computer, all trades, exposures and other situations interesting the organization in a world-wide sense.

This should definitely include tick-by-tick transactions, exposures and balances – which is a reason why systems operating in realspace are one of the major advances taking place in 24-hour banking. They integrate electronic messaging services and are vast improvements over realtime applications. But they also require:

- a global approach to information management
- valid interconnection methods among business units
- the ability to bring together at one place the company's capillary structure
- systems which meet instantaneous response requirements.

Realspace solutions require a totally different culture than old data processing and therefore they cannot be planned or executed by EDPers.

Their agents are the new breed of Wall Street's professionals: the *rocket scientists* – a cross-section of technology specialists and bankers working with supercomputers, using artificial intelligence, and focusing on new financial products, as well as the timely evaluation and control of risk.

In commercial and investment banking as well as in the treasury operations of industrial corporations, realspace solutions are necessary now that the post-industrial economy has moved from:

- quantity to quality of services
- a mainly transactional business to client consulting
- impersonal to individualized, personal services.

Risk management is a particularly sensitive issue in this connection,* because with derivative financial vehicles companies today assure an inordinate amount of risk – quite often without even knowing it.

From the expansion of business opportunity to risk management, realspace serves company goals – but also imposes rigorous communications requirements in respect to the globalization of business. It can be effectively supported through company-operated networks, but this calls for a change in goals and means, with object orientation being one of the new means.

In other terms, the implementation of realspace facilities offers a competitive edge, but it also demands an agile infrastructure in the form of a *global network* supported through intelligent artefacts. Current business processes take place under conditions quite different than those known by previous generations of professionals.

Not only is this transformation process ongoing, but it is also a natural evolution of the internationalization of business. Geographical and legislative restraints that stood in the way of the wave of change characterizing the banking industry, for example, are being swept away with the on-line network becoming the pivot point of *relationship banking*. At the same time:

- Sophisticated financial vehicles are now the means for attracting and keeping a bank's best customers.
- The impact of these financial vehicles is felt throughout the organization, serving as a critically important high-touch response to the rising levels of personalization of products.

However, as shown on a number of occasions, becoming an innovator in personalized networking services is not so easily accomplished. It requires the appropriate culture and top management commitment; also new, object-oriented technology as project 'X' (of which we spoke in section 3) helps document.

* See also D.N. Chorafas, *Managing Derivatives Risk* (Probus/Irwin, Chicago, 1995).

- Object programs are easier to extend and parametrize than other programs.
- In a networked sense, these programs are able to exchange messages attaching specific methods to a specific class.

Metaknowledge, of which we spoke in section 2, helps in the exploitation of business opportunities. It makes possible the identification of

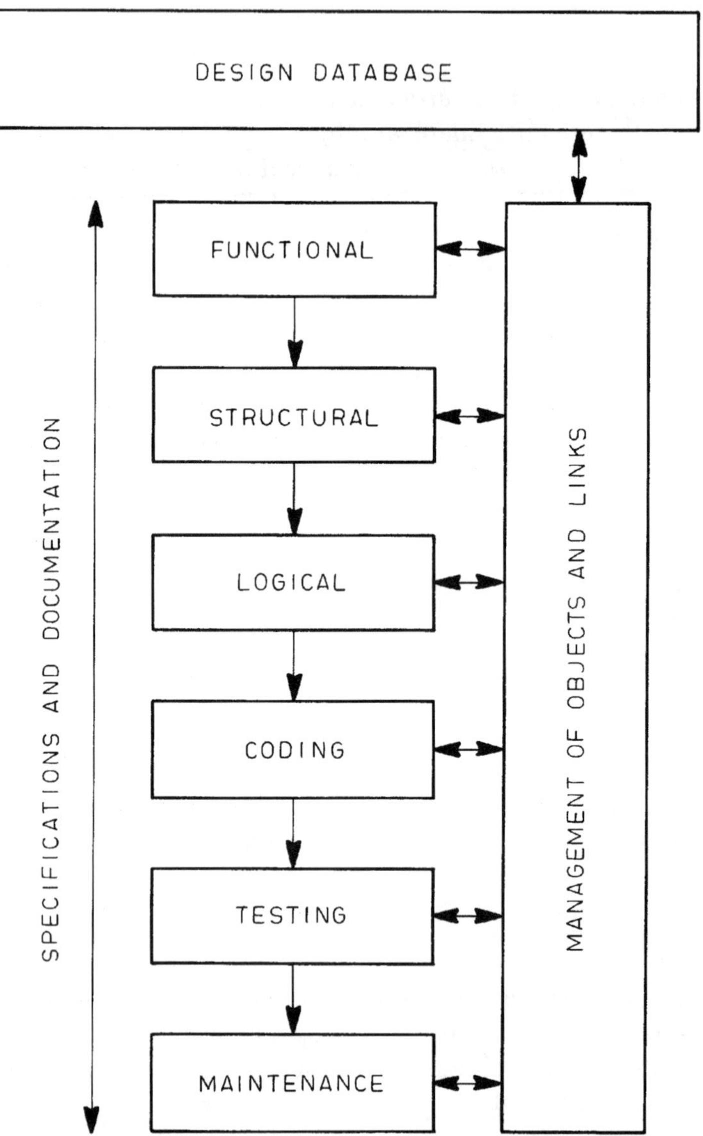

Figure 7.4 An object-oriented interactive software development environment

generic classes and methods leading to the solution of more general problems which can then be customized.

A number of interactively supported functions can be successfully exploited in moving from realtime to realspace implementation. Project 'X', which we discussed in section 3, not only achieved this transition but also accomplished it while preserving the use of legacy programs. The methodology which it followed is shown in Figure 7.4.

As the reader will appreciate, two factors underpin this transition. The one is an interactive design and development database which permitted concurrent software engineering. The other is the development of specifications for new objects and the encapsulation of legacy information elements, along with the provision of necessary links. Into this structure integrate all component parts of the system - functional, structural and logical.

5. The Benefit an Object Orientation Can Provide through Polymorphism

Let's start with the premise which has been made by Colin Crook, Chief Technology Officer of Citibank, that a systems architecture is a business architecture. Are object solutions able to make a significant contribution to the role that a business network architecture should play? The answer to this query is 'yes' – and an example is provided by polymorphism.

We have already mentioned polymorphism in section 2. There is a number of reasons why a realspace environment capitalizes on this facility. To understand them we should distinguish between *ad hoc*, parametric and generalized polymorphism.

- With *ad hoc polymorphism* different methods are selected, based on the type or form of operands.

This process is vital in applications such as risk management which evolve very rapidly during 24-hour banking. Market conditions change transaction by transaction, tick by tick, and the same is true of exposure. In fact exposure can change even if there is no new transaction affecting the bank's database – because the evolving market conditions impact on the trade book and the banking book.

- With *parametric polymorphism*, the user of the system impacts upon the objects through manipulation of parameters.

This can be done automatically by means of agents or directly by the user. The parametric process is particularly important in the experimental evaluation of business opportunities, as adaptive object-oriented programs specify essential classes and methods by constraining the configuration of a class structure or customizing its behaviour.

- *Generalized polymorphism* is the *alter ego* of parameterization, where the same method is used regardless of the type (or form) of the operands.

In this manner, for example, programmers are encouraged to think about families of programs by finding appropriate generalizations in describing their structure, functions and logic in an adaptive object-oriented sense.

The benefits of either class of polymorphism is that an adaptive object-oriented program may be used on different class structures. The process specifies the information to be supplied by a user implicitly, as contrasted to using explicit parameters by means of constraints. Alternatively, the method just described can be enriched with metaknowledge, therefore with higher-level constraints.

Whether in an *ad hoc*, parametric or generalized sense, the facilities presented by polymorphism can be instrumental in internal control. For instance, in confronting the many unknowns involved in *global risk management*, where essential requirements are:

- constantly monitoring the total performance of each financial instrument, client, industry, country, currency and interest rate
- establishing in realspace warning signals which enable decisive action to be taken as soon as risks exceed a pre-established level of tolerance.

In today's financial industry, the more lucrative deals are very risky. Derivatives, loans and investment opportunities have to be monitored constantly, including the synergy of risks.

A sound business network architecture will ensure that global risk management is central to any investment or trading decision. A policy of properly established *global risk* procedures should be embedded in all trading and investment systems – and should be mapped into the corporate database.

Companies need advance information to pull out of lines of business, as well as of areas, where the risk they are taking is judged to be disproportionate to the profits they make or hope to make. *Ad hoc* polymorphism responds to this requirement because, as the Barings bankruptcy of February 1995 and many others help demonstrate, terminal risks present themselves *ad hoc*.

To project on future risk and reward, management has to rely on computers, communications and software. This can be achieved successfully only when the information systems strategy is subservient to the company's business strategy, not vice versa, and when the tools which we use are able to handle the complexity of the situation we are facing.

Trading in derivatives financial instruments, loans exposure and investments must be monitored on several levels; the same is true of costs. No activities should be continued, much less undertaken, without regard to costs. Financial resources must be preserved at all time.

From global risk management to corporate-wide cost control and product innovation, management depends on realspace networks and sophisticated software. Properly used, the many aspects of polymorphism ensure that top-flight organizations are better positioned for survival. Only those companies which lead themselves into new levels of competitiveness can continue to exist.

6. Why Object Orientation Can Provide Flexible and Adaptable Solutions

Several of the practical examples we have seen help demonstrate that within the context of a business network architecture object-oriented approaches offer more promise than hierarchical or relational alternatives. Sophisticated software development and maintenance can be well-supported by the object paradigm, benefiting from the *ad hoc* and sharing mechanisms supported by inheritance, metaknowledge and polymorphism.

Data abstraction, too, is helpful in ensuring the coexistence of many different internal data representations. Figure 7.5 suggests that in the 1970s the use of abstract data types was limited – and so was the sophistication of software. But after the 1980s things have changed.

- Much of the gear behind this change has been the able exploitation of class concepts, inheritance, metaknowledge, metadata and polymorphism that came with object solutions.
- The same ingredients see to it that reusable modules are encapsulated in objects whose interface would be the same no matter what their internal representation.

The best results with object-oriented solutions have been obtained in domains such as computer-aided design (CAD), computer-aided manufacturing (CAM), computer-integrated manufacturing (CIM), complex market-oriented operations (forex, securities), cross-functional projects (risk management) and cross-departmental projects (cost control), as well as cartographical implementations, office automation (OA) and computer-assisted software engineering (CASE).

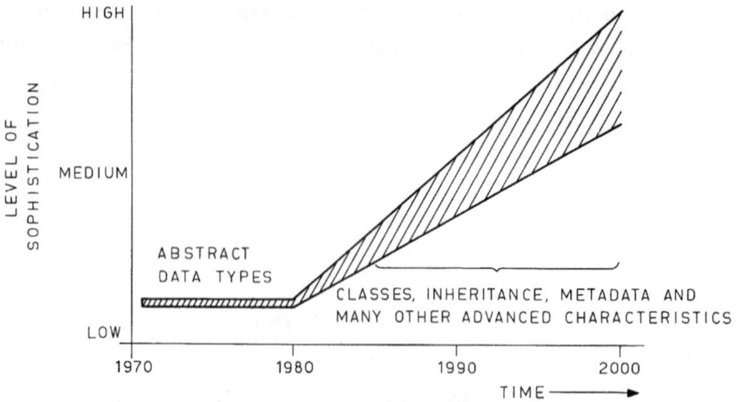

Figure 7.5 Effect on database management from object orientation

All these applications domains have in common rapid changes which can be effectively handled by active objects. That's why object orientation can provide flexible and adaptable solutions. Constraints could be seen as sets of objects connected in networks with message flows and other activities taking place in a business architecture.

All objects can have implicit interfaces expressed by their visual presentations and their physical significance. For instance, a system design would be a set of networked elements associated according to design rules in a part-whole ephemeral hierarchical fashion, with design rules maintained in an object dictionary being accessible interactively.

Object-oriented database management systems (DBMS) typically support multiple inheritance which, as we have seen, is an important tool in modelling complex data structures. It enables the structure to take on the properties and behaviour of items at the top of the inheritance tree and map them into its filials which may belong to more than one origin.

Knowledge software developers understand that performance is a critical issue in making the move to the new generation of distributed networked databases. But to get results they have to design their products for maximum throughput. Among the techniques used to optimize performance are:

- caching
- direct memory access
- hash-table indexing
- automatic clustering
- query optimization.

Object-oriented DBMS typically incorporate a data dictionary often implemented as a class hierarchy within the object database. This provides metadata descriptions that can be used by application programs to determine the form, location, and access methods for all system resources.

Since it is expressed as a class hierarchy, the object data dictionary can be easily extended to accommodate new requirements. For instance, it can be adapted to model the behaviour of networked data dictionaries from different vendors, or to reflect specific requirements, conditions and constraints present in a user organization.

A high degree of flexibility in database solutions is mandatory because the most important database problems of the 1990s and beyond are not precisely known. Moreover, software and hardware advances of this decade do not make brute force approaches attractive, let alone economical.

- The scale of the prospective applications is too great and the complexity is beyond what we have known so far.
- At the same time, the new generation of applications calls for the able management of heterogeneous, distributed resources.

To ensure that these prerequisites are answered in an able manner, we need to learn more about user-centred design, orienting database management towards a closer co-ordination with computer-aided systems engineering.

Such an approach requires discovering appropriate characterizations of the properties embedded in our business network architecture, going beyond formalisms to capture essential structure. As has been stressed on many occasions, past experiences may be helpful but only a new culture can assist in providing the solutions we need in the years ahead.

7. The Role of Frameworks in a Business Network Architecture

The preceding sections have explained the importance of object-oriented approaches and the contribution they make towards greater flexibility and more sophisticated software required by a business network architecture. But they have also underlined the need to integrate into the new solution a number of legacy programs which continue to exist. This integration is one of the objectives of object frameworks:

- Frameworks constitute a prefabricated structure, or template of a working program.
- The concept of frameworks is not new to the software industry; what is novel is the way of using them.

There exist three alternative ways of looking at a *framework*. The broader one is to interpret it as an infrastructure which consists of domain-wide reusable software, able to integrate into it other reusable and *ad hoc* modules in order to answer the requirements of a specific job.

The second way of approaching the issue of frameworks is as a set of object classes that embodies an abstract design for solutions to a family of related problems. By extension, framework-oriented programming is the exploitation of integrative object structures, along the lines explained in section 6.

Recently there has been a great deal of discussion about application frameworks because they provide support, and in some cases functional insertion by default, for other more elementary programming paradigms. This is particularly important in connection with parallel programming, whether on a single machine or in a wider network perspective.

Experts in the field would suggest a third way of looking at frameworks, through the object-oriented definition of encapsulation.* In their fundamentals, frameworks encapsulate a group of closely related classes, making it possible for the software developer to work at a higher conceptual level of the design.

- The focal point shifts to interactions among object types with which the designer, analyst and programmer need to work.
- The framework itself sits in the background supporting the effort of the developer and, in a way, guiding his hand.

This approach is vitally important to business-critical applications, which are central to an organization's mission. This approach enables major improvements on life-cycle experiences with technology, including a better understanding of software reusability criteria and of what it takes to reduce maintenance.

But while using software frameworks we should never lose sight of our goals. A primary purpose of frameworks is to assist human resources by improving the latter's efficiency, building user-friendly software environments behind which hardware details are hidden. Like the operating system for a serial computer, a framework for parallel systems must be:

- general purpose
- interactive
- multi-user oriented.

Therefore, the framework should be designed to support currently the execution of various processes, doing so with high throughput.

* See also section 2.

Supporting concurrent execution of parallel programs also requires advanced operating system features to co-ordinate the partitioning of resources among the programs, as well as to action dynamic repartitioning at runtime.

However, let us take good notice of the fact that frameworks are *not* a substitute for everything. The locality, the concept of grouping activities and the principle of balancing are guidelines for partitioning at the basic software and hardware levels. These are not the job of the framework but of the system design.

By contrast, the mission of the framework is user-oriented, providing designers, analysts and programmers a higher level of abstraction in order to integrate modules in a way supporting parallelism. Correspondingly, each operating system under the framework manages specific resources and co-ordinates user programs according to the framework guidelines.

At grand-design level, synchronization calls for system-wide failures to be supported by means of a flexible network management system. Let us emphasize that this duality of approach – framework to operating system and network system to framework comes none too soon. Crucial functions include:

- advanced intelligent routing
- addressing and flow control
- synchronization and deadlock prevention.

As hardware technology evolves, it is not really feasible to predict well in advance how the system will behave in a dynamic sense or where it may be usefully extended. The uncoupling of the system management environment from the underlying hardware makes it feasible to virtually manipulate the aggregate the way the architectural developer and/or system manager think best.

- One advantage of interfacing frameworks to systems functions is that this approach allows flexible extensions.
- Another advantage is that this is done without upsetting the applications environment or having to write entirely new kinds of device drivers for every application.

This flexibility is particularly important as a number of research projects reveal that in many applications roughly half the code involves fixing or working around problems and obstacles posed by configuration issues. Network level frameworks enable developers to revise their applications at a more rapid pace, without having to interact directly with hardware and the operating system primitives.

Interfacing all the way to the basic software framework solutions enables a higher level of code and design reuse than is practical otherwise. Theoretically this could be achieved through fourth generation language code generators, but these are usually based on procedural programming techniques and cannot easily provide the infrastructure and design guidance.

Within the perspective of a given network architecture, frameworks make possible a valid answer to both issues. They also help to extend the entire scope and concept of flexible, reusable software solutions – from developing applications to their renovation and maintenance. With appropriate skill applied to their usage, these solutions assist in making the business network more agile.

8. Capitalizing on an Object-Oriented Controllability of Software

As the evidence provided by the research which we carried out in the 1993 to 1995 time frame in the USA, the UK, continental Europe and Japan, helps document, the tension between *the need for innovation* and the requirements for practical and *immediate solutions* has increased. This duality always made the job of network architecturing a challenge. But both the factors entering into the solution equation and the objectives to be met have increased.

One of the objectives which has been in the background of many references made in this chapter, is *software controllability*. Its solution space is multidimensional because able answers necessarily touch a number of issues:

- the choice of network protocols and their seamless implementation
- remote access to distributed heterogeneous databases
- rapid prototyping for high-quality software development and maintenance.

High technology is underpinning a valid response to each one of these issues; it is also the means for paying attention to their synergy. Without high technology we can have neither innovation nor valid solutions in connection to networks, databases, human interfaces and software.

A similar statement can be made about the assurance to be provided that business networks supported by heterogeneous devices will interoperate. 'Interoperability is the Number 1 item on customers' agendas today,' said the marketing vice-president of a major American computer manufacturer. However, let us never lose from sight that the solution, for instance, to cross-database connectivity is not just *technical*. It is primarily *managerial* and it depends on whether or not we have the intellectual vitality to face the new era of information technology.

It may sound strange that the decision on whether or not all pieces of a business network architecture will operate perfectly both as stand-alones and as a system is primarily managerial. Yet, this is the way to bet. As long as top management relegates the responsibility of the scope regarding the business network architecture to technicians, the result will leave much to be wanted.

This does not mean that there is no technical responsibility. There is, but it comes after the business goals and grand design. The different components of the business network architecture, for example, may operate well as stand-alones, but this does not guarantee they will work as a system. In connection to integration:

- Object-oriented software offers many features and power.
- But it also introduces opportunities for errors.

Therefore the techniques designed to test object-oriented software must be very carefully examined, stipulating better ways to solve problems connected to networked resources, and demonstrating solutions which have been able to overcome some of the thorniest problems network architects have so far faced in this domain.

Software controllability is not an issue which has come with object-oriented programming. It is present with *all* programming efforts, but it must now be more carefully examined. *Controllability* is a term used in control engineering to mean the ability to put a system into a desired state by manipulating its input variables.

- Simply because a system is man-made does not ensure that people are always able to control it.
- Often significant efforts are made in vain to control an uncontrollable structure.

An example is provided by *multidatabases* which have their roots in the concept of distributed corporate databases reflecting incompatible systems designed along a mainframe mentality. Contrary to this, the right approach would be to support:

- database and knowledgebank concepts
- reliability and availability characteristics
- the synergy necessary to create and sustain federated databases.*

The theory of controllability defines the conditions under which control is possible. In its fundamentals, this theory is mathematical, but it

* See chapter 5.

is important also to have a concept of controllability for systems that cannot be expressed in a fully analytical, quantitative form.

Not only new tools are necessary, but also the proverbial long hard look and a change in methods. Those on the supply side of software have to ask themselves a tough question: 'Am I really adding value, or am I simply contributing to the problem?'

- As with networks and databases, there is a minor revolution under way in software development which is hard to define in a sentence.
- It includes not just object-oriented programming but also a whole new infrastructure – with the network at the hub of concurrent engineering.

The new concept of efficient software development must rest on the users' enlightened approach to self-service by harnessing the latest software technologies, with prototyping, knowledge engineering and object orientation at the top of the list.

Such strategy will ensure that current software development bottlenecks will be broken, and applications will be more finely tuned to the task which is targeted. Control of programs will be put back into the hands of users, through a significant paradigm shift towards end-user-actuated controllability.

The above is written in the full understanding that the expectations of the quality of architectural solutions involving networks, databases and software products are rising. At the same time, constraints on cost and human resources are tightening.

- Many companies have incorporated object-oriented technology into their software development process as a means of addressing this problem.
- The result is that top-level businesses have attained many benefits such as reduced development time, improved reuse and higher quality.

But at the same time, these companies discovered that constructing a highly available, stable and robust network using object-orientation requires new techniques and tools to test the software – not just program by program but also class level testing. There are no free outcomes with object-oriented approaches, or with any other methodology which we use.

8

Providing Efficient Networking Solutions in a Transaction Environment

1. Introduction

One of the issues which distinguishes telecommunications from other computer-based corporate services is that they are subject to the whims and rulings of regulators, which, as we saw in Part 1, ends up in a host of tariffs and legal issues. The laws of physics are the same in all countries – but this is not true of the laws of men.

Another main difference between computers and communications is costs. Costs are due partly to differences in tariffs but also in large measure to the efficiency of operations. In particular, tariff issues generate queries such as:

- How do tariffs compare from country-to-country, among those most technologically advanced?
- What sort of alternative schedules and breaks do they offer?
- How do they change over time due to competition and technology?
- How do tariffs dictate investment in network interface solutions?
- How should basic costs be integrated into the network services.

Tariffs vary widely between countries. Deregulated markets, e.g. America, the UK, Japan, tend to have lower tariffs. In fact, the lowest of all tariffs are in America where the Federal Communications Commission (FCC) switched in 1989 to a *price cuts* policy, rather than setting the floor price.* This opened the door to very tough competition.

Still another factor which distinguishes communications from computers is reliability. We have spoken of database availability. The

* See also D.N. Chorafas and H. Steinmann, *Intelligent Networks* (CRC Press, Boca Raton, FL, 1990).

telecommunications network must be by an order of magnitude *more reliable* than the computer systems attached to it.

Typically, we are aiming at much better than 99.99 per cent reliability in connection with networking. We should not forget that, other things equal, high reliability is incurring high costs. Yet, short of the 'four nines' policy a widely distributed computers and communications system will not be dependable.

But computers and communications also have common points, beyond the fact that a network interconnects the resources attached to it. One of the common points is synergy; another is costing and pricing.

With any solution in computers and communications, cost-effectiveness must underline design, administration and maintenance of all resources. We have to know cost and benefit, hence projected profit and loss (P&L) before we start any project – as well as when we make design reviews of systems already in operation.

Together with the emphasis on improving service and keeping costs low, the solution we are after must be *future-proof.* Not only the network should be able to provide a whole range of features, but it should also be possible to enhance these features over time as applications and systems evolute.

As we see in this chapter there are a number of issues which fall halfway between the computers and communications domain. Hence, we will start our discussion with wide area networks, continue with local and desk area networks, see some do's and don'ts with peer-to-peer solutions and end with recovery strategies.

2. Network Design for Transactional Applications

We said that any valid network design must be able to provide significant flexibility, growth potential, cost cutting opportunities, and a 99.99 per cent or better reliability. The network must be capillary, preferably wideband and definitely peer to peer.*

Both current and projected applications must be served in an able manner. Many of the leading financial institutions, manufacturing companies and merchandising firms, for instance, operate around the globe 24-hours a day and must be able to deliver services:

- at any time
- for any product
- anywhere in the world.

* See also D.N. Chorafas, *Handbook of Data Communications and Computer Networks*, 3rd edn (McGraw-Hill/TAB Books, New York, 1991).

Usually such networks are not being built bottom-up by starting from scratch. They represent an outgrowth of existing communications formats and disciplines which are often incompatible. Hence integration perspectives are at a premium.

In spite of heterogeneity, the network we have or develop must be able to handle transactions in a uniform manner. Any valid study will start with the resources to be used for transaction processing, and should do so end to end.

A valid approach is first to build a model of the network, then to derive from it a bill of materials, and subsequently to simulate each transaction in its use of network resources. This approach helps to establish per class of transaction:

- machines it uses
- software modules
- input/output
- database accesses
- communications time and cost
- people's direct labour
- overheads.

Computers and communications costs have to be taken together because they both impact on the cost per transaction. This is true for hardware and software, to utilities, people costs and overheads.

Hosts, databases, workstations, gateways and all of the nodes in the network have to be considered. Since the late 1960s, when it started, the concept of front-ending computer resources in terms of the communications discipline has evolved greatly, while many of the functions which were needed at the start are still necessary today. The solutions we now provide are at a much higher level of sophistication.

Among the main functions performed by front-end devices are load distribution, monitoring, journalling, analysis of statistics and associated corrective action. We are interested in load balancing in regard to both networks and databases. In a networking context, load distribution requires transaction routing taking into consideration the available resources and their usage.

Monitoring takes place in connection with resource utilization due to type and composition of transactions, including arrival rates and execution requirements. Message frequency, hit ratios, lock conflict and so on are performance indicators.

Corrective action can be taken with reference to performance problems due to significantly changed load composition as well as system configuration changes. Either of these cases presents the need for dynamic adaptation of routing strategy.

An integral part of any solution is the interconnection to be provided between the different networked resources. This should make possible the handling of all supported message types:

- from client
- to front-end processor
- to database, and
- back to client.

The fact that protocols have not been normalized in a fundamental sense does not mean that there are no design guidelines to be observed. There exist some international standards, though they have many dialects.

As a matter of principle, the smaller the message to be transmitted, the less the cost errors. But small message size and error control can be contradictory goals since error control requires more characters for parity reasons (error detection, error correction) and other constraints also exist.

The message from this discussion is that when we talk of network solutions with multiple resources, we are faced with conflicting requirements. Hence, any solution has to be well studied in advance.

- Many alternatives should be examined before choices are made because afterwards changes will be disruptive and costly.
- Both the cost of the networking solution as a whole and the cost per transaction being handled should be evaluated.

The transactions our network is handling may be simple or complex. An example of a simple transaction is deposit to or withdrawal from an account. A complex transaction will involve 'n' atomic parts. Analytical costing requires having a cost estimate of each. Hence the need for *unit cost analysis*.

Network costs should be charged to the user department of the transaction-handling facility. However, only after unit costing has been completed in an able manner, is it meaningful to talk of pricing strategy. Otherwise, it is not possible to ascertain whether we make or lose money with a transaction stream:

- The right pricing strategy can be documented on the basis of competitive prices, rather than internal costs.
- Only when it knows the level of its competitiveness, will the user organization be in a position to control its profit and loss (P&L).

In practical terms, this means that the Telecommunications department must be very much aware of state-of-the-art solutions and of competitive costs – as well as of the unwritten rule in networking that 'if nothing changes in technology, costs will skyrocket'.

Based on a number of studies, Figure 8.1 shows a trend graph of communications and computer costs under different hypotheses. Notice that bending the cost curve can be done in different ways.

- No solution is really ideal in the general case.
- Every implementation has its own characteristics which have to be studied.
- Real cost savings require very significant improvements over current conditions.

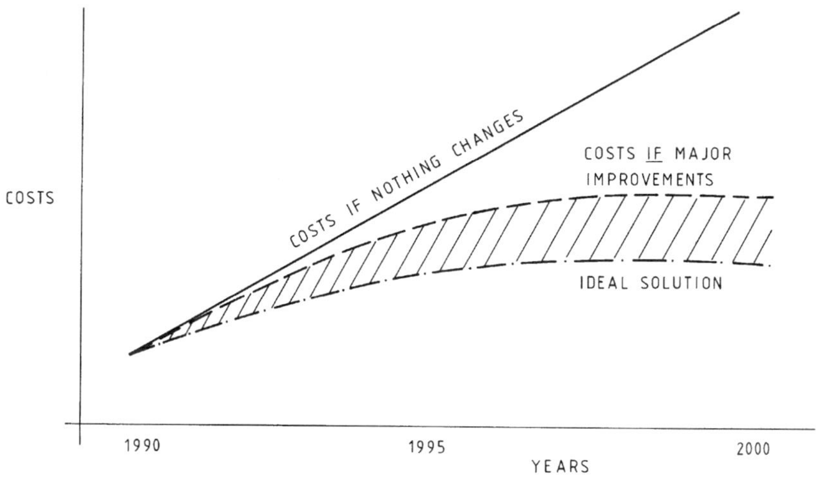

Figure 8.1 Communications and computer costs in the 1990s under two different hypotheses

Major improvements and, even more so, a very advanced solution have to be a steady culture rather than an exceptional event. They require a corporate policy which is established, communicated to everybody and enforced.

No single department can ensure success all on its own. Management should see to it that there is synergy among internal users – and that suppliers are selected not just because of their name but after a tough competition which considers all advantages and disadvantages.

3. Networking Solutions and Local Area Requirements

Since the early 1980s, cutting edge organizations have integrated all their communications services: wide area networks (WAN), local area networks (LAN), point-to-point connections, telephony, private branch exchanges (PBX), gateways and telex.* This integration has given significant results in terms of cost-effectiveness and has also caused a quantum leap in technology.

There is every reason why companies with important transactional requirements should follow this advice. Experience in business and industry helps demonstrate that there is a desperate need for a truly efficient internal network, which is most essential as the company expands.

- The goal should be value-added services, approached in an integrative way for all transactional requirements.
- But value-added services require a different, much higher level of reliability and of technology.

The communications department should have the skill to develop an efficient corporate network, but it should also be given a clear mission to do so.

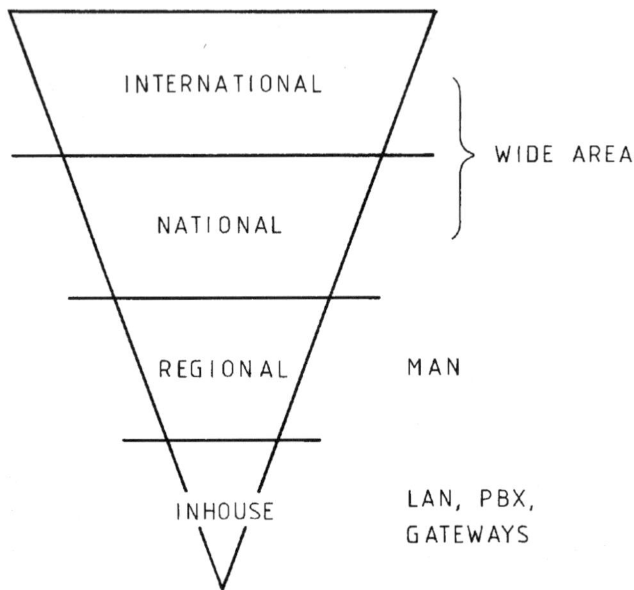

Figure 8.2 There are advantages in conceiving a network in a layered form, but the layers have to integrate

For a multinational company, the network will have four layers, as shown in Figure 8.2. The international and national segments require wide area solutions.

- On a national scale, wideband communications will be supported by optical fibres and microwave links.

* See also D.N. Chorafas and H. Steinmann, *High Technology at UBS – For Excellence in Client Service* (Union Bank of Switzerland, Zurich, 1988).

- Both optical fibres and satellites will be used internationally.

Metropolitan area networks (MAN) will typically answer regional requirements. Depending on the laws of the land, they will be private or public.

In-house solutions are strictly private involving local area networks, private branch exchanges and gateways, to MAN and wide area communications solutions. Databases will be interconnected through these facilities, and the same is true of workstations and other attached devices.

Efficiency should be a steady preoccupation from design to implementation, operation, maintenance and back to design. This life-cycle view evidently brings up the subject of new, more efficient protocols – for instance changing from 3270 to the TCP/IP.

- Confronted with a growing transaction challenge, both in sophistication of operations and in numbers, a user organization cannot afford to continue with the pseudo-workstations which work under the dumb 3270 protocol.
- Neither can the employees work efficiently with a policy of two and three dumb terminals* per desk.

Stated in a blunt manner, no firm can consider itself to be technology oriented if it continues to use point-to-point twisted pair and 3270 protocol. The required changes in local networking are no big mountain to climb and they are doable over a short timetable. This statement is valid provided top management is serious about seeing changes happen.

The best solution for local networking is a single, modern protocol to link workstations across the corporate network. This requires an approach to enable smooth transition to the high-bandwidth applications which characterize the mid- and late 1990s.

- Without such a solution, the user organization will not be able to join the new wave of office automation – no matter what the mainframers may be saying.
- Without integrative applications on intelligent workstations it will not be possible to significantly improve upon personnel performance.
- As a result, the operations of the company which decides to stick with backwards technology will be characterized by high labour costs and loss of competitiveness.

If high labour cost and low performance are the goals management is after, then it is fine to stay put in a stagnant technological environment.

* Or workstations which are paid at higher prices but used as dumb terminals.

Otherwise, the transaction management solutions should be characterized by evolutionary change.

It is not enough to look at what people do today in order to provide the basis for change. We have to project on what they will be doing tomorrow – which is not with the same mode they now operate. Able solutions for the 1990s call for:

- integrated workstations
- increasingly sophisticated servers
- TCP/IP
- knowledge engineering
- object orientation
- an open architecture.

These are only highlight points. Several other references could be added to bring the user organization forward, gaining leadership in an intense transactional environment which gets increasingly demanding all the time.

4. The Advent of Desk Area Networks*

Communications-based solutions must be able to provide a broad range of business services that user organizations are keen to employ. Short of these services, the organizations do not earn an income, no matter how technically perfect they may be. This principle has characterized the presentation in all chapters of Part 2 of this book.

The opposite statement is also true. Business and industrial applications can learn a great deal from communications principles – particularly the implementation of networks. By late 1995 the transition is clear:

- In the past network principles found their way from wide area communications to metropolitan area and local area networks.
- Today, this transition takes place from LAN to the evolving systems solution of *desk area networks* (DAN).

The low cost of microprocessors and experience with network solution are two of the reasons behind the advent of desk area networks. But a more rigorous reason is that of the evolving applications requirements – particularly in the domain of multimedia.

A good example of multimedia support comes from MIT's desk area network project, and the ViewStation design which is presented in

* This section and section 5 are a preview of a forthcoming book on high-performance computing and desk area networks.

section 5. Like project Athena and X-Windows in the early 1980s, the goal is a quantum leap in technology which can rapidly be put to productive use. DAN represents what is likely to happen beyond client-servers.

Let us rephrase this statement. While client-server solutions are today a peak technology, their time will be passing as newer, more imaginative and more fundamental approaches are taking hold. Therefore, to benefit the reader with a vision of what is to come, prior to reviewing client-servers (in section 6) we look into the concept and design of desk area networks.

People in the computers and software business who think about future requirements rather than those of the past, are apt to appreciate the huge transition which we experienced during the last 20 years – which goes well beyond breaking the von Neumann bottleneck:

- With mainframe architectures, we had one processor serving *n* users, *n* being a three- or four-digit number.
- With cluster solutions employing non-intelligent terminals, it has still been 1:*n*, with *n* a two- or three-digit number.
- With client-server, or PC-LAN-type solutions, the ratio is 1:1; which means one processor for one user.
- With the coming generation of desk area networks, we have an *n*:1 relation – with *n* processors serving one user.

One, two or three dozen processors at the disposal of a single user, is the new basis of an efficient architecture. In fact, it is the only one which can handle in an able manner a business-type multimedia environment.

Even if few systems specialists and even less company executives at this time are able to appreciate what these processor-user relationships really mean, the foremost companies are already taking advantage of them. They also pay due amount of attention to *human interfaces*, which is another way of exploiting:

- network intelligence
- gigastream channels.

A great part of the success of the information superhighway will depend not on how much fibre is laid down and how many gigabytes flow through it, but on well-designed consistent user interfaces. The task is challenging because it is part of normalization which must:

- overcome current diversity
- accommodate the different requirements of potential users.

As we saw in Chapters 3 and 4, Internet and other commercial networks are delivering interesting services, but these networks are incompatible and the need to learn diverse interfaces severely limits their utilization and discourages users from signing up for more than one system. This heterogeneous situation is like that of any system before standardization. The nineteenth-century telephones had similar shortcomings.

Another issue connected to making the use of network intelligence and broadband cost-effective is the thorough revamping of *transaction* and *query* services. For instance, transaction servers are designed for applications such as order execution, billing, credit-card processing and banking. Query servers elicit new information from existing data.

Increasingly, intelligence-enriched queries imply *database mining* achieved through high-performance, massively parallel computers. A company might, for example, mine its customer database for clues to the potential of a market or of a customer account – exploiting both private and public distributed databases. Or, it may mine in realtime multimedia databases, which poses megastream transmission requirements. In all these cases, 'n' microprocessors per user are of great help.

5. ViewStation and the New Forms of Visualization

Prognosis regarding future applications of technology, and their possible aftermaths, is not possible through daydreaming. The serious researchers would be keen to visit the most advanced laboratories; not necessarily those of some mainframers where inertia and bureaucracy call the tune, but surely those of the foremost organizations which have made their mission to become leaders in a dynamic market.

Precisely along this line of reference, the meetings we recently had at MIT covered two major areas of interest. Both of them can be significant in terms of retaining technological competitiveness in the coming years.

1. *ViewStation* and *desk area network* which will, by all likelihood, constitute the intelligent workstation solutions of the mid- to late 1990s.

Currently, three projects in three different continents address desk area networks. ViewStation in Cambridge, Massachusetts, is one of them. The other two are MANNA by the Gesellschaft für Mathematik und Datenverarbeitung in Berlin, and the RealWorld Project by the Electrotechnical Laboratory in Tokyo. All three are government sponsored.

ViewStation is a multimedia-oriented, distributed desk area network at an advanced stage of development. The software MIT develops permits the user to:

- address his or her programs and files *as if* they were under his or her desk

- in reality these programs and files are separated by hundreds or even thousands of miles.

This solution also makes it feasible to keep somewhere in the background aging equipment and old software modules – while making their integration and use fully transparent to the end-user.

These paragraphs present both the technical interest and the business perspectives of ViewStation. The project makes feasible the allocation of *n* microprocessors to a single user, as explained in section 4, doing so in a flexible manner which makes possible the development and exploitation of an end-user-oriented business systems architecture.

2. Pioneering work, conducted at MIT's Media Laboratory addresses *new forms of visualization* – constituting necessary additions to any professional's skills and technological toolkit.

MIT is not alone in this approach. The core of another meeting, in Salt Lake City, with Evans and Sutherland (E&S) has been *realtime simulation*. Like other defence contractors, E&S capitalizes on the expertise which it has developed in virtual reality applications with the military and other US government agencies, such as the Coast Guard.

- This technology transfer effort seems both achievable and rewarding – hence, it should be of interest to any company.
- There is much that can be gained in financial and industrial environments by capitalizing on realtime simulation expertise.

Similarly, at a workstation-oriented level of reference, the work by Visual Numerics (VN) of Boulder, Colorado, in *realtime visualization* is new and promising, allowing several two-dimensional charts and tables to be replaced by one three-dimensional visualization.

Like E&S, Visual Numerics capitalizes on its experience from engineering to enter the finance and other business markets. In fact, the two companies complement one another in their applications.

- Banks employ VN's 3-D colour graphics in connection to forex, securities and derivatives trades, as well as the presentation of stockmarket prices.
- One of these banks uses PV Wave to map the visualization approaches of its competitors, and extrapolate the type of decisions these can reach from such output.

Interactive visualization requires a steady data stream, whether from realtime data collection or from database mining. For this purpose, another research meeting was held in Silicon Valley with nCube. The strength of this parallel computers company derives from its close association (by means of common ownership) with Oracle. It designs and manufactures parallel processors of hypercube architecture, but unlike its competitors it blends Oracle's database management experience into its products. This leads to a dual business perspective:

- *Disk farms*, which essentially means very competitive database computers by exploiting redundant arrays of inexpensive disks (RAID) and parallel processing.
- *Media servers*, for multimedia databases and switching centres which will be found everywhere in the infrastructure of the coming information superhighway system.

British Telecom and Bell Atlantic have awarded media server contracts to nCube and Oracle – and they now jointly work on their development. This is a subject which recently started to attract the attention of every telecommunications company, because it constitites a new product line and a significant business opportunity. User organizations should take note.

These are the perspectives which will be characterizing transaction and query systems in the coming years, as well as the networking solutions underpinning them. Their implementation will be calling for a great deal more than client-server solutions offer today. This said, however, we should take a look into what is involved in the able use of client-servers.

6. Variations on Adopting Client-Server Solutions

A *client-server* approach to the architecturing of a computers and communications system can mean different things to different people. Yet, the concept is simple and it can be put in a couple of sentences if we adhere to the fundamentals.

The *client* computer is the end-user oriented engine. It operates on-line and typically sends a request over a network to a *server* computer, which then carries out the task. The client may be a workstation and the server a database, number cruncher supercomputer, gateway or just another workstation.

Part and parcel of the client-server concept is the principle that end-users at client machines should not need to trouble themselves over the location of the server(s). These might be under the next desk, in another city, or on a different continent.

In this systems-oriented way of looking at solutions, one can say that client-server computing has been around for years but its potential has grown rapidly with the arrival of:

- more robust networks and increasingly sophisticated user interfaces
- greater quantities of power available on workstations through mighty microprocessors
- new software tools which change the sense of programming
- system integration architectures enabling seamless access to computer resources.

*System integration** has several definitions, but essentially means putting together, in a way that it can effectively operate, the best mix of software and hardware to solve a user organization's problems. This should be the goal of every company as well as of the technologists which it employs.

An open architecture and system integration are closely connected to one another. They both demand considerable expertise on the part of the user organization's computing and communications services. But beware. All mainframe vendors say that they are experts in system integration, this being one of their several false claims.

Clear-eyed user organizations are quick to recognize that properly implemented client-server solutions lead to significant cost-effectiveness. But wares vary in performance and in prices.

- A leading bank benchmarked workstations respectively belonging to a proprietary and an open architecture – including all software and hardware – and found that the cost difference was 3:1 in favour of the open system.
- A known electrical and mechanical engineering manufacturer completed a benchmark of open architectures versus a proprietary solution. A 5:1 ratio favoured the open option with regard to savings in costs.

Both the open and the proprietary architectures billed themselves as client-server. The message is that client-server is *just a name*. Often the performance of top-end workstations can match that of low-end mainframes and maxis for a fraction of the cost.

Solutions have to be sound from the start because, as the network grows, more and more will be needed in terms of added systems functionality as well as in terms of integration. It is time to adopt the open architecture as a culture and benefit from the much greater performance it makes possible. Just as it is time to look at object-oriented solutions, beyond those that relational approaches can offer.

Knowledge engineering and object-oriented programming have a key

* See also D.N. Chorafas, *System Architecture and System Design* (McGraw-Hill, New York, 1989).

role to play with client-server computing, as the industry as a whole moves more towards truly reusable software. Application will be split into standard processes (objects); they will reside in different locations and be called when required – and this is just as true of communications as it is of computers.

Section 4 presented the thesis that new software development technology turns the 70:30 split of the programming budget between maintenance and new developments on its head. This happens because:

- The use of shells for rapid prototyping tremendously accelerates program development and also produces more accurate software.

Productivity improvement ratios of 5:1 and 10:1 through the use of shells are not uncommon. Even higher ratios can be achieved with *visual programming* capabilities.

- Software maintenance is essentially reduced to a new rapid prototyping job. The rest is done by the compiler.

New tools able to assist the maintenance job within that environment include *program visualization*, which is a process opening interesting professional perspectives.

Another significant advantage of the suggested approach is end-user programming, which can be instrumental in altering our concepts of software development. End-user programming can significantly ease the backlog which exists today in terms of computer applications.

7. Pitfalls with Proprietary Peer-to-Peer Approaches

Architecturally, peer-to-peer denotes the lack of a central authority commanding over the operation of the network and its component parts. As we have seen on repeated occasions, the network is a federation of communicating workstations and servers, each with its local transactions but also sharing global transactions.

In a proprietary, vendor-oriented sense, the peer-to-peer programming model has been promoted with the introduction in the mid-1980s, by IBM, of the low entry network (LEN). This was subsequently renamed APPN – advanced peer-to-peer networking architecture.

Companies which decided to remain in the IBM world and at the same time wanted to get out of the overly restrictive centralized solutions, adopted APPN. This architecture involves two types of devices:

- network nodes, which provide routing
- end nodes, which primarily receive and send information.

APPN is based on IBM's SNA LU6.2 protocol and the APPC, CPI-C and CPI-R programming interfaces which rest on that protocol. Using a model of chained transactions, programs establish long-lived sessions. A program sends and receives one-way messages over a conversation instead of making procedure calls.

This, of course, runs contrary to what we said is the modern approach with remote procedure calls, and is a good example of how the user can be locked in with proprietary approaches. It is also a first-class case in demonstrating how fast a relatively new protocol (introduced in the mid-1980s) can fall out of favour.

With APPN's two-way alternative, each conversation is half-duplex: one of the participants is in send mode and the other in receive mode. While the sender must explicitly turn over send control to the receiver, the receiver cannot start sending until it receives.

LU6.2 theoretically allows commit from anywhere but practically has many constraints. Of the three protocols being used:

- APPC is the original and is very complex.
- CPI-C came as a first SQL version, but does not fit with transactions.
- CPI-R is an evolution of CPI-C supposed to handle transactions.

There are three levels of synchronization in the protocol: 2, 1 and 0. With *Level 2*, programs in the conversation tree execute in a transaction, while *Level 1* and *Level 0* are much more restrictive.

Level 1 has no transaction context. Each program can acknowledge receipt of a message, by issuing a confirm signal. This indicates that the program has processed the message or messages. Correspondingly, Level 0 features no application level of acknowledgement to receiving message(s).

As a result of this approach LU6.2 compatibility requires much more by way of detail and definition than a general protocol reference. However, as a peer-to-peer protocol and architecture APPN is more flexible than the hierarchical SNA – but also leads to a more complex programming environment.

An implementation example is Sears, Roebuck which has become one of the first users to enrol in IBM's Quality Partnership Program.* Under this program, IBM will work closely with selected top users at their sites to:

- test its new mainframe software products before they are released.

* Announced in March 1992.

- enable both sides to fine-tune a new release.

In order to appreciate the size of this effort, we must be aware that Sears Technology Services has 400,000 users on its network, which serves about 18,000 sites world-wide. '[The company] sees it as necessary over time to migrate to APPN, because it's potentially superior to the sub-area architecture,' suggested a Sears executive.*

Sub-area routing is a networking scheme used in SNA, in which mainframes are the hosts and central processing points for all network applications. To move away from that model, Sears has developed a three-step plan to gradually convert its hierarchical SNA network to a peer network:

- The first step involves integrating APPN network node software in up to 100 IBM mainframes at Sear's three data centres.
- This will mean upgrading the VTAM communications software now on the mainframes to VTAM Version 4, which incorporates the network node software.

Associated to this transition is a whole mainframe upgrading process. While experience with the implementation of this approach is not yet available, a number of references help document that an outright conversion to a new client-server environment may be by far the easier and less costly way of renovating transaction processing systems. This is precisely what many leading manufacturing companies and financial institutions are doing in America.

8. Queuing Transaction Execution Requests

Queuing helps solve transaction handling problems particularly when there are many users and the number of processes exceed the number of available processors – which always leads to trouble. Attention also should be paid to the fact that some transaction processing software will not work in any other way than by queuing.

Seen from the perspective of an enabling procedure, transaction queuing is an implementation mechanism for multitransaction requests. A typical sequence of actions is exemplified in Figure 8.3. However, there are negative aspects associated with the procedure.

A first negative is the increase in response time. The value of modern transaction systems is largely dependent on fast response. Delays mean system degradation. Furthermore, most transaction processing systems do not assume (and some do not allow) queued requests to be interactive.

* *Communications Week International*, 20 April 1992.

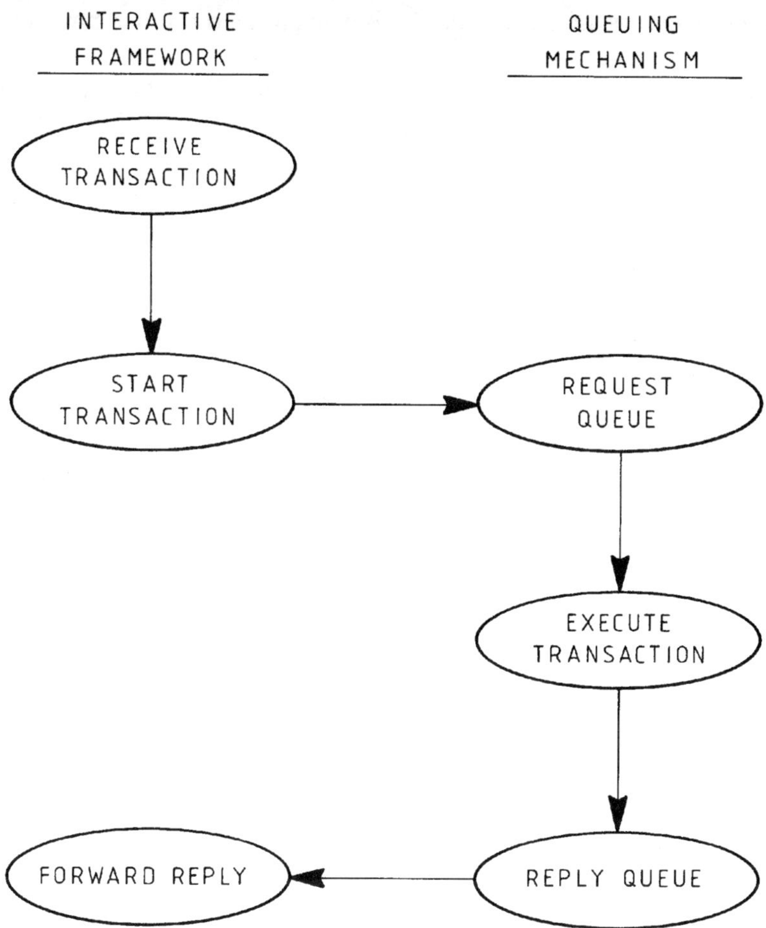

Figure 8.3 An approach to the development and operation of transaction queuing procedures

Since many transactions have priority over other transactions, queuing is not that simple a process either, contrary to what one might think by looking at the bare mechanics:

- A client sends a request to a server, and waits for the server to run the transaction.
- But the server may be down when the client wants to send the request.
- Or, the client workstation is down when the server wants to send the reply.

To serve in a meaningful manner, the queuing mechanism must know what is happening. The network should have intelligence for load balancing across many servers – and each server must have enough knowledge for priority-based scheduling reasons.

These are processes quite difficult to execute with old software structures, and this is why the example we saw in section 7 will quite likely run into trouble. When systems become big and complex, a new departure is the best strategy. Patchwork will not do the work.

If queuing services are run at global rather than local only level, the network must be able to control work requests by moving them through queues in an optimized fashion. If the queue is persistent, the client can in principle find out the state of a request. But this depends on available software and is not generally assured.

Queue forwarding helps in terms of a greater flexibility in a system sense. It is possible to have the elements of one queue forwarded to another queue because of resource availability. Also, queue elements can be forwarded periodically, if programmed to do so.

A number of improvements may be necessary to save communications costs, redirect work to idle resources or for other reasons. One reason, for example, is improving response time.

- Queues permit asynchronous processing.
- Therefore, they can be helpful in handling long transactions.

Another way of looking at queues is as databases which can be created, scanned and destroyed. Queue forwarding can thus be seen as a database-to-database exchange as it enables the forwarding of elements from one queue to another.

Several technical issues must be ensured in connection with a valid queuing mechanism. For instance, some requests like security violation should be reply-queued even if the transaction itself aborts. This adds systems dependability at the expense of more transaction overhead. In terms of transaction semantics, it is proper not to confuse the queued transaction stack with program-to-program queuing as a non-transactional communications mechanism. Queues can have different functions and aspects and, under certain conditions, may make feasible better coherency control. *Coherency control* is necessary for data sharing and this requires the avoidance or at least detection of buffer invalidations. Just as important is to always know where the most recent version of information elements contained in the database is located.

The assurance of the latest version of information elements (IE) needs to determine where an up-to-date object version can be obtained. If not locally available, the system must read the IE from disk or request them from another component database. Updates and modifications can be exchanged among subsystems across an environment of shared database resources.

One of the key issues in choosing a coherency control scenario is the aftermaths to be expected from the update propagation solution to be chosen. The choice to be made must assist in controlling:

- input/output overhead
- response time for update transactions
- lock holding time due to data contention.

These are transaction processing problems and networking issues at the same time. Coherency control is dependent on the protocol(s) being used. Choices should point to less communication overhead as well as avoidance of lock conflicts, therefore ensuring database dependability.

9. Failure Modes and Recovery Strategies

Experience with the design, implementation and operation of communications systems suggests that the proper identification of reasons and subsequent recovery from failures can be a tricky business. There are two types of exceptions an on-line applications environment has to cope with.

1. Reasons causing transactions to abort, whether locally or globally.

Background reasons may be due to the transaction flow or the operating environment generally. Foreground reasons are triggered by the transactions themselves. For instance, the losses of state are associated only with the transaction(s).

2. Reasons causing the operating system to fail – whether at server level or in a network sense.

Issue 2 can be more serious than 1 above because it entails a loss of the memory state. Here comes the major difference between recoverable and non-recoverable resources.

With both types of errors the key issues are: what *state* is available to the exception handler? What *actions* can the program take to recover?

In terms of state, when a transaction aborts, all recoverable resources must be restored to their original state – that is, before the transaction started. The cause of the abort must also be known so that the corrective action is focused.

Had the abort been caused by the execution of a given operation, the program needs both the statement's exception and the reason for the abort. However, certain aborts can be spontaneous, unrelated to the application program which is executing at the time the failure has occurred.

Experience with real-life situations is the best guide on how to proceed. Therefore, the following references are based on the experience with monoprocessors and multiprocessors, which is reasonably rich. From such experience we will extrapolate behaviour under network perspectives, which however needs a few more years to be thoroughly validated.

Based on the fundamental issues related to state problems, a system failure causes all transactions active at the time the failure took place to abort.

- This type of failure destroys the state of all non-recoverable resources such as the contents of main memory.
- Hence, any IE needed for exception handling must be saved in the resource manager of the database.

To a significant degree, the cause of *abort* would be part of the application program's state, while the necessary recovery procedure should be more generalizable.

Precautions have to be taken as the program might abort for other reasons than transaction itself, for instance, for system reasons. A good approach is to process aborts and errors through an exception handler. The details are dependent on whether transactions are *chained* or *unchained.*

When transactions are chained, they execute sequentially but a program can specify the end of a transaction (whether commit or abort). The milestones are:

- start
- commit
- abort

but they are handled in different ways by the various transaction processing routines. With unchained transactions, the program identifies the start and end of each operation. Some statements may execute outside a transaction. However, most transaction monitors offer a chained programming model.

A procedure relative to actions-related transaction failures ensures that the program automatically branches to an exception handler. In a chained model, this routine handler is part of a new transaction. In the case of a non-chained approach, the exception handler is responsible for transaction demarcation.

Actions are particularly affected with system failure, since the program state is also lost. Provided the necessary software is available, the system will only recover programs with recoverable control state. Transactions supported by this feature can be restarted.

The proper strategy ensures that each request is run once and only once. This can be best arranged in the transaction monitor mode which supervises request execution, and contrasts to the batch environment which calls for rerunning procedures.

Closely associated to recovery strategies are the savepoints which relatively few companies observe. Precisely because of rerunning policies, since the early 1960s when batch programs of a certain size have been written, the advice has been to build at frequent intervals *recovery points*, or savepoints.

- A routine traps intermediate results.
- This avoids rerunning the whole application from the start.

But programmers rarely follow this principle even if it serves recovery requirements well in the case of system failure, thus easing the recovery burden.

With certain modifications, the savepoints strategy can be carried to a transaction environment where each program has a local state and parts of that state can be recoverable. A recovery point policy ensures that each program makes the values of its recoverable resource permanent though transparent.

Since a transaction does not need to abort back to the beginning but calls on trapped intermediate results, this feature can significantly improve recoverability. It helps in optimizing both a computing and a communications approach.

The subjects covered in this chapter, and the systems requirements they impose, are characteristic of the area of overlap between communications and computers. They are also software-intense issues, which need to be addressed in a consistent and thorough manner whether the study concerns communications or computer systems.

During the second half of the 1990s many of the preoccupations which dominated computer applications will enter into the communications domain. Inversely, a number of issues which so far have been generic to communications will have to be solved at the computer applications level. The best paradigm to demonstrate this permeability is transaction processing – hence, the decision to include this chapter in the book.

Part 3

Communications Companies Address Network Design Problems

9

Technological Breakthroughs Leading to New Network Designs

1. Introduction

New network designs and a range of equipment options can contribute to better private networks. Organizations are now replacing dumb multiplexers used on point-to-point circuits with more sophisticated ones. These act as bandwidth managers capable of dynamic switching and routing.

Mesh networks are being built that are much more cost-effective and more reliable than the old structure, but the question is: can step-wise change bring real benefits? The most important change is the newly found emphasis on *network intelligence*. However, as we have already seen, few organizations have the skill to obtain valid results – or even the culture to do so.

In the past, the large majority of networks did not really get designed. They simply grew as traffic increased, as users realized they could save money using a leased circuit, and as telcos provided that circuit. Over the years, the outcome has been that:

- The network became simply a collection of discrete, point-to-point leased circuits.
- These were put in place over a number of years without a properly laid-out technical plan.
- The adoption of parochial architectures, pushed by the vendors, contributed to inflexibility.
- High tariffs by telcos made it uneconomical for lower traffic parts of the network.

Faced with major problems in network operations, advanced user organizations have decided that it is high time their strategy regarding communications and computer networks must change – and that they themselves have to address design issues.

Forward-looking companies start to capitalize on technology to improve on price and performance, and look for quality of service as well as for reliability. But such efforts are often frustrated because users have to deal with old established telco monopolies and a tariff mentality that comes straight out of the Middle Ages. We have seen many examples on tariff issues in Chapter 3. This chapter shows why new technologies make old tariff structures obsolete.

2. The Need for Experimentation in Connection with Communications Networks

Because we know that with the exception of countries where there has been true deregulation the telco mentality will not easily change, we must be willing and able to study alternatives. Experimentation in regard to communications networks should include not only lines but also various types of components facilities and services, as well as their functionality and cost characteristics.

Circuit cost-distance variables can be represented by a graph on which the break points and segment slopes are specified for each facility type. Networks should be thoroughly analysed in terms of:

- structure
- functionality
- cost
- reliability.

A model built to represent the network should account for the fact that its whole structure in principle provides a single interactive environment developed to respond to a variety of communications functions. Hence, the appropriate description should involve:

- *network representation*, describing the network topology, service demands and equipment features
- *planning algorithms* necessary to estimate, map and optimize network functionality; as well as for scheduling reasons
- *user interfaces*, at every point which the network serves, including the ability to redefine network functions and services.

Planning and design algorithms can be instrumental in helping to determine the specific size, routing, and costs associated with the particular network being studied. The simulation of user interfaces allows the network planner to operate, understand and correct network planning failures in regard to end-user service.

On-line network management databases are necessary to store device and traffic information, and provide data for experimental planning models. These models typically cover traffic forecasting, blocking factors in connection to local and remote links or switches, routing schemes and the optimization of outside plant facilities.

Stored in easily accessible databases, network description files should cover each line and each node. Organizational data includes the network configuration, while geographical references reflect location and co-ordinates of the node. Uptime statistics provide information for reliability analysis.

- A distance matrix gives internodal distances, associated usage figures and bottlenecks.
- A cost matrix provides the cost for each circuit joining each node pair.
- Traffic data specifies traffic demand for each node pair, as well as projections on such demand.

A trunk specification file contains records of existing and potential trunks to be sized. The basic information includes lower and upper bounds on the size, an index to the transmission facility menu, routing exceptions and access models.

Any valid network study will pay significant attention to end-to-end blocking factors. Many telecommunications equipment manufacturers and service providers are very inaccurate when they assure their customers that there is no blocking in system performance.

- Because system performance depends both on design characteristics and on traffic flow, the moment comes when the limits are reached.
- Therefore, it is wise to experiment on system behaviour. With the aim of obtaining results which permit to forecast saturation, and of sizing the network.

In Figure 9.1, end-to-end performance in connection to communications traffic shows blocking levels. An ideal network performance with practically zero blocking is never achieved. There is no way that every traffic stream experiences the same end-to-end blocking: one per thousand in this example.

There are, however, different choices which should be experimentally proven. We must look for a solution space between an acceptable condition where no stream is exposed to more than, say, three-per-thousand blocking, and one where a significant number of network users is exposed to high levels of blocking. Such an approach is shown in Figure 9.1.

There used to be a time when, in a telephone network, the appropriate unit of measurement for saturation was *Erlang*.* But the Erlang is

* After the name of the Danish engineer who developed the measurement procedures just prior to World War I.

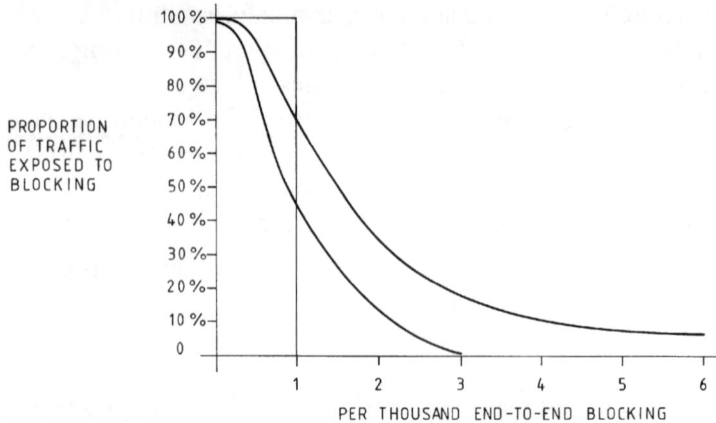

Figure 9.1 Zero end-to-end blocking is now feasible, but the situation should be under control

fairly deterministic and therefore it no more constitutes a valid unit of measurement. The new unit of measurement needs to be fuzzy – and many companies are now working on this issue by modelling through fuzzy engineering.

3. Evaluating the Benefits a Renewal Strategy Can Provide

Experienced telecommunications managers and astute network design engineers appreciate the breadth and depth of a study necessary prior to making a decision on whether to proceed with an overlay or a full-blown replacement strategy. A great deal of competitiveness, now and in the future, is embedded in this choice.

By articulating a set of basic functional components that underlie cost and benefit, sticking to an open architecture, and providing means to recombine network elements to create new services, user organizations make available to themselves the possibility to switch vendors. They also obtain results more quickly and at a lower cost than a static network policy can ever allow.

Many user organizations rest a significant part of the renewal of their network on routers and gateways. Routers come in several types and different levels of intelligence. They:

- operate at network connectivity
- use hierarchical addressing
- require end system participation.

Most importantly, routers are transparent to higher layer protocols, are more intelligent than bridges, can be local or remote and are more or less suitable for a variety of topologies.

Remote routers connect geographically dispersed subnetworks and are usually quite sophisticated. Local routers may be little more than bridges with routing functions. These are often called *brouters*. Routers:

- can be distinguished by routing scheme
- may be static or dynamic
- may feature a single or multiple protocols.

Static routers require a network manager to update routing tables whenever a change is made. Dynamic routers use routing protocols to continuously update all nodes on the status of the network. Single protocol routers connect two networks using the same protocol. As the name implies, a multiprotocol router supports more than one protocol.

Figure 9.2 suggests that routers are attached at the lower physical level but operate at the network level (level 3) of ISO's open system interconnection (OSI). Among the ISO network routing protocols is the 8473, an international standard version of Internet Protocol (IP), formally defined as MIL-1777. The fact that there is a large number of network and internetwork routing protocols, is one of the problems.

CCITT-recommended protocols include X.25, X.28 and X.75 associated with packet-switched public data networks (PSPDN); Q.931 protocol used with digital end-to-end connectors with the integrated services digital network (ISDN); a Q.704 and Q.714 designed for signalling connections supporting ISDN and the emerging intelligent networks.

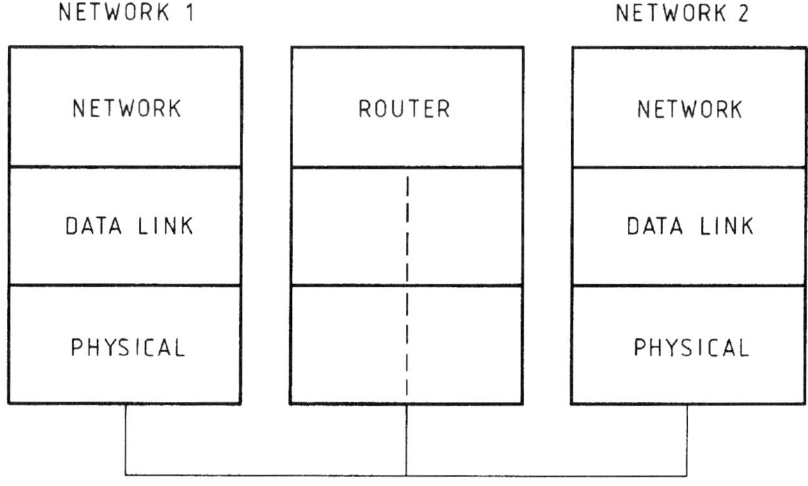

Figure 9.2 Routers attach at the physical level but operate at the network level of ISO/OSI

Compared to routers, the gateway technology is, essentially, a point-to-point solution. Each local area network has a high-end personal computer which serves the function of a:

- bridge connecting similar LANs, or
- gateway that links LANs to other communications systems.

These might include X.25 networks, asynchronous communications, SNA architecture or other. While the different disciplines vary, the functionality consists of routing work requests from individual workstations or servers to the resource(s) addressed. Such requests may come from any component attached to the network.

Since routers are software and hardware devices which come at considerable cost, there is plenty of room for experimentation and optimization. Typically, this requires simulation, but few user organizations really master the technology which is necessary; from mathematical models to knowledge engineering.

Network simulation is not just the better way of being sure of returns on the investments which we make – and the service which we get – it is the only serious approach as networks become more polyvalent, and therefore so much more complex.*

There is also a need to pay extraordinary attention to drawbacks which exist with network solutions, particularly those relating to component parts and associated services. One of the evident examples is the limited availability of certain features in public networks, such as international frame relay.

- Local access to frame relay nodes is still dependent on inadequate and expensive local infrastructures.
- Lack of standards even characterizes old networks such as ISDN, which was supposed to be the saviour of the telcos' old plant.

Long in development but now available from carriers across most of Europe, ISDN is still incompatible from one market to the next. Yet, the biggest clients, the multinationals, want a common range of services with common interfaces available from telecommunications suppliers across the world.**

The case of incompatibilities and high costs is made worse through relatively low quality in communications channels due to lack of com-

* For a discussion on this issue see D.N. Chorafas and H. Steinmann, *Implementing Networks in Banking and Financial Services* (Macmillan, London, 1988).

** From section 8 onward we discuss another major drawback in the form of high prices of public data services – to which reference has already been made in Chapter 3.

prehensive network management. It is further aggravated by the professed (by the telcos) uncertainty about technical directions, though the answer is rather evident: radio networks and optical fibres.

4. Using Fibre Optics in the Loop

Both companies and nations able to read tomorrow's newsprint today appreciate that when it comes to transmission capability, the answer is gigastreams on fibre. Fibre-in-the-loop systems have experienced a slow initial deployment, in part due to high equipment costs.

- As prices drop, network designers become more attracted towards photonics, while at the same time competitive pressures escalate.
- Operators are turning to fibre to provide much greater network capacity at a much lower cost.
- This dual influence is leading to a growth of the fibre-optics market, with a corresponding drop in prices.

Photonics has become an attractive proposition both on land and for undersea information highways. At the present time, an estimated 200 fibre-optic underseas systems are in operation.

In America, railroads are busy exploiting the right of the way through fibre-optic cables. In Japan, the Central Railway took advantage of optical fibre cable laid along rail tracks, to enable business travellers on moving trains to communicate with their homes and offices. In fact, through photonics the Central Japan Railway has enhanced its services to fight competition from other forms of transportation.

Fibre-optic applications in offices are no longer something really new. For five years, Japan's NTT has cabled the Twins towers of its Tokyo headquarters – one with optical fibres, the other with coaxial cable – and has, in effect, put the two systems in competition with one another.

Rapid advances in optics are moving industry towards an environment in which optical fibre can be delivered to the home as cheaply as copper wire. This tends to promote photonics highways between offices, factories and homes, making possible the proliferation of two-way television and networked distribution systems handling compound electronic documents.

- Innovation in optical communication revolutionizes not only the underlying network but also the computational infrastructure.
- Emerging local, metropolitan, and wide area networks have transmission speeds ranging from 50 MBPS to over 1 GBPS.

- Such channel capacity is providing bandwidth for many distributed high-performance applications.

These references are important because while photonics technology is already well-established for long-distance voice communications, an intensive implementation over short distances is novel. The concept is to capitalize on data rates ranging from megastreams of 100 MBPS to gigastreams of 1 or more GBPS.

This is how leading-edge user organizations are thinking, but it is not necessarily what happens in the majority of cases. A surprisingly large number of companies are still blinded by their EDPers and the tendency to hang on to the old wares of their preferred computer vendor. The *status quo* often dominates and, with this, inertia. As Figure 9.3 suggests:

- The resulting approach is a naive 3270 protocol, underutilizing the personal computers and perpetuating incompatibility in the connection of terminals.
- An improved solution is the necessary step towards the more advanced technology discussed in the preceding paragraphs.*

The transition towards improved connectivity is urgent and absolutely necessary. Oncoming lightwave systems using wavelength division multiplexing (WDM) will allow a single fibre cable to carry multiple high-speed communications channels.

- This may reach a combined data rate of terastreams, that is 10^{12} bits per second (TBPS).
- Its availability will fundamentally change the way hardware and software are designed and implemented.

Partitioning optical fibre bandwidth into several subchannels through WDM, permits existing electronic communication equipment to fully use the potential of optical fibres. Wavelength division multiplexing can support multiple channels over a single physical link, with each physical link viewed as a set of parallel logical links.

- The effective implementation of WDM calls for new technology such as the use of non-linearities in wave propagation. For instance, *solitons*, which are isolated waves that travel without change of form and have recently attracted considerable attention.

The pulse spectrum of a soliton, as well as its shape, changes little over great distances. Hence, solitons may lend themselves better than conventional pulses to wavelength division multiplexing.

* This is an intermediate step since buses have limitations, as we discuss in section 5.

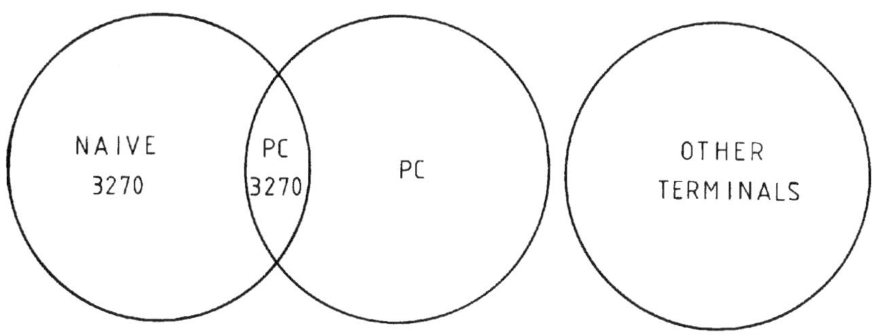

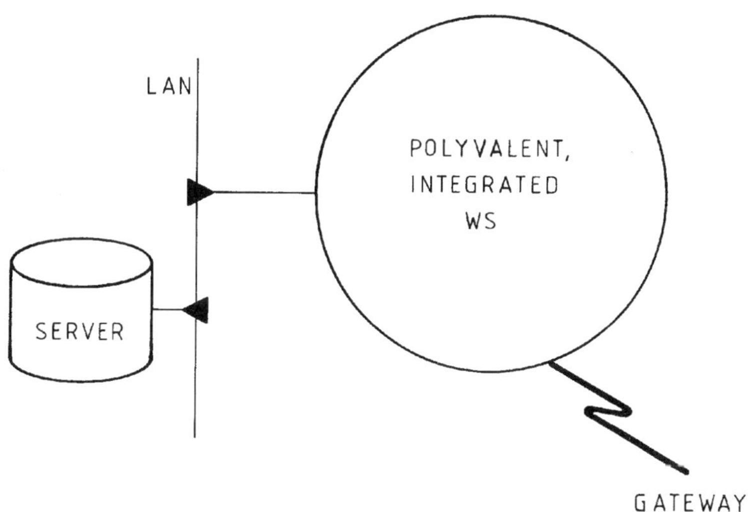

Figure 9.3 The best way to spoil a project is to maintain the *status quo*

Some of the estimates currently made give non-linear solutions an advantage of as much as five in data throughput. It is quite important to notice that the interest on solitons comes also from other sources, for instance, non-linear type studies in financial analysis.

5. Frame Relay and Asynchronous Transfer Mode

With the characteristics of electronics devices approaching physical limits, parallel, distributed processing has been widely advocated as a promising approach for high-performance communications and computing. This approach is strengthened by the fact that there is a significant amount of exploitable parallelism inherent in many applications.

To effectively use parallelism a system must be able to greatly reduce the communication overhead between processors. The communication architecture to be adopted should be independent of the applications themselves, but also efficient, reliable, and cost-effective.

- An interconnection of communicating devices through a crossbar, would be prohibitive in terms of costs.
- But, a shared-bus interconnection might be inefficient and less reliable than necessary.

For these reasons, present research is directed towards designing interconnection networks whose performance and cost lie somewhere between the aforementioned two cases. Such interconnection networks, have an architecture which integrates switches and links, permitting multimedia communication between processors and storage devices. Depending on the timing approach, switching mode and control strategy, each set of topologically equivalent networks can have different operational characteristics, giving rise to different system behaviours. The timing approach is one of the most important attributes of the communication system. The two types are:

- synchronous
- asynchronous.

Synchronous control techniques are characterized by the existence of a central, global clock that broadcasts clock signals to all devices in a network so that the entire system operates in a lock-step fashion. This has been the most widely used approach since the 1950s and therefore it is well-understood.

Asynchronous network solutions operate without a global clock. Communication among operational units in networks and computers is performed by means of handshaking. As a result, they have good expandability and modularity, but are rather novel in conception – and hence rather difficult to design.

- *Asynchronous switching* methodologies have been introduced in long-haul network design, not only in computer architectures.
- The *asynchronous transfer mode* (ATM) is presently being established as the new design discipline in telecommunications.

In all likelihood, ATM will find itself at the heart of computer design of the coming generation of networks; most particularly of broadband communications systems. ATM is characterized by fixed cell length, which is and is not a drawback, consisting of 5-byte header and 48-byte user information.

The protocol enables switching with pure hardware. Hence, switching can be performed nearly as fast as physically possible. However, fixed cell length is not optimal for voice traffic or for data.

- For voice, even a smaller cell than 53 bytes might do better.
- For data, a cell length of about 1500 bytes would have been a good value, depending on the application.

Table 9.1 compares different communications disciplines: Frame relay, ATM time division multiplexing (TDM), X.25 and FDDI. Particularly important is the contrast in terms of applications domains, main benefits to be derived from each of them, individual drawbacks, the ISO/OSI layer to which they apply, the frame or cell length and the standards being observed.

Frame relay is one of the favoured implementations of *fast packet switching* using variable length frames. It is a protocol suited for data communications, not for voice. The main goal is to have a faster interface between the network and end-user equipment.

The frame structure of frame relay corresponds to ISO Layer 2. It is described in the CCITT Recommendation Q.921, and enables packet switching to be actioned at high speed. Above the data link layer, frame relay is protocol transparent.

Another difference between ATM and frame relay, which is not shown in Table 9.1, lies in the fact that the asynchronous transfer mode has been practically adopted as the American standard, while frame relay dominates European implementations. The US applications, have started with the government's Sonet network and are finding their way into in-house systems.

6. The Fragmentation of Services Connected to Public Networks

Many experts in the telecommunications field foresee that the public telecommunications network will become fragmented at the operator level, with new and major interoperator boundaries to be administered. Compounding the challenges is the fact that customers have different views of what matters most – as well as different wishes regarding the protocols to be chosen.

Table 9.1 Comparison of communications disciplines

	Frame relay	*ATM*	*TDM*	*X.25*	*FDDI*
Main application	data	data, voice, video	data, voice	data	data
Main benefits	low overall delay, flexible	high-speed, channel sharing	best suited for voice	good for value-added services	good solution for MAN
Main drawbacks	limited value-added functions	high cost of hardware	assigned time slots	long delay per hop	sensitive to interrupts
OSI layer	2	2/3 (ATM adaptation layer)	2	3	1, 2
Frame (or cell) length	variable	fixed: Header: 5 bytes; Info: 48 bytes		variable: 128 bytes as typical maximum	variable: 4,500 bytes maximum
Standards	CCITT I.122	CCITT I.121 (B-ISDN)	CCITT G.700	CCITT X.25	X3T9.5

- One of the technically, and politically, difficult issues which will be revealed is protection against carrier underperformance.
- The good news is that users will have a choice among systems integrators and a number of suppliers of underlying services.

This issue of best choice is likely to become more urgent in a world of digital networks in which fundamental control tasks, such as routing and service provisioning, are moving away from currently established operators. There is a growing number of service providers and users, some generalists and some specialists, hence:

- New strategies are necessary to face the challenges posed by network pluralism and protocol incompatibilities.
- There is a need for proper definition of rules that could commit dominant providers to normalized network features.

Interoperability across networks is and will remain key to the future, but the variety of protocols we have seen in Table 9.1 greatly complicates this mission. Many user organizations now require that network providers follow standards, rather than their own parochial architectures and protocols.

Norms and standards are no longer just a question of access to physical facilities, but also to the higher levels of functionality in intelligent networks. At the same time, both carriers and user organizations want to protect their intellectual property rights in complex and expensive network software.

- While practically everyone agrees that standards should be observed, there is no universal opinion on what they should look like.
- Though only people who lost all good sense talk of SNA and 3270, the example which we saw in section 6 about differences in frame relay and ATM is most actual.

Today, many networking analysts believe that private implementations of ATM/Sonet have all but destroyed any justification for the American National Standards Institute (ANSI) to continue work on either the slotted, hybrid-ring version of FDDI, known as FDDI-II, or the planned gigabit successor to FDDI, called FDDI follow-on LAN (FFOL).

Some experts in network planning are advising potential corporate users of FDDI that, if they intend to employ a number of isochronous multimedia applications and do not plan to upgrade until, say, 1998, they should leap directly from Ethernet and from token-ring to local

ATM, bypassing FDDI entirely. Various considerations have driven developers from shared-media topologies to this conclusion.

- The move from a shared-media LAN to private switching networks capable of interfacing with public networks has been long overdue.
- Developers seeking to combine high-speed packet data switching with video-conferencing could reap particular benefits from ATM implementation.

The ATM notion of bandwidth-on-demand is just as important for reducing costs at the local level as it is at the public network level. Many technical issues are currently shared between local area networks (LAN), metropolitan area networks (MAN) and wide area networks (WAN).

The added factor in the foregoing consideration is that shared-media technologies have the problems of a peak bandwidth that needs to be significantly high. This might be acceptable with a moderate number of users, but as the number of nodes goes into the hundreds:

- either the effective bandwidth per node shrinks
- or the cost of implementation skyrockets.

Such issues are rarely evident in most vendors' offers – which are either incomplete or represent the co-operative effort of different companies. From a regulatory and antimonopolistic viewpoint, one of the toughest dilemmas in the new telecommunications environment will be deciding when co-operative agreements and marketing alliances are in the interest of customers or, alternatively, when they constitute abuses and antitrust violations.

Since such alliances will increasingly be the norm, the pressure on antitrust authorities and regulatory bodies will increase. Not the least of the problems is ways and means to control powerful global network service providers, acting outside the jurisdiction of any particular authority. Making high-technology telecom capabilities available to everyone at an affordable cost will not be that easy.

7. Implementing a Two-Way High-Definition Television

Practically every communications and computers manufacturer today believes that its future lies in multimedia networks. Hence the drive to adopt an all-embracing strategy of developing in-house asynchronous transfer mode chips, network adapters, hubs and switches.

Added to this drive for self-sufficiency is the fact that survival is often seen through strategic alliances, and the longer-term aim is forging new markets. This dual approach however requires:

- enormous cultural changes to face the challenges of new networked multivendor information systems
- the proper definition of the domain where the evolving communications technology will be at its best, for users and for vendors.

As far as the technologies which we discuss in this chapter are concerned, they could prove to be instrumental in connection to two-way high-definition television (HDTV). There are also many applications domains which might benefit from them.

One application for very large bandwidth using two-way high-definition television is flat screens on the wall like huge windows. These *communications windows* enable the user to converse with business partners, do teleconferencing and exchange documents. Beyond this:

- virtual reality applications could help in bringing together far-away people and places, compressing them into the same screen for effective investment and other decisions
- other applications include medical analysis and diagnosis, two-way entertainment, on-line police checks of fingerprints and other indices.

But is HDTV and its standard a sure bet? What about the colossal research investment in analogue solutions which are now being abandoned in favour of digital, as has happened both in Europe and in Japan?

The challenge of a switch out of analogue services started as far back as October 1992. 'D2-MAC [Europe's intermediate HDTV standard] is dead,' proclaimed André Rousselet, then president of Canal+, the French-based broadcaster.* But few people were ready to listen at that time. Testifying before the Parliamentary Office of Scientific and Technological Choices, Rousselet, a former supporter of the MAC standard said he believed digital television

- will be able to carry more signals per channel than MAC
- will arrive before broadcasters are able to amortize their investment in MAC.

It took more than a year for Europe's telecommunications ministers, company executives and laboratory directors to understand that message. Then, in mid-1993, the authorities of the European Union agreed to abandon a previous strategy which called for an analogue transmission standards for HDTV, in favour of digital technology.

This decision came after the British blocked a plan to develop the advanced television market in Europe, because the proposal relied on

* *Electronic World News*, 12 October 1992.

analogue standards. It was followed, in February 1994, by the Japanese who publicly accepted that analogue HDTV technology would be rapidly outmoded. As a result, Japan wrote off all its investment in analogue HDTV.

But there are even doubts on HDTV as such. In July 1993, when he was still the CEO of Apple Computer, John Sculley said that he believed digital compression television has a better chance in the future than HDTV. At the annual convention of the National Association of Broadcasters, in Las Vegas, Sculley:

- questioned the commercial viability of HDTV
- stated that no one has yet figured out how to build a digital HDTV set at an affordable price.*

To a very substantial extent, the challenge is one of targeted markets and what they can afford in terms of prices. Both the public telecommunications offering and the in-house networks are going through a major shake-up – a message which has not yet filtered through to the majority of people concerned by this change.

8. The Growing Competition in Pricing Network Services

Pitfalls and wrong directions are compounded by the fact that the huge monopoly-type telephone networks are not able to keep up with technology start-ups. The massive infrastructure investment by monopolies cannot be easily written off – even if it is giving way piecemeal, to demand-led new network solutions.

This trend will continue. As a result, opportunities for user organizations multiply as more operators emerge. As volume grows for low-cost services, small networks made from efficient high-technology switches supplant big networks. This is precisely what happened to information systems as networked personal computers and workstations took over from mainframes.

- Whichever standard takes over, from line protocol to a high-definition discipline, head-on competition in telecommunications should bring lower rates and better service for both cable and telephone services.
- This is really the market-led start of dismantling the old monopolies, as both the telephone industry and the cable companies plan to launch multibillion-dollar investments in technology.

* *Communications of the ACM*, Vol. 36, No. 7, July 1993.

Large investments in high technology will make possible advanced business services and consumer-oriented products such as education via interactive video, sophisticated on-line shopping and remote medical services. In order to capture the evolving markets, total US spending on telecommunications equipment is expected to grow between 6 per cent and 8 per cent per year.

At the same time, at the deregulated telecommunications environments of the USA and the UK, there is a steady and significant drop in tariffs due to stiffening competition. The evolving new tariffs with broadband services will turn the economics of providing traditional telephony upside-down. The almost *infinite bandwidth* available with fibre optics will probably mean that:

- it will not be worthwhile charging for ordinary telephone calls, or low-speed data traffic, such as email
- instead, subscribers could simply pay a fixed *monthly rental* – or a price based on the consumption of HDTV programmes.

In all likelihood, there will be no unique tariffs scheme. Each telecommunications carrier will have its own cost and benefit structure. Even today, before the huge new investments and new offerings, the prices quoted for the same service by different value-added networks are widely diverging.

For the user organization this is good news, since it provides an excellent basis to play one communications provider against another, and thereby enlarge its business opportunity. As an example, Table 9.2 presents the quotes by four different vendors for the replacement of a current network which had outlived its purpose.

The quoted prices are indicative, but the order of magnitude as well as the differences between the offers by the different networks are real. Note that further study indicated the offer US Sprint made was by far the best all-round opportunity the user organization could obtain.

Other network services vendors who participated in this competition

Table 9.2 Quoted prices among telecommunications vendors (the current network cost is $3.5 million per year)

1. *US Sprint:* $0.75 m/year with new technology, also installing its own switches on the nodes.
2. *Competitor A:* $1.3 m/year, well below current cost – but with the same old system.
3. *Competitor B:* $1.5 m/year, but average technology with multiplexers or individual lines.
4. *Competitor C:* $4.5 m/year plus a $0.5 million entry price.

were vague. One of the major computer manufacturers, who now expands into long-haul network systems said that it needed to work for two or three months to define what was to be done prior to making an initial offer.

Another computer vendor made an offer which was higher than all four in Table 9.2. But it sugar-coated this offer by saying that the leadership it had in the data processing business will show advantages in the telecoms sector, aiding in the understanding of multimedia applications! The user organization doubted, correctly, that it will be that easy to change from the culture of 'biggest is best' to the 'small is beautiful' solution. Yet, this is what a highly competitive telecommunications and software environment requires.

9. New Communications Solutions Depend on Sophisticated Software

As we have seen in section 8, increasingly intense international competition is forcing businesses to become both more efficient and cost-conscious. New intelligent communications networks and knowledge-enriched software technology are enabling novel organizational forms, processes, and roles.

- Advanced technology makes it possible to share vast amounts of information within organizations.
- This is a fundamental reason why the re-engineering business processes are now becoming common; with knowledge and information being the pivots.

A combination of competition, demographics, and changed views of global competition have shown that communication, co-ordination and learning are not mere peripheral activities. Rather, the construction of shared information systems is an essential part of any human enterprise.

- Intelligent networks empower people and companies to create, share and communicate all forms of information at any time and from any place.
- Sophisticated software fundamentally improves the way we work, produce, buy, sell, govern, learn and play.

The challenge lies in the vision of the future as well as the ability to ensure that our products and services continue to be key building blocks used to construct value-added solutions. Increasingly, people and companies buy solutions – not just hardware or software.

Many cognizant people now believe that the period of organizational change we are entering will be as significant as that which followed the Industrial Revolution – and networks will be the infrastructure. The successful organizations of the next few years, and of the early twenty-first century, will be very different from those of today.

- The change will create significant opportunities for people and companies.
- But it will also bring enormous problems which need to be surmounted.

For instance, the importance of managing information efficiently throughout an engineering organization has never been more crucial. With the concept of concurrent business operations taking hold in many companies, keeping all important data accessible to everyone within an enterprise is a major competitive advantage.

Top-level organizations are taking a careful look into the emerging era of new business opportunities with the goal to help find novel and pragmatic answers to diverse questions that concern society at large – not just the financial and industrial sectors:

- What will happen to the growing numbers of people whose jobs are disappearing in today's downsizing efforts?
- In which way will the transformation of know-how affect business operations and employment opportunities?

Underpinning the answer to these questions is what will happen to industry structures when electronic markets and information highways make it possible for buyers and sellers to find each other easily, on a global scale, without the classical intermediaries.

There are many other practical questions to be asked in connection with the instantaneous transmission of information by intelligent broadband networks. For instance, in which way should traditional accounting measures be augmented to reflect a broader view of a firm's intangible assets, liabilities, and long-term prospects? How can this be done in a global sense?

The control of exposure due to derivative financial instruments in the international market brings into consideration the need for sophisticated analytical tools which are able to go further and deeper than classical accounting ever made possible.* As the bankruptcy of Barings in February 1995 documents, the risk was taken by the Singapore office of a British bank, through speculation on the Tokyo stock market index, in trades done in Osaka.

* See also by D.N. Chorafas, *Managing Derivatives Risk* (Probus/Irwin, Chicago, 1995) and *Chaos Theory* (Probus, Chicago, 1994).

There is no alternative to the thorough study of current exposure as well as of hypothetical but plausible future risks. This requires that organizations are experimenting with new technologies from realtime simulation of products and processes to top-level management control based on any-to-any networks.

Knowledge and information are crucial ingredients in elaborating new organizational solutions, systematically creating and refining coherent scenarios of future possibilities. Precisely along this frame of reference has been advanced the concept of the information superhighway.

As we see in section 10, however, monopolies have neither the brains nor the motivation of providing sophisticated telecommunications networks connecting offices and living-rooms, using interactive computers and advanced software artefacts. Cost considerations are just as important, as has been underlined on several occasions.

With the advent of virtual company and virtual office solutions* the living-room will double as the office for many, perhaps most, people. But teleworking will spread faster in a deregulated environment than in one which is under the thumb of the government and its bureaucrats.

10. Telecommunications Developments in the European Union

The governments of the European Union have pledged themselves to abolish the barriers to the intra-European flow of people, money, goods and services. But do the European governments really mean it? Is this supposed to be applicable in all domains and most particularly in telecommunications?

- Though bankers and brokers would clearly benefit from an integrated market, most governments resist the trend toward a common European central bank.
- In continental Europe, the different telecommunications administrations remain huge government-owned bureaucracies, which seal the borders to competition.
- At the same time other protectionist measures still flourish, no matter the rhetoric about Maastricht and the Unique Act of the European Union.

Germany, for example, has passed legislation that would make it expensive for middle-size, family-owned businesses to sell out or merge across

* See D.N. Chorafas and H. Steinmann, *Virtual Reality: Practical Applications in Business and Industry* (Prentice-Hall, Englewood Cliffs, NJ, 1995).

frontiers. But at the same time the government squeezes the Mittelstand by cutting down on the research grants given to German universities – because of the huge deficits in financing the former East Germany's chaos.

Knowing politicians, we expect all of the present governmental barriers still to be here four years hence. Also in place will be the uncertainty which, for the last few years, has characterized what direction Europe would take in opening its telecommunications markets.

- What the European governments and their protected monopolies fail to appreciate is that continental Europe is not able to dictate the pace of reform.
- Telecommunications is more than ever a global industry with Americans, British and Japanese competitors threatening to leave the continential Europeans way behind.

The decision not to touch for the time being Europe's voice network monopolies, and this at least until 1998 or later, has been near-sighted and politically weak-willed. Its ramifications go far beyond the telephone business and hit at the heart of economic progress and competitiveness. Current telco positions are:

- steadily eroded by foreign competition
- threatened by foreign ideas and technology.

The fate of the telecoms services sector is a reflection of Europe's inability to grasp the many other pressing political and economic issues. It can mean that all the countries together and each one individually, lose in many ways, as innovation stagnates and big business looks elsewhere for cost-effective communications services.

The situation is made worse by the fact that Europe's communications sector is fragmented and ill-prepared for the coming onslaught of competition. Some knowledgeable people think it is heading toward irrelevance; others believe that it has gone beyond repair.

Indecision prevails at many levels. In 1987 the European Commission established the ground rules for a so-called *competitive* telecoms market. The problem is that not everyone really believes in such a thing or is even interested to take this philosophy as the basis of a European network infrastructure. If there are no takers, there is no progress.

As long as carriers act in what they think are their own interests and ignore business, industry and private customers, and as long as governments are indecisive or run scared from liberalizing markets there is going to be decay. The European telecommunications industry is doomed to lag behind those of the USA and Japan, which are working feverishly on strategic communications investment.

In fact, down to the bottom line, the whole issue of the information superhighway is just one huge business investment. If it succeeds in the USA, it will put American telecommunications industries at a colossal advantage over the Europeans. This will be a big jump forward and it will become increasingly difficult for others to catch up.

10

Choosing the Right Direction in Research and Development Investments

1. Introduction

One of the basic premises underlying the new telecommunications systems is that rapid progress towards the solution of complex issues relating to users, products, customers and markets, is essential to fulfilling many of the missions of this decade. This will be even more crucial at the beginning of the twenty-first century which is, after all, only a few years away.

The term 'rapid' is not used only in an *R&D* sense but also, if not mainly, in regard to *time-to-market*. 'By the HPCC folk?' asked one of the reviewers. 'This is not one of their preoccupations.' The reference made to HPCC is to the High Performance Communications and Computers project sponsored by the US government – and the answer to this remark is that time-to-market should be a major preoccupation of the sponsor and of the researchers of any project involving communications, computers and software.

The products we design are for the user. The market is an excellent criterion. How can we assess new products in computers, communications and software without describing the numerous task environments and thousands of runs in each one of them?

Evaluation is a complicated issue and analysis has to take place at many levels. Considerations include not only product characteristics such as functionality, quality and cost, but also:

- market reaction to the application domain's breadth and importance
- effectiveness and uniqueness of resource utilization
- comparison to alternative products and market efforts.

Experimentation is essential. Obviously, any one of the applications models or simulators to be developed would capture only a fraction of the relevant product and market dynamics. But *if* the results of experimentation will make it feasible to evaluate competitive advantages, then we can position ourselves against the market forces.

Advances in computing and communications technologies can accelerate the product development process in all disciplines. Cost-effective results can enable companies to integrate new knowledge and better methodologies into their product and market strategies, doing so in a national as well as a transnational sense. We take computers and computing as the focal point in demonstrating cost-effectiveness.

Because of global networking, from managerial productivity to product development and marketing crucial processes are increasingly dependent on the close interaction of people located in distant places. There is a global business perspective which greatly influences new advancements in technology.

Typically, managers and professionals are sharing and accessing computational resources across countries and continents. By so doing, they can appreciate that the sophistication of the approaches put at their disposal is instrumental in facing the challenges of the years to come.

2. An Infrastructure for Resource Sharing

High performance computing and communications technology is *knowledge and innovation intensive.* It usually engages the entire organization, a concept well-documented if we look back to the recent past:

- Building upon fundamental research of the early 1980s, a new computing technology of scalable parallel processing computers has emerged.
- The foremost companies in manufacturing, merchandising, finance and other services are now effectively using supercomputers, gaining an edge,
- The 'haves' and 'have-nots' in technology will be further differentiated when by the late 1990s, practical applications achieve sustained performance improvements of a 100 to 1000 times greater level, compared to current systems.

Most advanced laboratory projects address both computers and communications, and rightly so. Resource sharing requires increasingly wideband networks moving from kilostreams to megastreams and gigastreams.* Figure 10.1 shows this transition in an applications-oriented sense. Based on projections by the US High Performance Computing and Communications program, this figure distinguishes between steady and bursty traffic requirements. These are the two main classes

* KBPS to MBPS and GBPS.

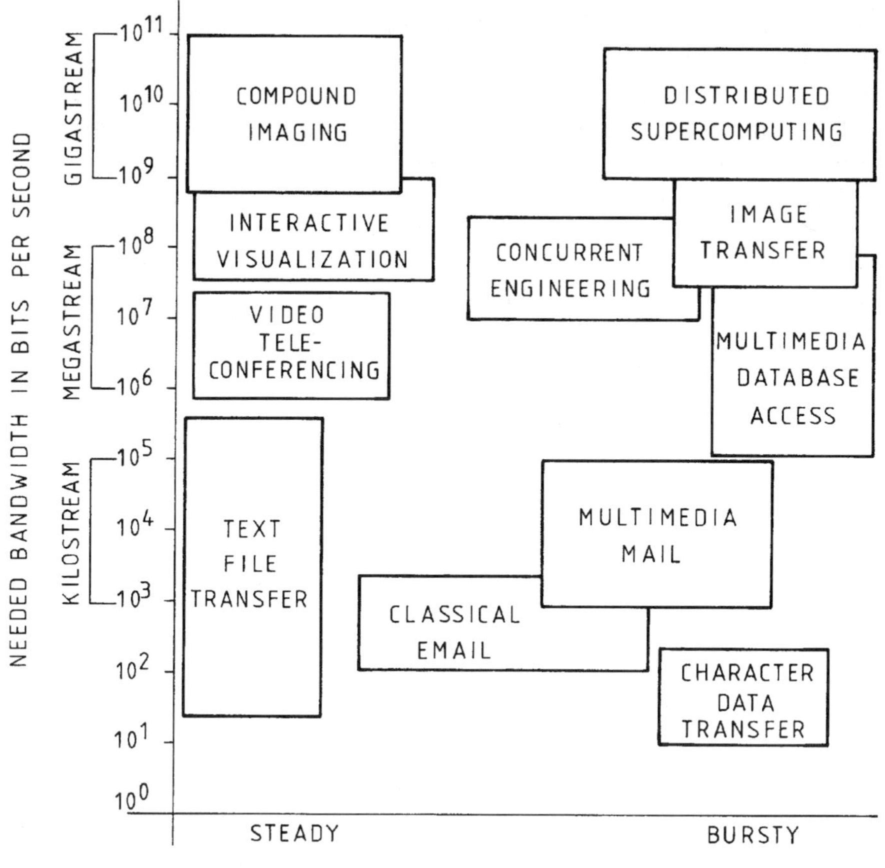

Figure 10.1 Applications on the US National Research and Education Network: traffic characteristics and bandwidth

of communications challenges to be faced during the coming years by networks, in terms of function and performance. They will characterize many applications by the end of this decade as well as into the twenty-first century.

Made by the Office of the President of the United States, the aforementioned projection accounts for the fact that the industrial and financial sectors of the economy will keep on providing major sources of innovation. But they will do so more effectively if they are supported by cost-effective solutions in addressing grand challenge problems. The cornerstone to success, some specialists suggest, is:

- rapid transition of laboratory results into new products and services
- a focused effort to assure that their market impact would be felt immediately.

In this sense, advances in high-performance computing are seen as an *enabling technology*, making possible impressive developments in almost every scientific, engineering and business discipline. There is a complex web of interdependencies, with each area contributing to progress in other areas or, alternatively, placing stumbling blocks in the way.

Because of these dependencies, achieving and maintaining a proper balance in the sharing of resources should be a primary goal and the most important priority in the current context of the R&D environment. Striking such a balance should be part and parcel of any strategic plan. Another key criterion is the ability to provide wide dissemination and application of new technologies thereby:

- enhancing existing know-how
- speeding the pace of innovation
- serving organizational goals in an able manner.

In a fiercely competitive environment, corporate goals are best served through rapid product introduction, cost cutting, gains in productivity, improvements in quality and market competitiveness. They are promoted by making high-performance computing and networking an integral part of the design, production and marketing process of the organization itself.*

Admittedly, the transfer of technology from research to development and from there to business applications might be a slow process due to a number of barriers. Hence the need to properly co-ordinate the whole effort, with priority given to:

- technology transfer operations
- design reviews and audits
- a close eye on timetables, quality and costs.

Not everything is to be found in technical breakthroughs alone. For instance, conducting research on new protocols and related security primitives is necessary but not enough. We have to effectively use the results which are obtained in related domains such as networking and databasing. Experience suggests that this statement is true in terms of applications involving:

- heterogeneous databases to be accessed in seamless manner
- sustained gigabit network speeds with very low bit error rate**

* 'Let's (rather) do research on how to allow everybody to *slow down* (*sic*),' suggested an EDPer. Crazy but true.

** For instance 10^{-11}, 10^{-12}. See also Chapter 1.

- standards able to provide effective interoperability
- enhanced user interfaces to distributed systems.

Just as important as the dissemination of technological developments is the ability to transfer the acquired *applications knowledge*, so that it becomes widely available throughout the enterprise. Managers and professionals, not only research scientists, should be the first beneficiaries of this effort.

'How can everybody be first?' asked a reviewer. This question evidently misses the point. Currently in the typical organization, some 90 per cent of the IT budget is dedicated to trivia and administrative work which is nonsense. By contrast, first priority should be given to managers and professionals – who should attract the lion's share of attention in systems solutions and financial allocations.

3. Who Finances the Researchers?

The American HPCC effort sees the development and usage of powerful system design tools as being closely associated to the research which must be done. This reference is valid for computer-aided design (CAD) through to new means for computer-aided software engineering (CASE), as well as the work necessary for enabling multiple platforms to work together in the analysis, simulation and testing of:

- products
- systems
- markets.

In his election campaign, President Clinton made frequent reference to the Japanese model of indirect government financing. Achieved mainly through the Ministry of International Trade and Industry (MITI) the Japanese approach all three issues: products, systems and markets at the same time. Who will finance the American researchers?

The overall strategy for HPCC in America builds on government agency strengths, by giving appropriate organizations the responsibility to co-ordinate activities, integrating their participation in various task areas. These agencies can be divided into the following main groups:

- Department of Defense (DOD) with the Advanced Research Project Agency (ARPA) and the National Security Agency (NSA)
- Department of Commerce (DOC) with the National Institute of Standards and Technology (NIST),* National Oceanic and

* Formerly, National Bureau of Standards (NBS).

Atmospheric Administration (NOAA) and the Advanced Technology Program administered by NIST
- National Science Foundation (NSF)
- Department of Energy (DOE)
- National Aeronautics and Space Administration (NASA)
- Environmental Protection Agency (EPA)
- Department of Health and Human Services with the National Institute of Health (NIH)
- National Library of Medicine (NLM).

All participating agencies conduct research and development in each of the areas of activity in HPCC. The Office of Science and Technology Policy bears primary responsibility for the administration of the Federal Program* – or 'sort of', as some people tend to suggest.

Most of these organizations have ample technical and operational expertise needed for deploying high-performance systems. NSF, for example, has developed national networks for the research community and it has been promoting computer projects since the early 1950s, financing a significant number of initiatives in computers and software.

The careful observer would however suggest that – contrary to MITI – none of the government agencies mentioned has direct market experience. This is a gap the American government needs to close in order to improve project efficiency by emphasizing the all-important time-to-market.

Stated in a different manner, nobody would ever challenge the scientific credentials of the US agencies. Due to their past involvement with computers, communications and programming efforts, they are well positioned to support basic research in communications technology, software developments and computational science. But high-performance computing and networking also needs clear-cut commercial perspectives.

An instrumental element in this is market expertise, which constitutes a prerequisite to a better bottom line – the profit and loss statement and cash flow. When it started on a well-financed basis resting on available expertise, the HPCC project had good chances for moving ahead on a rapid and sustainable timetable on the technology front. But it needed a similar support in terms of *global marketing* – which it did not get. Now it is in the dolldrums.

* Details can be found in 'Grand Challenges 1993: High Performance Computing and Communications', from the *Supplement to the President's Fiscal Year 1993 Budget* (Office of Science and Technology Policy, 1992).

4. Project Virtuosi by Nottingham Trent University and British Telecom

Developed at Nottingham Trent University by a team under Professor Steven Gray,* and partly financed by the British government and Nottingham County Council, as well as companies such as British Telecom, GEC and BICC, *Virtuosi* is a well-focused virtual reality project:

- designing *virtual clothing*
- to be worn by *virtual models*
- on a *virtual catwalk.*

Virtuosi is a good example of an interdisciplinary project, which required that mathematicians and fashion designers collaborate in the creation and display of 3-D clothing items. The goal has been to permit a designer and a buyer to explore interactively the virtual world. They work together in creating and evaluating garments prior to sampling and manufacture.

The aim of project Virtuosi is to provide a set of interactive computer tools for designers, permitting them to develop and display clothing attire. Realtime simulation is used to make the designer-buyer relationship interactive, as well as to enable remote virtual meetings. Along this line of reference, the research team is investigating methods by which mannequins can be represented in a 3-D environment, including:

- an analysis of the human form
- identification of the best method of representing skin, limbs and joints.

A new device produced by Telmat, a French company, is used to identify accurate measurements. Its contribution is to permit realtime *anthropometrics* (the measuring of people) through a combination of cameras and *shape recognition software.* This approach helps to create 3-D representations of the subject that are both proportioned and accurate.

When completed, the computer-simulated mannequin and attire will emulate the form, movements and poses of a real fashion model. One of the most ambitious parts of the research programme at Nottingham Trent University is the creation of realistic cloth models, including:

- virtual fabrics that accurately represent the properties of real cloth
- the ability to drape, pin and cut such fabrics in a virtual world.

* The project team comprises specialists from other universities (Manchester, Nottingham and Lancaster) too.

There is, however, no unanimous opinion on the practical applications of a realistic representation along the stated goals. Some people think that, at the moment, fashion on the computer is just fun. Their thesis is that because clothes are so tactile, there is little point in trying to sell them by virtual reality.

The researchers at Nottingham Trent have a different view: the static and dynamic views being projected permit users to see the effects of different types of material. The graphics show colour and surface textures, as well as physical characteristics of construction and structure.

The Nottingham Trent researchers are constructing tools needed by designers to create garments in a virtual world, and also specifying the nature of the interaction users will have with the environment. They also provide a *navigation system* allowing interaction with the virtual world over and above the fact of effectively interconnecting two or more system users.

This concept is known as *Computer Supported Co-operative Working* (CSCW). The chosen solution relies on the same telecommunications infrastructure as the *Fashion Intelligence Navigation System* (FINS) – also developed by Nottingham Trent University. The project provides direct links to computer aided design (CAD) and targets a quick response from design innovation to customer delivery.

5. The 'Spirits' Project by British Telecom, NTT and Other Companies

What has been written about in section 3 about focus on time-to-market which should characterize government-sponsored projects, is even more true when it comes to private industry. Sometimes, however, co-operative efforts sponsored by many companies have a tendency to stay in the laboratory and collect dust, rather than going to the market and earn money. An example is 'Spirits'.

The Multivendor Integration Architecture (MIA) is a project which was started in Japan by NTT.* In 1993 it was transferred to London, rechristened 'Spirits' and focused on on-line transaction processing (OLTP) services. It is now sponsored by British Telecom, NTT and Belcore, as well as IBM, DEC, Hewlett Packard and NEC.

In the background of this project lies the concept that computer-based solutions must be able to provide a broad range of business services. Hence, they should be flexible enough to include different computer makes and models, each covering the area of business in which the vendor's approach is the most profitable or the most advanced.

* See also D.N. Chorafas and H. Steinmann, *Solutions for Networked Databases* (Academic Press, San Diego, CA, 1993).

The trend towards multivendor environments is not only due to a corporation's need to answer in the best possible manner software requirements, but also to the active competition that has developed during the last decade. This enables user organizations to overcome costs through a well-managed computer procurement policy.

Companies which know how to put into effect a multivendor approach to procurement have been able to reap considerable cost benefits. However, they also found that *multisourcing* is not that simple because it involves many issues:

- avoiding the duplication of development and maintenance of application programs
- overcoming allocation and scheduling difficulties in resource sharing in a network-wide sense
- increasing the efficiency of operation in spite of differences in operating systems and methods.

Part of the goal set by 'Spirits' is network-wide access to heterogeneous databases classically designed along local reference terms. In a multivendor environment, computer connectivity is often difficult because different computer equipment typically use incompatible communications interfaces. This limits machine capabilities in resource sharing.

The usual result of this state of affairs is duplication in resources such as databases and workstations, programming products developed for incompatible operating systems, as well as data input and clearance addressed to a variety of computers. There is also a need for special hardware and software for interfacing reasons, raising the overall cost of system development, installation and operation.

Telephone companies have many reasons for being interested and paying attention to this subject, *directory guidance* services is one of them. Another is record-keeping and billing, as the most important clients are now getting into the habit of asking for on-line information and verification of their bills.

- The first practical issues to which 'Spirits' addresses itself is on-line directory guidance for yellow pages and white pages.
- The aim is to make it feasible for computers from different vendors to talk to each other at a common platform level, enabling users to share databases.

When a valid system interconnection interface is established as a common communications protocol, it is possible to bring together into one aggregate a variety of platforms, eliminating wasteful duplications which currently exist in applications programs and skills. Transparency makes it also possible to reduce operating expenses for system design and implementation.

Another prerequisite for sound systems design is that users should have virtually the same display and visualization standards on whichever workstation they work and wherever they go. This can be achieved through a common human user interface. The latter also makes possible more effective on-the-job training of users, helping to reduce overall expenses and improve job performance.

Still another important issue is that of reusable software which is particularly acute in industries where the information systems infrastructure and product line offerings tend to merge – as currently happens with telecommunications companies which face the challenge that there should be compatibility between the two fields of:

- automatic switching
- information processing.

As the walls between switching and computing are being torn down, databases, communications protocols, and workstations need to be fully incorporated into networks in order to keep providing competitive solutions. In conclusion, efficient approaches require the standardization of *software platforms* and interfaces.

6. Digitized Video and Media Servers by British Telecom, Bell Atlantic and Oracle

More imaginative than 'Spirits', and a better income earner if it succeeds in reaching the market target it has set itself, is the *media server* projects British Telecom (BT) and Bell Atlantic have undertaken with Oracle and nCube. The two projects work separately from one another, though the vendors act as liaison.

Media servers are a natural fit with BT goals, because in Europe British Telecom has set its sights on leadership in the multimedia domain where both broadband and database technology underpins business opportunity. It is no accident that since 1993 interest in multimedia servers became concrete and solutions have been actively sought after:

- Increasing cost-effectiveness has created a crossover line where multimedia implementation becomes a practical proposition at affordable cost.
- While the unit cost of millions of instructions per second, gigabytes of disk storage and megabytes of PC memory will continue to fall, current levels are low enough to permit practical multimedia applications.

Both British Telecom and Bell Atlantic have signed with Oracle and nCube a multimillion dollar contract for the server development. British

Telecom has acquired three nCubes and, in collaboration with the vendors, works diligently in developing multimedia solutions. But the effective development and implementation of media servers requires a change in culture – not just better technology.

The digitization of video content is a significant step, but it is not an overwhelming procedure. At Oracle, the digitized video project started in mid-1993, when a group of young engineers worked on a program for sending video clips across a network. One of them got the idea of trying the program on as many as 1000 processors at once.

However, while broadcasting a digitized film is fairly easy, serving up 100 different films to 100 houses at 100 different times can be a programming nightmare. The concept has been to:

- use a parallel computer engine (nCube)
- split the video data into 1000 different segments storing each of them on a different disk drive.

Each drive is controlled by its own microprocessor. One processor coordinates all the others so the film flows seamlessly in the correct order. This process can ensure that when a new viewer orders a film – whether this order is 20 seconds or 20 minutes later – the first drives can start delivering the requested service.

This is the strictly technical part of the project. The need for change in culture is due to a number of other developments which have progressed in parallel, but few people properly have correlated them to develop a pattern. Yet, they revolutionize what we know so far in computers, communications and software. From a telecommunications viewpoint, the topmost references are:

- massive infrastructure improvements all the way to the local loop
- the merger of different technologies, including HDTV and digital audio
- the move towards realtime encoding of information in a digital form
- the availability of efficient compression technologies.

Part of the business opportunity rests on the fact that growing amounts of multimedia information are available digitally. But the primary reason propelling the sort of project BT has undertaken is the new generation of computer-literate users.

Taken together, these two reasons ensure that the *digital demand* has arrived and it pushes for new media servers. It also calls for cost-effective solutions – hence the interest in multimedia servers with hundreds or thousands of processors, gigabytes of central memory, terabytes of disk memory and broadband input/output. For instance, the project undertaken by British Telecom and Bell Atlantic with Oracle and nCube targets:

- over 10,000 simultaneous video streams
- 1500 title video databases.

The multimedia architecture under development is supporting both magnetic and optical disk farms, a video file system, video server software and communications network software addressing digital video. All this looks fine technically, but we have some reservations as to marketing perspective. Corporate usage rather than consumer entertainment should have been the main target.

7. The Synergy Necessary to Get Results

Success in the projects which we have seen in sections 5 and 6 rests to a very large extent on the synergy which should be obtained between communications, computers and software. Another key factor is cost-effectiveness. Costs cannot be allowed to remain high in an industry such as computers and communications where low-cost services increasingly set the market pace.

A well-orchestrated consortium of research funding organizations is a necessary contributor to a successful R&D effort in high technology; but it is not enough. The synergy necessary to get results calls for other major players.

1. The business sense which should prevail in research laboratories of hardware firms, particularly the upcoming computer companies with a track of advanced designs.
2. Imaginative software development efforts which can particularly be located among the leading software firms and in university projects.
3. New applications horizons requiring the deep co-involvement of user organizations and the best minds to be found in foremost laboratories.
4. A steady training effort by academia to develop technologists and users able to *think in parallel* and employ in the best possible manner the new technology.

'That's the easy part,' stated one of the reviewers from academia. The answer is: 'Really?' If it were that easy, why has it not yet been done? Changing the culture of people is not easy. It is one of the most difficult and demanding jobs that exists.

Without the synergy of the outlined four main contributors to a high-performance effort, the results will be well below those wanted. No matter how much money is spent on the advanced R&D programmes, the outcome will resemble that of a tramway which speeds downhill with the brakes applied to only one of the four wheels.

Are there major implementation domains which can offer the opportunity for imaginative applications and at the same time a market large enough to justify the investments? Is there a candidate to replace the market represented by the war industry now that the world-wide use of high-performance computing seems to have moved beyond its traditional government-sponsored base?

The answer is 'Yes!' The need for high-performance computing and communications is spreading rapidly throughout the manufacturing, commercial and financial industries. 'We now live in an age where finance and science are inseparable. High-speed simulation by supercomputers is indispensable in solving the problems of *risk* and *return*, especially in today's unpredictable world of finance,' suggested a senior banker in a recent meeting.

Indeed, the financial world of tomorrow is being created on the high technology of today. No wonder that since November 1992, major American banks have been setting up advanced projects in financial analysis with the:

1. Massachusetts Institute of Technology
2. Santa Fe Institute
3. Los Alamos National Laboratory
4. Lawrence Livermore National Laboratory
5. Argone National Laboratory.

The aim of a committee created with the blue ribbon nuclear laboratories of the USA is to develop centres for financial technology, some of which are co-financed by the Department of Energy. The products will be powerful financial models through cross-fertilization of business and the most advanced domains of science.

The research effort supporting US industries generally and the financial industry in particular will be bolstered as the US Administration plans to shift a significant amount of money from military to civilian technologies. A good deal of this funding will most likely be distributed by the Advanced Technology Program of the Commerce Department.

Among the leading US banks, the research themes which are currently being selected are expected to have a major influence on the financial markets and on the management of banks and brokerage firms. These themes include:

- *non-linearities* encountered in economics and finance

- *fractals theory* by Dr Benoit Mandelbrot
- *chaos theory* by Dr Edward Lorenz and Dr Mitchell J. Feigenbaum
- *butterfly effect*, focusing on aperiodicity and unpredictability
- *chance, uncertainty and blind fortune* theories by Dr David Ruelle
- work on *artificial life* by Dr Christopher Langton.

The deeper goal is to solve problems that defy accepted ways of working in banking and finance. These projects will view the development and interpretation of patterns, particularly patterns that appear at different scales at the same time.

Both deep models and surface models will be elaborated, the latter focusing on visual programming and program visualization. Some of the projects go beyond *visualization* as we know it today in terms of user applications, to include:

- *visibilization*, making visible very small and very big items or concepts
- *visitraction*, making visible phenomena lacking a direct physical interpretation.

These high-end implementation fields fit well with the giga instructions per second computer power some advanced projects aim to develop and deliver at reasonable cost. Figure 10.2 dramatizes this reference by showing where GIPS power will most likely be used.

The message from the points made in this section is that something big is happening in sectors of the economy such as banking, and the way things are going can be appreciated from the list presented on page 223. The second, third and fourth institutions on this list are the top-most nuclear research laboratories in America – whose physicists are now going to work on finance.

An example is provided by Santa Fe Institute, an intellectual offspring of Los Alamos, full of Nobel prize winners in physics and biology. The goal is to develop simulators and inference engines which can handle:

- new financial paradigms
- very powerful decision models.

Throughout the First World, the laboratories which won the Cold War turn their nuclear scientists toward finance, permitting US banks, brokers and other financial institutions to reposition themselves in the world's financial markets through high technology. Non-traditional financial analysis enables banks to position themselves against the forces

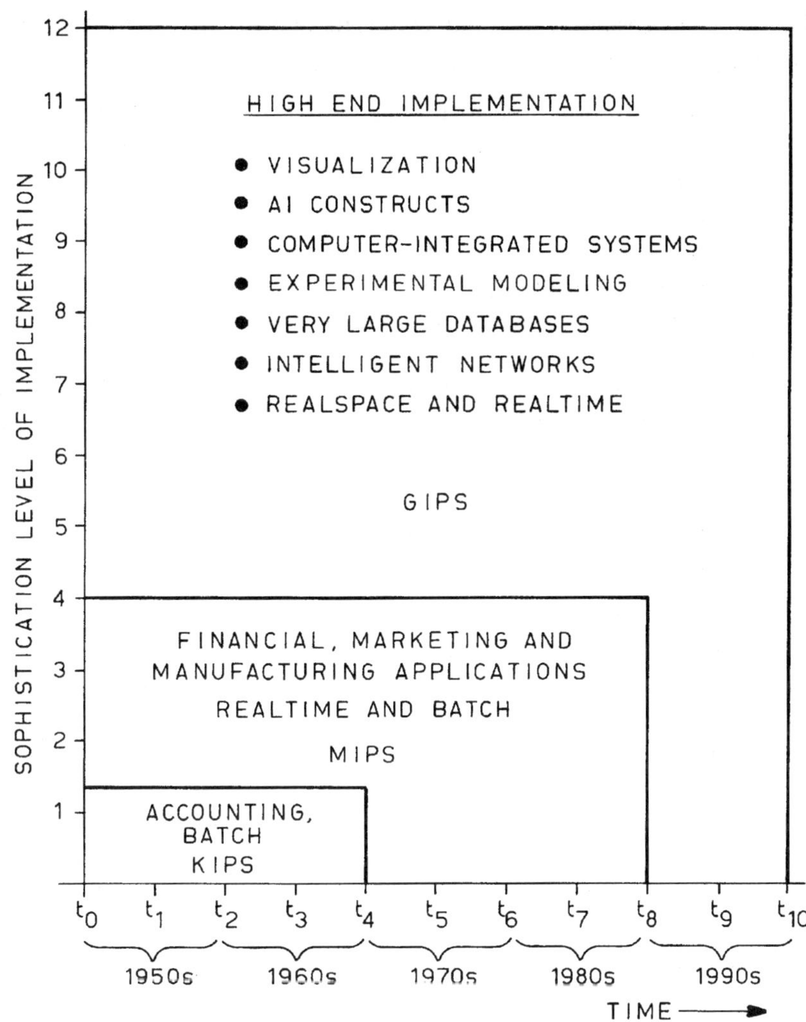

Figure 10.2 Areas where GIPS power will most likely be used

of the future, gaining a competitive edge in a market more competitive than ever.

8. Targeting Solutions which are Knowledge- and Innovation-Intensive

How much individual organizations and people will benefit from the funding of a research program, and its aftermath, is largely a function of their own involvement. The bottom line is the results they will be able to obtain in market-oriented terms out of sponsored R&D.

According to the strategic plan for the 1990s set by the US Executive

Office of the President, in what concerns overall direction the outlined national goals will be realized by achieving a synergy between:

- computational performance of one trillion operations per second (10^{12} ops, teraops) on a wide range of important applications*
- a national research network capable of one billion bits per second (10^9 bits) or gigastream of information transfer
- large and growing distributed databases, working in a federated way and seamlessly accessible by a significant number of users
- development of associated system software, new tools as well as improved algorithms and heuristics for a wide range of problems
- an increasing production of PhDs and other trained professionals per year, particularly in computational science and communications engineering.

These prerequisites are seen as necessary to enable effective utilization of new technologies, and for reasons of promoting advanced applications development commensurate to the aims to be reached and resources being invested.

At the national level, it is projected that the goals will be met through a co-ordinated government, industry and university collaboration. The results must be able to support solutions to the important scientific, technical and business issues of this decade.

In terms of computers and communications programming, for example, it is projected that experimental products and processes will be exploited with expertise enriched by knowledge engineering. This should be done in a manner able to provide a fast feedback to software designers.

The type of projected grand challenges for which sophisticated software will be most crucial can be illustrated through examples on broad classes of computing problems. Figure 10.3 shows some of the problems which require significant improvements in computational methods. Note the similarity between this technical figure and the more business-oriented graph which we saw in Figure 10.2.

Both Figure 10.2 and Figure 10.3 deserve careful study, most particularly in those aspects in which they converge. From the past to the present and the future, three time frames are outlined, each with its corresponding computational performance objectives:

* The petaops is the longer-term goal.

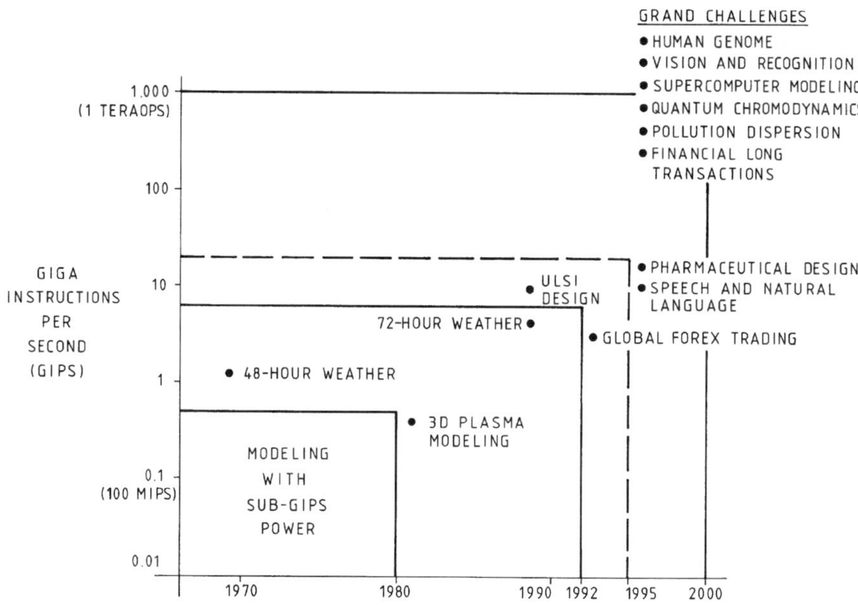

Figure 10.3 Grand challenges and teraops needs

- Prior to 1980, the applications were simple, even accounting for realtime operations whose implementation started in the mid- to late 1960s.

Modeling was one of the foremost applications at that period and simple models could be handled with a few MIPS. Complex models required more power, but usually at the sub-GIPS level.

- During the 1980s and early 1990s the scale of problems changed and so did the need for supporting computer power.

Three-dimensional plasma modeling and 72-hour weather forecasting are implementations requiring between 1 and 10 GIPS. The giga instructions per second are no more a longer-term goal; they are something of the past.

- A number of applications in the 1996 to 2000 time frame will call for more than 10 GIPS, and by the end of this decade up to 1000 tera instructions per second (1 petaops) will quite likely be needed.

It is easy to appreciate that this is an *exponential growth* in computer power requirements which, as many experts now suggest, is not only possible but also most likely.

Among business-type implementations breaking the tentative 10 GIPS ceiling are global foreign exchange trading and very complex transactions. Examples in science include ultra-large scale integration (ULSI), new pharmaceutical designs, and truly automated speech recognition including natural language understanding.

Among the grand challenges by the end of this decade will be the human genome project,* quantum chromodynamics and pollution dispersion. Let us also underline that:

- while the human genome and quantum chronodynamics may be very imaginative projects in biology and physics, they don't represent enough of a market to sustain rapid developments in computers and communications
- only an expanding market can generate the demand which promotes expensive R&D work with breakthroughs able to create new demand and a self-feeding development cycle.

Correctly, the US Administration is laying plans to shift federal research funds from military to civilian purposes, increasing optoelectronics funding, advanced materials and other critical technologies. And we should also mention the commendable initiatives in high-technology finance.

9. The Case of Market-Oriented R&D Developments

An article in *Business Week* explained why 'R&D managers have to focus research more clearly on the step beyond invention – *commercializing discoveries*'.** This article correctly underlined that the chosen strategy must provide a fast time to market but without swamping creativity, even if conceptually this type of conflict is hard to avoid.

- Classical, relatively slow computational approaches make this dual objective hard to achieve.
- By enabling rapid action, high-performance computers and communications liberate energy for imaginative applications.
- Scientists and businessmen must be proactive rather than reactive in a world where managing invention is an incredibly intricate pursuit.

Corporate laboratories often attack a problem with high-powered multidisciplinary teams. Yet even the most ambitious efforts still depend on the talents of a few key individuals whose brainpower should be magnified and made more generally available.

* Which is a scientific grand challenge problem, but it can also lead to major breakthroughs in database management.

** 'American Inventors are Reinventing Themselves', *Business Week*, 18 January 1992, p. 48.

'Only 5 per cent to 10 per cent of the people in a lab are the fuel that keeps it going,' says Greg E. Blonder, head of the materials and technology integration laboratory at Bell Labs. 'You lose them, and the whole organization goes.'* An analysis done by a major US automaker in his own laboratory showed that 10 per cent of the researchers with patents produced 80 per cent of the inventions.

Not only does Pareto's law hold well for achievements in innovation, but obtained results suggest that far from being leading experts in one narrow field, great inventors typically *cross disciplines*. Often, it seems, it takes the fresh perspective of a generalist, rather than the deep knowledge of the specialist, to get very commendable results.

It is the opinion of the authors, documented through 40 years of practical experience, that the most imaginative future projects will be interdisciplinary. Their synergy will come to require even more than is currently projected in terms of computers, communications and software facilities. Such multidisciplinary projects will have common needs in:

- advanced programming technology and knowledge-intense programming environments
- interoperable object-oriented database management solutions
- efficient parallelization tools for realtime implementation
- increasingly efficient end-user visualization, visibilization and visistraction
- emphasis on deep testing and optimization
- on-line performance measurement with feedback.

Not every one of these projects fits under the currently sponsored programs in computers and communications, yet government financing is a very important ingredient to success. How can these two issues be reconciled?

The answer is by rechannelling defence money, while largely keeping its flow within the same laboratories which contributed the weapons systems breakthroughs. The Clinton Administration seems to be tuned in this direction.

Currently, the US military gets much more than half of the $76 billion in federal R&D. Over time, this will most likely be changing from 60 per cent defence to 50:50 which will mean a shift of $7 billion into civilian projects. America will most likely see aggressive civilian technology programs – and that's the sense of many of the references this chapter has made.

Through the example of the Santa Fe Institute, section 7 has given a glimpse of what this shift in funding might mean. While it is still too

* *Business Week*, 18 January 1992.

early to tell how profound an impact the redistribution will have, the fact is that – worried about their own funding – federal laboratories are now joining research deals with American companies.

Lawrence Livermore National Laboratory, for example, has signed deals with General Motors (GM), Boeing, Caterpillar, and others to disseminate its technologies. In one $3 million project, Livermore is working with GM to develop an advanced laser that could help the automaker improve how it cuts and welds body parts. It is also being discussed that the US Administration will:

- nurture high-technology industries through the appropriate R&D tax credits
- create dozens of manufacturing-technology centres to help small businesses apply the latest techniques.

The interaction between R&D and market behaviour is known for decades. What is new is the rapidity of growth. As the examples which we saw in Figures 10.2 and 10.3 help in appreciating, the regression curve connecting computer power goals by implementation area is exponential. Somehow, there seems to be no tapering off of power-intense requirements that can be foreseen at this point in time.*

10. The Growing Call for a Cultural Change

Many computers and communications experts are right in their belief that co-ordination of developments concerning advanced hardware and software technology – including languages, shells, prototypes, algorithms and heuristics – will be critical to ensuring efficient use of hardware among a range of user entities. This is hardly surprising as it is known from more classical computing, but its importance has not always been appreciated in all circles.

Another basic prerequisite is knowledge-engineering enriched networking. On-line computers will increasingly fill important functions in all phases of *learning processes*, providing flexible instruments for interactive operations as well as for rapid gaining of further experience. Their use will help provide the value-added skills needed to function in an increasingly competitive world.

Following this line of reasoning, account should be taken of the growing synergy between the development of more powerful interactive computers and the more advanced communications capabilities.

- As computing technology progresses, greater demands are placed on network bandwidth and very low bit error rate.

* Eventually, there will be tapering off, but we are not yet at the level of estimating it.

- As users conceive new instruments and increase their database accesses, they require even higher network performance.

This synergy of developments leads to truly distributed computing, allowing a given job to be executed on several different machines. Assignments and their optimization will be directed by knowledge-engineering artefacts at the network's nodes.

Networked high-performance computers will communicate partial results among themselves, sharing different facets of computation and jointly assemble an end answer. Networked federated databases will use a growing bandwidth in multimedia information exchange.

Interactive communications are inherently capable of taking place at speeds that stress local area network technology and are a hundred or more times faster than possible digital transfers on today's long-haul networks of the ISDN type. To support the growing number of demanding applications, a substantial amount of directed research and development effort is scheduled to take place in the areas of:

- communications protocols
- high-speed computer interfaces
- network switches and trunks.

Multigigastream networks represent a change in kind, not just in degree, from today's solutions. This adds up to a *cultural change* of magnitude in terms of design, implementation and usage of the increasingly important capabilities that HPCC technology was expected to make available for practical use.

The same statement is valid in another domain: that of networked databases. For a large number of applications, databases have locality. But as business perspectives expand and computer resources are interconnected, there is also a growing amount of global database usage.

- A cultural change is necessary if the effort of reconciling the global and local database requirements is going to be successful.
- The concept should be that of *shared resources* on a federated basis.

Solutions to complex problems of present-day business and technology require intensive study to understand the involved relations and interactions. High-performance computing can shorten the time of calculation, but a cultural change is necessary to cut down the delays involved in the discovery process, by allowing the development of accurate simulations to point out the most promising directions.

The underlying concept is that of exploring the possibility of various combinations of elements that may lead to new business opportunities. The cultural change necessary in this particular domain is the appreciation of the market forces.

Results which have been studied so far from massively parallel computing systems and advanced parallel software technology, tend to suggest that we should promote the conception, design and validation of multidisciplinary solutions. On-line experimentation must also be carried out to allow the optimization of complex market-product interactions throughout the operational landscape of the corporation.

11. Massive Parallelism and Cost-Effectiveness

While not all high-performance computers are or need to be parallel engines, the way to bet is that for the foreseeable future massive parallelism will carry the day. One of the basic reasons is that parallel processing can significantly reduce the cost of handling large, computation-intensive problems. It can also contribute to cross-database seamless accesses to heterogeneous resources, through dedicated processor assignments.

Another major advantage of parallel computer designs is that they are *flexible* in terms of the applications which they run. Networked nodes with stand-alone processors can be reconfigured, with the basic software helping to adapt the system to specialized problems. Parallel engines are *scalable*, easy to expand, making it feasible to run several smaller problems concurrently.

One of the reasons for massive parallelism is that it offers much higher potential performance than conventional designs. Contrary to what happens with mainframes, massively parallel machines follow the price-performance curve of semiconductors – and, furthermore, hardware is adaptable to the job, starting with a low-entry price tag.*

The net effect of these reasons accentuates the huge difference which exists today in terms of computer pricing. Note that price differences alone make investments in mainframes and vector processors highly unwise.

These considerations are less important when one client dominates the high-performance computing landscape, as happened with the military for over half a century. But they become crucial with diffused applications perspectives, as the civilian industry is entering the picture and is caring very much for cost-effectiveness.

Sometimes people have distorted impressions because of being influ-

* 'Wait till the IBM machines arrive,' said one of the reviewers. If you have time to lose, then wait.

enced by what has been known from the past. 'The mainframes primary claim to fame is input/output power, not computer power,' said an EDPer who glanced through an early draft of this text. This argument forgets that by and large what are today considered to be I/O-intensive jobs is a relic of the punched card era:

- Not only the I/O of most companies is still punched-card oriented, even if the punched cards themselves are no more to be seen, but also the database organization.
- A recent study has shown that because of punched-card images, companies use only 5 per cent of their disk storage, while they pay 100 per cent of the cost of the equipment.

All these are what we call *cultural issues*: all I/O should be *on-line*, not on paper; databases should be redesigned for distributed implementation and easy access; program development should be done by the end-users themselves through visual programming. Parallel computing is one of the goals; not the only one.

With end-user oriented applications programming models in mind, a most vital issue is that of understanding the process of productizing a parallel program. Here starts the software challenge and this involves three major steps:

1. *Decomposing*, that is dividing the application into a set of parallel processes and information elements to take advantage of parallelism.
2. Effectively *mapping* onto the computer the way processes and information are distributed among the nodes.

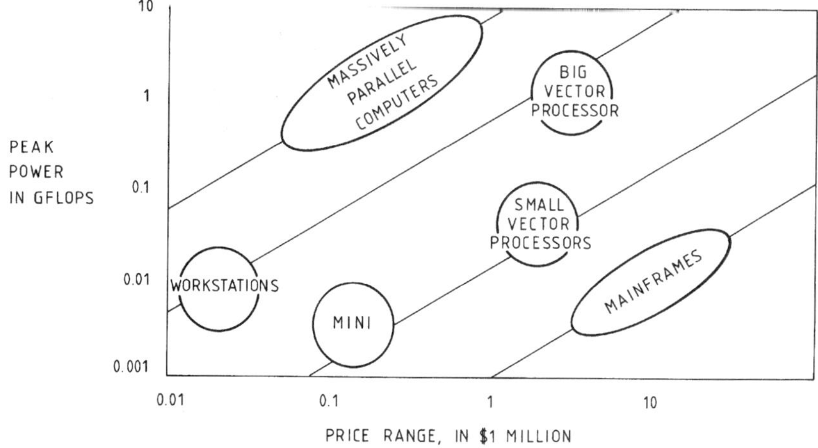

Figure 10.4 Improvements in cost-effectiveness with massively parallel architectures

3. Dynamically *tuning* the system to the application environment to improve its performance.

Benefiting from the performance trends shown in Figure 10.4 and applying what is suggested by the foregoing three points, are, for any practical purpose, two sides of the same coin.

12. Thinking in Parallel

The effective usage of parallel machines requires that we are able to *think in parallel*, and at the same time decompose our applications into their constituent elements, each to be run on dedicated processors – without losing sight of the integrative perspective.

As a technical term, decomposing means to break the application apart into a set of parallel processes and information elements – that is, objects. The way to approach this issue depends on the nature of the problem: its processes and structure of the data.

An example helps to better appreciate this reference. A leading financial institution in New York bought a hypercube with 32 nodes for mortgage-backed financing (MBF) applications. MBF is done in pools and it was found that:

- With eight nodes working on the same pool the response time was minimized, then tapered off.
- This was achieved by decomposing the operations pertaining to a mortgage pool into atomic elements, a process which apart from speed also provided a better insight into the operation.
- At the same time, it was possible to process four pools of mortgages in parallel on the same computer, further reducing the overall time necessary for the application.

Since problem decomposition is both the first step and the one that guides the entire application process, it is appropriate to be familiar with the available techniques. Understanding how these techniques can be applied to the new generation of problems leading to advanced solutions at affordable prices, is particularly important.

The able implementation of decomposition on a parallel computer requires, among other things, balancing the load among the processors. All nodes dedicated to an application should be busy during the entire time the application is running.

Mapping is the step that directly determines the load balance, so that nodes with smaller workloads do not sit idle. The job is doable, but quite evidently it requires a different frame of mind as well as skills, than those used with naïve languages such as Cobol, PL/1, SQL and the like.

We said: '*The job is doable.*' But as one of the reviewers was to suggest: 'It is not always doable, unless sophisticated techniques are used.' Both statements are correct.

- Throughout this book *we write of advanced approaches.*
- The junk in information technology's backyard has no place in modern business.

Both the applications perspectives which we saw in this chapter and new departures in basic software are necessary for the development of an advanced generation of systems solutions. As we saw in the preceding sections this includes:

- R&D for systems departures which open broader applications horizons
- infrastructural needs, such as broadband (gigastream) telecommunications networks with intelligence at the nodes
- education and training to make feasible the able exploitation of the developed resources.

The ability to face the competitive challenges of the mid- to late 1990s is conditioned by the ability to develop and sustain a new R&D structure. Able solutions have to be polyvalent and rest on synergy, including hardware and software manufacturers, telephone companies, university laboratories, user organizations and governments.

The objective of such a program should be to lead in world standards and to be effective in the global market, particularly that of the First World. Since competitiveness is at stake, industry should be highly supportive of such a project because client-server computing and high-performance computing are the best way available today of increasing cost-performance – and therefore market effect.

11

Towards the Global Information Age at the NYNEX Laboratories

1. Introduction

The global information age is a synergy of business and technology which stretches the boundaries known to exist with respect to computers and communications systems. Global information perspectives characterize many of the state-of-the-art projects currently running at the better-known laboratories where a broad range of expertise makes it feasible to develop solutions which might have been considered far-fetched just a few years earlier.

One of the most challenging roles in this effort is to identify the emerging technologies that are going to be applicable to the needs of business, industry and the consumers.

- This identification is a task which must be carried out not only now, but also four, five and ten years into the future.
- As such, it requires a sound group of experts able to break new ground with a vision of bringing technology to fruition.

The ability to *study the future impact of today's decisions* is the prescription for making possible ever more sophisticated solutions bringing to the user community all the benefits of the latest developments in communications technology.

Within this perspective, as this and the following chapters will show, present and coming network technology addresses a whole web of connections over which information in all its forms is transported. But networking is indivisible from:

- *presentation technology* which involves the ways end-users interact with each other as well as with products and services
- *computer technology* including languages, software and databases that lie behind the presentation and make it possible.

In communications technology intelligent nodes, satellites and optical fibres with their *megastreams* and *gigastreams* are revolutionizing the transport site. Most particularly, wireless solutions are introducing a high degree of mobility to narrowband communications.

The now familiar modern application of wireless is the cellular telephone. Cellulars have grown rapidly in recent years and refinements continue at a rapid pace. Many companies are working to improve the efficiency and responsiveness of cellular networks to made them even more useful to users.

An example is a monitoring system* that can relate data on traffic patterns and reflect on fluctuations in demand to optimize allocation of power to various cell sites. This requires knowledge engineering but makes feasible the handling of high traffic without delays. As we will see in this chapter, artificial intelligence artefacts have become the cornerstone to competitiveness in the telecommunications industry.

2. The NYNEX Science and Technology Laboratories

Four hundred scientists work at the NYNEX Science and Technology (S&T) Laboratories, at White Plains, New York. A great deal of this work is focusing on applied research and development. According to the statistics NYNEX provided, their profiles divide in the following way in terms of professional expertise:

- 41 per cent computer science
- 23 per cent electrical engineering
- 9 per cent telecommunications
- 7 per cent business background
- 6 per cent psychology majors
- 5 per cent mathematicians
- 5 per cent physicists
- 4 per cent other disciplines.

These statistics are a telling example of how deeply computers and communications have integrated. NYNEX is a telecommunications company, yet more than 40 per cent of the professionals in its laboratories are computer scientists, a large percentage among them being knowledge-engineering experts.

A great deal of the work is in applied research and development. There is no lack of interest in basic research but most effort in this domain is directed through co-operative projects with Bellcore and 20 different university research centres.**

* By NYNEX.

** In 1994, NYNEX S&T Laboratories had a $240 million budget versus $3 billion at Bellcore.

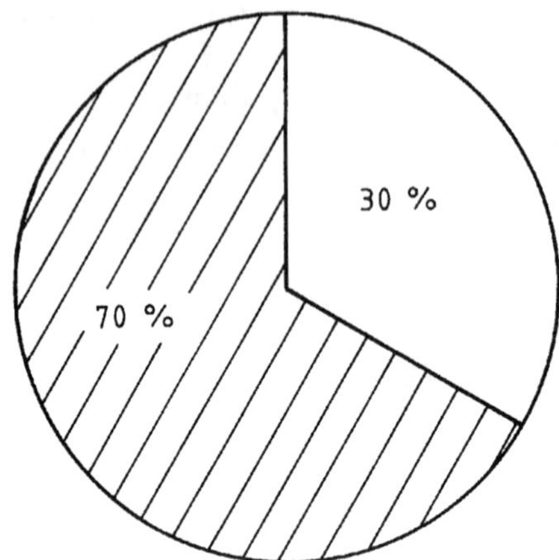

Figure 11.1 Research and development at the NYNEX Science and Technology Laboratories

Bell Communications Research (Bellcore) is a research facility organized in the 1980s and financed by the Baby Bell companies. It is jointly owned by the seven regional Bells, while the mission at NYNEX Science and Technology is to adapt Bellcore's generic work and apply it to the specific needs of NYNEX's customers – both within the New England region and around the world.

As seen in Figure 11.1, in dollar value some 30 per cent of the work at the NYNEX Science and Technology Laboratories is forward-looking exploratory development. The balance is client specific, often concerning co-sponsored projects.

Five main areas of activity have been identified during our meeting at NYNEX Laboratories, the latter three being rather recent and growing much faster than the first two areas:

1. *Electronics* Work focuses on computers, lines, switches, circuit termination equipment and other devices. Particular emphasis is placed on miniaturization and on accomplishing more sophisticated operations through knowledge

engineering. The smaller size of equipment requires less power and permits faster operation and more storage capacity in the same space.

2. *Photonics* Fibre-optics technology is opening new worlds in transport capacity. Research work focuses on improvements in light sources, detector systems and other domains. It is projected that fibre-optics transport capacity will double every two years during the 1990s.
3. *Informatics* NYNEX puts under this heading the melding of formerly distinct communications and computers technologies. It is correctly perceived that this requires increasingly complex methods of processing and presentation which must be developed to turn masses of data into useful information – as well as to manipulate this information to meet the needs of individual users.
4. *Ergonomics* The underlying concept is that technological developments are driven by human factors because products are useful only if they are used well. Studies in ergonomics ensure that products are designed for the comfort and convenience of users, with complex new technologies interfacing with the users in simple, natural ways.
5. *Intelligent software* Intelligent software was described at the laboratories as one of the pivotal technologies that tie the information industry together and enable the creation of sophisticated applications. Since software technology makes feasible further advances in electronics and photonics, NYNEX capitalizes rapidly on the leading trends in the field.

Both directly and through Bellcore, NYNEX also participates in the development of industry standards. To provide universal, world-wide communications, individual equipment manufacturers and service providers need to adhere to common standards, hence the involvement in the work of the major national and international standards committees.

3. Gaining Competitiveness through Knowledge Engineering in Networking

If one was to define in a few words the NYNEX Science and Technology Laboratories mission this would be through the emphasis which it places on time-to-market: bringing to commercialization by providing a value-added resale of telecommunications services. A major ingredient of this effort is knowledge engineering.

The strategic plan is sound. Value diversification is the way to growth and survival. Today the bulk of the telecommunications solutions is supported through plain old cable services. But this is not necessarily so for the future.

The more aware telephone companies can see that the prime mover in the market are the customer-driven applications that require high technology to be answered in an able manner. Therefore, particular emphasis is placed on expert systems by creating knowledge-based artefacts that emulate the decision-making processes of human experts.

- Experts make decisions based on their accumulated knowledge and experience.
- At NYNEX, an expert system is given information about a problem, and its rules interpret this information.
- Then they arrive at the conclusions a telephone expert would have arrived at in similar circumstances.

NYNEX has developed expert systems that diagnose problems in the telephone network, plan large and complex telecommunications aggregates, and maximize network efficiency. Intelligent tutoring systems increasingly are useful as training aids.

Knowledge engineering also assists in making improvements in database design, providing for better storage management and for accessing complex and voluminous information more easily.

- Artefacts have proved to be adaptable to the requirements of specific applications.
- As customers' needs evolve, the laboratories continue to develop ever more sophisticated techniques to meet those needs quickly and cost-effectively.

Other projects focus on multimedia. The NYNEX laboratories develop multimedia services that involve much more than impressive displays. Behind them lies the technology for transmitting, storing and retrieving voice, data, text, graphics, images and video – with particular emphasis on presentation technology.

To enhance the presentation aspects, NYNEX uses knowledge engineering but also developed a number of multimedia storage capabilities, including files and archives for storage and retrieval operating at network speeds.

There is an advanced electronic mail service capable of forwarding, storing, delivering and tracking multimedia messages in multimedia envelopes. Other projects focus on directories of resources and facilities. The goal of another of the advanced projects which currently is in process is *virtual reality*.

In a discussion on the development of intelligent networks, NYNEX did not explicitly mention the desk area network (DAN) and ViewStation projects supported by the Advanced Research Projects Agency (ARPA). But Bellcore is a key participant in this project and no doubt there will be major repercussions at NYNEX.*

- DAN, ViewStation and virtual reality applications are closely linked.
- As we saw in Chapter 8, DAN aims to capture, edit, store and display multimedia at desk level.

The whole project and its components greatly benefit from artificial intelligence, as do other network structures under study such as the wireless LAN that enables the user to move away from stationary installations, while remaining connected to computers and networks.

An extension of this reference is the *personal communicator*, which is no futuristic vignette. Movable kiosks, hand-held terminals, wireless office communications systems using digital radio technology, all require portable links in a wireless communications setting – and major investments in R&D.

The emphasis on portable communications is another way of emphasizing the need of keeping the human interface simple and agile even when confronted with the challenges of an increasingly complex technology.

- The operations we perform in order to use the devices at our disposal are the doors into the world of technology.
- They should be efficient, easy to adapt to, and of an affordable price.

Such goals may seem contradictory but in reality they are complementary and doable. NYNEX is using knowledge engineering to program a computer to do something that would be considered intelligent if a person did it. This has created many opportunities for exciting new products.

Stated in simple terms, this is the way companies which understand the direction of the coming years apply themselves to the task. We will examine in detail some of the outstanding projects at the laboratories, but prior to doing so we should review the way the NYNEX Science and Technology Laboratories are organized.

4. Organization and Structure of the Laboratories

The NYNEX Science and Technology Laboratories address themselves to what was characterized during our meeting as critical domains, of

* The other participants are MIT, the University of Pennsylvania and IBM.

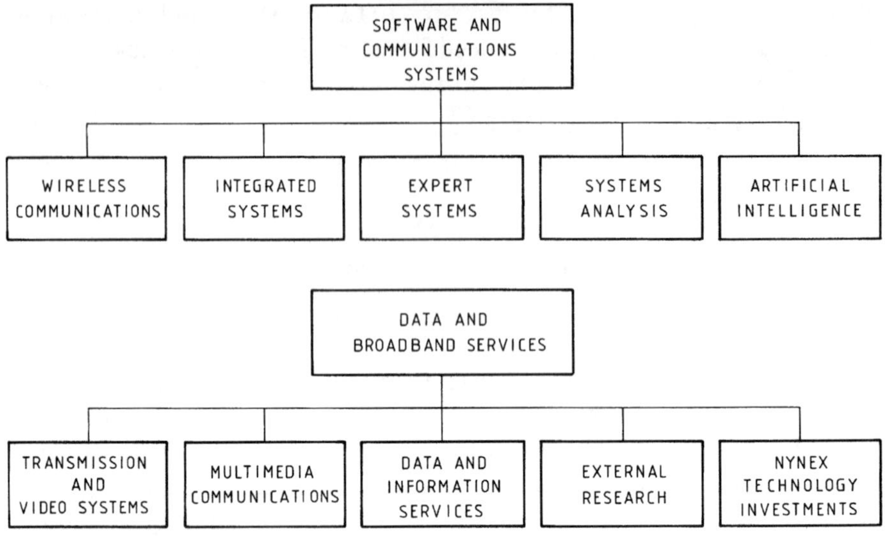

Figure 11.2 The organization of R&D at the NYNEX laboratories

which there are three. In *information transport*, the critical domains include optics, radio links, switching, intelligent networks and network management.

In *information processing* the critical areas identified are multimedia storage, software tools, expert systems and transaction control. Under *presentation technology* come human interfaces, image processing, workstation software and geographic information systems.*

In terms of background and skills, some 20 per cent of the professionals working on these projects have a doctorate degree, another 20 per cent a master's degree, the others have a batchelor degree. Two major R&D divisions can be distinguished as well as a logistics organization. Figure 11.2 shows the main divisions in this research and development effort.

1. Under *Software and Communications* are as diverse fields as wireless communications, integrated systems, expert systems, systems analysis and artificial intelligence.
2. *Data and Broadband Services* include: transmission and video, multimedia communications, data and information services, external research and technology investments (venture capital).
3. The *Support Organizations* include: general counsel, intellectual property, strategic information management, program management and quality assurance.

* We see what is included under this heading in section 10.

Under the *Wireless Communications* department of the *Software and Communications Systems* division, come cellular radio, wireless loop and geographic information systems, as well as craft access, wireless data and intra-premises.

The *Integrated Systems* department addresses itself to new voice service concepts, speech systems development, intelligent peripheral platforms and input media. The Network Services Development Center is part of this effort.

Four different sections come under *Expert Systems*: strategic expert systems, adaptive expert systems, intelligent decision support artefacts and work systems design. The component parts of the *Systems Analysis* department are: requirements and specifications, software development, operator services automation, and channel switched network services – including prototyping and testing.

The reason for *Artificial Intelligence* R&D being a separate entity is to handle projects in speech recognition, speech synthesis, neural networks, and intelligent character recognition. Also human factors from man–machine interfaces and ergonomics to intelligent tutoring systems.

Three major research departments are part *Data and Broadband Services*, the other major division. Under *Transmission and Video Systems* fall projects in fibre-optics research, network simulation and analysis, residential broadband, cable television and high-definition television (HDTV).

The research sections of *Multimedia Communications* includes prototype development, concept validation and testing, new application, and identification of services and multimedia. The multimedia section addresses both databases and software applications – but there is a separate section on multimedia trials focusing on:

- medical
- publishing
- education
- manufacturing projects.

The sections under *Data Information Services* are: broadband networks, ISDN, intelligent call management, MAN/LAN functions, data services and network management. Also transaction services and applications, as well as evolutionary support for data services.

Some 40 to 60 scientists work in each laboratory section and a major part of the mission is not only to improve system performance but also to *reduce cost*. 'If you can save a few seconds of the operations time, you save millions of dollars,' said a senior executive.

The laboratories have to respond to the requirements of a sophisticated client base which includes 400 companies among *Fortune's* 500.

Therefore, they have to keep with peak technology because otherwise they would lose the best of their customers, who depend on high tech for their continuing competitiveness.

Several projects are co-sponsored and focus on cross-business perspectives. Paramount had visited a week prior to our meeting at the laboratories, to evaluate the quality of transmission in connection with Liberty Cable, a competitor to Manhattan CATV. 'Everybody is now looking for partners because alone they cannot do everything,' a cognizant executive suggested.

5. The NYNEX Shuttle

If one was to choose one out of the several projects seen at the NYNEX Science and Technology Laboratories, that would be the *Shuttle*. The NYNEX Shuttle is an in-house prototype network service providing multimedia communications and information capabilities. It is currently used within and between laboratories. The following applications are available:

- *Two-way video communications* which operate on a networked basis, a significantly better alternative than point to point.

Four parallel windows are presently supported. A project in process aims at 16 parallel windows.

- *Flight recorder* used to record and catalogue the contents of meetings, that can later be retrieved in a relational database.

This corporate memory facility contains a full-motion video documentation of meetings and sessions.

- *Manufacturing and maintenance* is an application which demonstrates how the Shuttle can provide video mail.

Live video-conferencing is an objective already met and this is also true of access to remote video libraries in a manufacturing environment.

- *Lesson planner.* Teachers can use the Shuttle to find information, browse through it and assemble it as the basis for class discussion or homework assignments.

This last application is being exploited primarily in the NYNEX franchise area (New York, New England) to provide added value to the telephony network. *Long-distance learning* is being developed in co-operation with the State University of New York (SUNY) and is a fully interactive system.

Two-way audio-video conferencing effectively replaces the need for people to travel. But it requires a *multimedia network* with central office

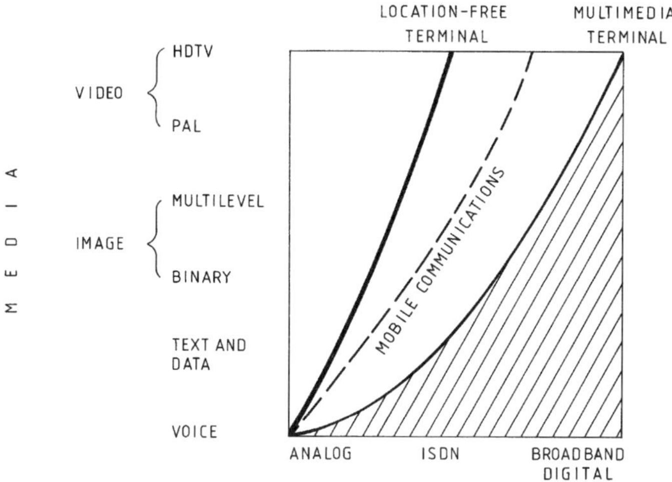

Figure 11.3 Evolution of networks and terminals

software for controlling the service and for billing. Terminal devices can run under Macintosh, MS DOS, Windows and Unix Motif.

The four parallel video-conferencing windows presently supported require T-1 lines (1544 MBPS); the 16 parallel videos in the future will need T-3 lines. Networking is live; there is no frame freeze and therefore ISDN cannot help.

The current implementation of the Shuttle at NYNEX features 35 geographically spread users. A significant role is played by knowledge-enriched session management software and primitives which enable calls to be placed to different locations using the telephone network.

- There is very fast response to dialling up, on the public network.
- The system handles four-way calling and can work with 16 simultaneous calls.

For any practical purpose, the NYNEX Shuttle represents *the integration of telco, telecom and broadcasting* which will become more widely available through the deployment of broadband fibre-optic cable. This will have a tremendous impact on the evolution of networks, terminals and supported services as Figure 11.3 shows, with the role of ISDN limited to that of a passing bridge between the old world and the new.

Today there is still uncertainty over the future demand for services such as videotelephony and high-definition television. But the low cost and high flexibility of the new media are expected to break that resistance. Metropolitan area broadband communications are seen as the solution. MAN and HDTV are interrelated; they can also be a pork barrel.

'The key to success is affordable cost, informality and flexibility,' the responsible executive suggested during the demonstration. 'There are no fixed preconditions for usage.'

Applications like the NYNEX Shuttle as well as the video on demand, NetWindow and Geographic Information System (which we will study in the following sections) do not fall out of blue sky. In the background is an ingenious research strategy. The NYNEX Science and Technology Laboratory prides itself as being a leader in:

- information transport
- network services
- system services
- intelligent applications.

Information transport problems involve moving voice, data and images among system components, including logical and physical facilities. *Network services* extend from system design to methods used to maintain the collaborative environment where sessions take place.

The role of *system services* is to assure the interface between applications and networks, making the development of both easier and more economic. *Intelligent applications* enable users to improve their productivity, service quality and time-to-market.

A basic strategy is that all applications are *user-driven* in their design, development and implementation. 'We apply process engineering to re-engineer the age-old solutions,' a senior NYNEX executive was to comment. 'Our work is entirely focused on the need of our customers – with the goal to improve performance, reduce cost and increase revenue.'

6. Two-Way Television

The NYNEX Shuttle is not only peak technology but also the tip of the iceberg regarding the implementation of two-way television. Interactive television which will eventually enable the user to talk back to the tube is the latest buzz trend in America and Japan, and is becoming so in Europe.

- Some financial analysts suggest that interactive video may be a $6 billion business by the year 2000.
- By then, an estimated 25 million users will be wired for participation in two-way broadband interactive networks.

Already 100,000 households in Spain are wired for interactive television, in what promises to be one of the largest experiments of this kind. But we should not get the mistaken impression that interactive television is something that is two or three years away in terms of wider impact on society.

- As a technology, interactive television is here and it is presently available.
- But in terms of large-scale implementation it is, most likely, five to seven years down the line.

Much will depend on the early real-life tests. For instance, on Spain's TVE public broadcast station where an estimated 100,000 households have booked up since January 1993 to Interactive Systems' Telepick service.

To have no illusions, let us add that the services provided by TVE are in no way comparable to the advanced features of the NYNEX Shuttle. What the Spanish subscribers can do is to participate in quiz shows, phone in for redeemable coupons, catch up on soap operas they missed, or engage in arguments with other participants on a talk show.

Something similar has occurred for the two-way television services that are or will be supported by the Benelux countries which went on-line after Spain; Germany, Switzerland and Scandinavia, which are scheduled for hook-up by the end of 1993; and the USA, Australia and New Zealand, added in 1994 (ten years after Orwell's *1984*).

Will these real-life experiments be successful? Side issues might one day provide the main thrust. Spain's Telepick, for instance, has caught the imagination of the Nielsen ratings service whose main product is measuring the exact participation of viewers to TV shows and advertising campaigns. Through the TVE box and its two-way feature, Nielsen believes it can tell advertisers not simply how many viewers were watching a particular program, but how many picked up the telephone and ordered coupons.

This, however, is not really networked two-way television and, as can be appreciated, many companies have their own interpretation of the theme. What often passes for interactive TV can be little more than quicker channel access – while what the term really means is state-of-the-art technology that virtually allows the viewer to dive into the screen.

Will interactive television become a virtual reality playfield? It is too early to answer this query as the answer will surely depend on a number of factors: technologies, services, costs and user acceptance. The best bet at the moment is: 'It might.'

Whether implemented in the office or at home, the use of interactive television will need an infrastructure which goes from broadband communications to intelligent software. We have seen how many projects at NYNEX focus on knowledge engineering; as the following sections document, broadband is another priority project.

7. Promoting Broadband for Business and Industry

NYNEX plans to deploy fibre, with an introduction to fibre in the loop systems currently under test. Known as *video on demand*, a switched video service is currently demonstrated. Samples of video are compressed to 1.3 MBPS and used to illustrate multimedia quality that can be transmitted over the existing plant.

Such effort is tuned to the fact that distributed communications and computing environments are rapidly evolving to meet changing user requirements and that solutions don't have to await totally new installations:

- New, bandwidth-intensive applications such as graphics, image processing and video-based transmission place increasing loads on networks.
- A bundle of communication technologies are being developed in response to market demands for higher transmission rates.
- Switching mechanisms such as frame relay, cell relay and the asynchronous transfer mode are under intensive study.

The goal of some of the ongoing projects is to match state-of-the-art developments in broadband technology and to investigate the strategic implications for user organizations. Work done at the NYNEX laboratories provides the knowledge and insight needed for planning communications networks during the rest of this decade.

One of the projects, Media Broadband Service (MBS) focuses on a network-based multimedia communications capability which permits the sharing of images and conversation for collaborative work among geographically dispersed locations.

- MBS consists of network transport, session management, industry-specific applications software and display.
- Available as demonstrators, some of the applications under development centre on health care, publishing and travel.

Aspects of this work are incorporated in the Media Broadband Service trial with Boston hospitals and publishers. Emphasis is placed on network-based visual communication capability which enables realtime sharing of images in support of collaborative work among geographically dispersed locations.

Fundamentally, the MBS program rests on studies conducted by NYNEX Science and Technology Laboratories which examined how people interact in the context of doing work, and resulted in several conclusions. Among them:

- Work is typically accomplished by communities of interest which need to be effectively networked in order to obtain commendable results.
- Such communities are established and sustained by information exchange which take place in the context of work sessions.
- The conversations that people and work centres have with each other form a network of relationships which help to expand the previous results.

Media Broadband Service applies the outlined principles in a way that emulates a conversational type of work environment, rather than a traditional computing environment. Applications driven by session management technology are oriented toward: articulation, expression, response, dialogue, exchange and even improvisation.

At the hub of session management is a proprietary software developed by the NYNEX laboratories. It provides a platform for network services enabling applications to take advantage of the session through a toolkit. Designed to reflect real-life situations, this enables individuals in different locations to engage in collaborative work sessions that involve:

- accessing and sharing image-based information across a wide variety of workstations and servers
- possibly extending the obtained advantages toward other environments where image-based conversation plays a significant role.

Utilizing high-speed fibre optics, MBS enables users to make concurrent critical decisions related to images. Sessions can be databased and then transmitted as multimedia mail for additional collaboration at a later time.

Most importantly, MBS makes use of an open architecture that support a range of interactions. This approach parallels another imaginative research project financed by grants from the National Science Foundation, ARPA and the Corporation for National Research Initiative (CNRI) known as the *Gigabit Network Project*.

8. The Role of the Gigabit Network Project

As is the case with DAN and ViewStation, there is no evidence the NYNEX laboratories are directly involved in CNRI's Gigabit Network Project. Yet, many of the research efforts at the S&T laboratories have to do with gigastream technology. Hence it is wise to take a quick look into what this project means.

Though from one project to another the specific objectives in terms of deliverables may diverge, the background goal of research on gigastreams is:

- To create test beds for the design and development of networks that operate with data rates of about 1 gigabit per second (GBPS), and eventually higher.
- The availability of GBPS networks can enable a major paradigm shift from data and text-based to image-based communications.

In appreciation of this fact and of its long-term impact, five contracts awarded by CNRI address network architectures and incorporate potential applications for GBPS networks. Test-bed goals include:

- distributed computing using multiple high-performance computers and workstations
- realtime processing of composite high-speed multimedia streams.

As is the case with MBS, current experiments being undertaken under the Gigabit Network Project perspective explore the feasibility of group collaboration over wide areas, as well as the use of GBPS networks to develop simulated environments.

Not only is gigabit speed researched but it is also enriched with knowledge engineering to obtain balanced network capabilities. Proper balancing is important to the success of *metasystems*. The network must provide a flexible way to connectivity at bandwidths dynamically required by applications between:

- computational nodes
- information storage locations
- user interface resources.

This must be executed any to any, in a manner independent of geographical location. Achieving a national metasystem which integrates computers and communications *will change the nature of the computational process* itself by providing the capability to collaborate with widely dispersed locations on grand challenge problems.

These efforts bring into perspective the concepts of *theoretical simulation* and of *navigation* among scattered and heterogeneous databases, possibly containing incompatible information elements. The term 'theoretical simulation' is used in connection with performing a considerable variety of logical and numerical experiments using:

- high-performance computing

- intelligent databases
- gigabit networks.

The aim is to create a world in *metasystem* memory where experiments take place *without the constraints of space or time*. This is the longer-term aim of research projects which concentrate on broadband communications, and it is absolutely indivisible from performance computing.

9. Leading Projects which Define Tomorrow's Telecommunications

Promoted by the NYNEX Laboratories, NetWindow is an advanced network management platform which combines intelligent features with ergonomic design. In addition to functions such as alarm surveillance and statistics gathering, the system assures computer-aided testing and on-line diagnostic capabilities.

NetWindow has been originally designed to help in the major change which characterizes the passage from teletype (TTY) terminals to frame relay services with the aim of automating some of the functions. It:

- monitors switches for frame relay services
- alerts the network manager about required retransmissions
- judges if retransmissions happen an inordinate number of times, indicating that a part will soon fail
- pre-allocates switches and circuits to customers two to three months ahead, based on forecasts.

The forecasts NetWindow makes include priorities and commitments concerning future resources which will be required, evaluated against available and projected network facilities.

The main issue is effective network planning. The second issue is resource management of thousands of frame relay lines. The third issue is surveillance and intelligent diagnostics. All are supported through knowledge engineering.

While this product has been developed for the telcos, NYNEX senses that there is market demand for it on behalf of user organizations. According to the developers, NetWindow has applications for both the end customers and the public carriers.

Another related product is *tools and methods* for network services specification. Current projects target a set of tools, methodology and training to aid in the specification of network services. Results are expected to assist in the:

- clarification of requirements

- reduction of ambiguity in specifications
- detection and correction of design errors.

Still another project along a similar frame of reference is the Intelligent Packet Network (IPN). It introduces knowledge-engineering principles and artefacts to network access security, mnemonic addressing and dynamic carrier selection. It also contributes to the use of virtual private networks.

The first release of IPN incorporated a database for mnemonic addressing, as well as on-line audit trails, logging all network access, and it supported closed user groups. Current IPN developments include the addition of Private Network Administration (PNA) which:

- allows a physical network to be carved into many separately owned and remotely administered virtual private networks
- includes further plans for the expansion of call processing activities and support for enhanced call redirection/deflection.

Two other projects seen as twins are Channel Switched Network Services (CSNS) and Intelligent Private Line Networks (IPLN). These are central-office based, digital backbone data network supports for dedicated leased line and private T-1 networking services.

CSNS/IPLN enables the utilization of intelligent channel banks and intelligent multiplexers, offering digital cross connect to control and switch customer network components. The adopted approach includes a family of functions:

- network access to the service node
- interoffice bandwidth between service nodes
- value-added nodal services such as sub-rate multiplexing and proactive testing
- network management, supervision and control.

There is also the *Automated Function Node* (AFN), a multi-functional development platform providing for the automation and enhancement of existing services or the addition of new ones.

The AFN platform facilitates *rapid prototyping* of trials for new services. It has been deployed as an intelligent adjunct to analogue and digital switches integrating new technologies, such as speech recognition. Some of the currently deployed services in AFN are:

- voice-operated intercept system
- multifunctional operator workstation
- automated credit quote

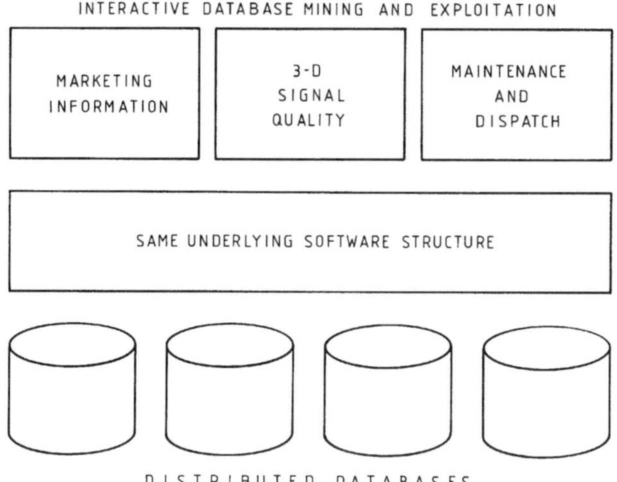

Figure 11.4 The NYNEX Geographic Information System provides a common information infrastructure for database mining

- customer contact voice response
- force and facilities data management.

Finally, there is *Smartstick*, a *database mining* artefact which provides for quickly and easily attaching and retrieving voice messages to documents. It also helps in transactions. Examples of applications are the transaction of purchases or payments and tracking the location of documents or forms.

10. The Geographic Information System

The best way of looking at the Geographic Information System (GIS)* is as a knowledge-enriched artefact for the exploitation of databases. Among the applications to which GIS is put are:

- database mining
- data analysis
- statistical analysis.

The competitive advantage of this approach is that it is done with space orientation layered by area of functions. As seen in Figure 11.4, the same underlying software answers a range of applications which are characteristic from marketing to maintenance. All applications are enriched with routines making possible *interactive visualization.*

The *Marketing and Planning System* (MAPS) of NYNEX is based on GIS

* GIS is Unix based, the DBMS is Ingres. It runs on Sun computers.

software and is targeted for use in market forecasting, outside plant engineering, and customer services. MAPS/GIS is employed to perform complex spatial analysis. It also enables the viewing of spatial distributions of data through interactive computer map displays and graphical user interfaces. Typical marketing applications include:

- high and low population distribution
- high, average, low income bracketing
- a combination of the above two and other demographic criteria
- analysis of business locations
- zooming on business locations within a buffer zone – for instance two-mile radius
- definition of where future infrastructure may be needed for investments such as fibre installation.

All these analyses are assisted through knowledge engineering and provide a first-class example of where database mining and intelligent artefacts converge.

MAPS/GIS applications range from the evaluation of customer needs to business opportunity research. Such an approach has a wide implementation potential not only in telephony but also in banking and in the service sector of the economy at large.

Also based on a GIS infrastructure, the *Signal Quality System* (SQS) is a decision support tool used to plan and maintain mobile communications. By integrating the functionality provided by Geographic Information System software, SQS allows the user to:

- simulate and analyse system performance
- alter parameters such as transmitter location and antenna type
- experiment on power levels and radio frequency.

Another interesting application of GIS is the *Dispatch of Repair and Installation Vehicles Efficiency* (DRIVE). It helps dispatchers optimize workload distribution among field technicians, taking into account reasons of failure, skills, availability and projected driving times. The user interacts with the software through computer map displays and graphical user interfaces.

The dispatching system operates in realtime. The signal quality database is updated every time a change takes place. The user is provided with tools for interactive experimentation based on signal variation as a function of traffic.

Another expert system which fits into a similar frame of reference is the *Maintenance Administration Expert* (MAX). It is used to diagnose line troubles and helps to cut down on double dispatches and other erroneous dispatches, therefore improving trouble resolution times.

- MAX is deployed in 43 maintenance centres in New York Telephone and New England Telephone.
- The drivers of this project have been cost savings and better customer service.

Still another knowledge artefact, the *Automated Transmission Link Analysis and Simulation* (ATLAS) manages a network of advanced test, simulation, and analysis equipment. By replicating any known combination of transmission impairments, ATLAS can provide a complete analysis of the impact of those impairments on new services and associated equipment.

As a testing tool, ATLAS is capable of stressing a system beyond its engineering limits with exhaustive sampling and variation. As NYNEX was to comment, by utilizing this expert system:

- New services and product can be thoroughly tested and evaluated under a variety of network conditions.
- This is done without the need for lengthy and costly field trials, increasing greatly the productivity of telephone engineers.

This range of activities in which we use expert systems is a good demonstration of the results obtained through the able use of artificial intelligence. It also demonstrates the range of interests handled by the NYNEX Science and Technology Laboratories.

11. Experimenting at the Customer Technical Center

Compared to the high-technology work which we have seen in the preceding sections, what is done at the Customer Technical Center (CTC) can be classified as relatively low technology. Yet it has its place, as the following examples help to document.

CTC is a facility used to identify and meet the communication needs of the *consumer market*. It is a place to observe and record customer reactions and responses to products and services under development, as well as those currently offered.

The scope of the NYNEX Customer Technical Center has been projected to cover residential issues, people in motion, small businesses, retail and other relevant markets and applications. The procedures have been designed in a way to enable efficient screening of customer criteria for current and potential market reasons.

- CTC effectively tests customer interaction with NYNEX products from new prototypes to enhancements.
- During testing, customers can be observed and video-taped to assure that valuable information obtained through observation will be used.
- The main aim is to obtain feedback from customers as they interact with the NYNEX products, both current and planned.

By means of real-life tests conducted at the Customer Technical Center, the observation and evaluation done during the live performance centres on what users like or dislike about the product. For this purpose, NYNEX sets up an environment like a train station, a living-room or a kitchen, and runs the service or product under test on a small scale.

For instance, one of the tests in a mock-up of a train station (including the setting and the noise) was a new public telephone for use with chip cards and debit cards. The goal was to evaluate three different European telephones in terms of user-friendliness.

Other, similar tests were done in mock-up living-rooms and kitchens for videophones. Still others focused on mobile telephones with some ten different telephone products from an equal number of manufacturers.

NYNEX experts observe the customers during the test and obtain feedback which is tabulated and analysed. This proactive experimental process is instrumental in finding out the problems which are involved in terms of simplicity of use, easiness to learn, default and so on.

The findings of this in-house market research help to stimulate thinking and therefore to extend existing telephone services as well as to prototype new ones. This is achieved by:

- having available multiple modular environments with sound effects which simulate real-life settings
- constructing specific environments such as a home, office or public place to permit rapid gathering of data from various customer perspectives.

CTC contributes in optimizing product evaluation and service development by refining concepts, identifying winners and speeding delivery. As such, it offers an important intermediate step between engineering testing and field trials.

The background idea is that problems must be detected and corrected at an early stage, thus saving both time and money. NYNEX correctly considers the Customer Technical Center as an unprecedented way of testing technology, leading to the creation of more user-friendly and competitive products and services.

As the management of the laboratories aptly remarked, important technological developments take place not only in business but also in customer products. An example is the *Voice Dialing Service* also known as Voice Activated Telephony Control (VATC). Through voice dialling a customer can:

- go off-hook
- speak a previously programmed speech utterance
- have the network react as if an associated digit string had been dialled.

VATC also includes the functionality required to review, add, and delete the name-number entries that have been previously programmed. The subscriber does not have to buy special telephone sets to take advantage of voice dialling. All of the equipment associated with the service is contained within the switching network central offices.

Another example is the *Flexible Recognizer*, a speaker independent speech recognition module eliminating the current constraint of limiting the speaker independent recognition vocabulary to digits (0–9) or yes/no. It allows users to program their own vocabulary and change that vocabulary as often as they like.

12

Networks for Intelligent Buildings and Intelligent Cities

1. Introduction

Intelligent cities, at the level of metropolitan area networks, and intelligent buildings, in connection with local area networks, are excellent cases of *high-performance communications*. As with computing, high-performance communications solutions must have a market scope.

Regarding market scope, right after the US Congress passed the High Performance Computing Act, in January 1991, a group of leading businessmen suggested that this was not enough and it should be extended. The chief executive officers from America's 12 leading computer companies have subscribed to this opinion.

These 12 CEOs, who are known collectively as the Computer Systems Policy Project (CSPP), have asked Congress to expand the high-speed network beyond the needs of the research community. In their statement, they are urging the federal government to make advanced computing and communications services widely available to heterogeneous segments of the economy, from hospitals and schools to industrial companies and financial institutions.

CSPP contends that there must be explicit co-ordination and accountability regarding the development of an intelligent network which will impact on America's future, as well as a clear mechanism which draws on industry expertise.

This multifunctional approach is considered to be fundamental in developing, co-ordinating and managing the implementation of the information superhighway initiative. There is a great deal of truth in this argument:

- While we are now looking toward gigastream capacity, it is doubtful that the node wire will answer the communications requirements of the next ten years.
- High performance will be increasingly associated with the knowledge-engineering artefacts embedded into nodes and lines.

Implementation of knowledge engineering will most likely take different forms. It will range from proactive knowledge robots designed to enhance customer service to diagnostics constructs for fault identification and preventive maintenance (see also the references made in Chapter 11 in connection to the NYNEX projects).

The networks being contemplated in America, Japan and other countries of the First World, are totally different propositions than those characterizing the communications notions which we have had so far. Its longer-term goal is *community intelligence* to be promoted by a number of intermediate milestones which are elaborated in the present chapter.

2. Components of a Program Focusing on Community Intelligence

The intelligent network the US Federal government proposes to build as an information highway will be providing a modern and efficient infrastructure. Everyone seems to be in agreement regarding its need; three key questions however remain to be answered:

- Should this network serve only the research community or also business and industry and eventually the American homes?
- How much high technology should there be in the design, implementation, operation, diagnostics and maintenance of such a network?
- Should the US taxpayer be asked to foot a wide-ranging implementation bill?

If the answer to the last question is yes, should government financing limit itself to the backbone, or cover also other issues more closely connected to implementation details. What about government subsidies due to frontier projects such as knowledge robots, and two-way television?

These are in no way idle queries. They are quite practical. A good example of the implementation of a new generation of proactive robots has been with *intelligent buildings*. These were first advocated by the United Technology Building Systems (UTBS) in the USA in 1981, and came about in July 1983 with the inauguration of the City Place Building in Hartford, Connecticut – but since that time the underlying concept has gone a long way.

UTBS was responsible for controlling and operating such shared equipment as air-conditioners, elevators, fire control and disaster prevention devices. The company further provided communications and office automation (OA) shared tenant services using local area networks

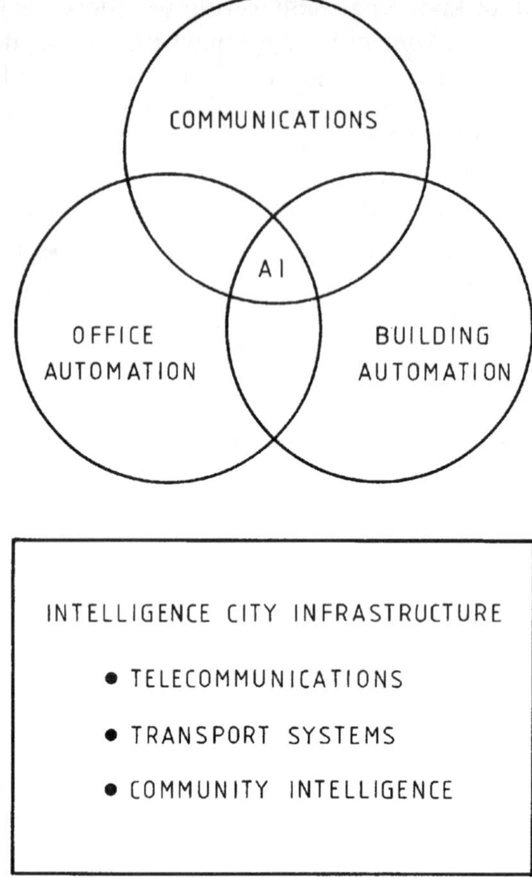

Figure 12.1 Evolution in intelligent building and emerging intelligent city requirements

(LAN), digital private branch exchanges (PBXs) and computers. The Hartford structure can be considered as the world's first intelligent building.

Slowly, the concept of intelligent buildings has spread to include not only those for which shared tenant services can be provided but also company-owned establishments, hospitals, schools and shopping centres. As a result, the practice of intelligent buildings now contains the notion of providing both:

- comfortable living space, as a bundler of software and hardware supports
- the needed information infrastructure, like telecommunications and building automation (BA).

Figure 12.1 presents the developing trend which, as we see in section 3, tends to include a great deal of formerly independent services now offered in an integrative way. Without the minimal doubt these developments impact on industry, technology and society at large.

- When truly broadband channels at metropolitan area networks (MAN) and wide area networks (WAN) levels arrive, they will turn the economics of providing traditional telephone services upside down.
- Because of the almost infinite bandwidth available with fibre optics, it will not be worthwhile charging for ordinary telephone calls, or low-speed data traffic such as email.

Instead, subscribers could simply pay a fixed monthly rental. This, for example, could be based on the consumption of high-definition television (HDTV) programs, and value-added services. Much of the competitiveness of such services will rest on knowledge engineering, and on microminiaturization to reduce power requirements and swamp costs.

American research and development in miniaturization technologies is rated the best in the world. But the Office of Technology Assessment (OTA) warns that the country is in danger of lagging behind other nations in time to market, commercializing the fruits of the leading research efforts.

- OTA stresses the importance of maintaining the lead in miniaturization technologies and in embedding knowledge into the chips.
- This includes everything from electronics and photonics to sensors, in a wide variety of applications.

Leadership in miniaturization and in knowledge engineering, and their timely implementation, is so important because it helps to create new markets and enhance existing products. Holding top spot in this field will add billions of dollars to the gross national product of the nations where they are developed and implemented.

Precisely under this perspective, a multimedia highway implemented by means of a broadband nation-wide intelligent network from desk area, to local area, metropolitan and long haul, is one of the best investments, in the sense that it is sure to show results. This proposition reflects the fact that multimedia communications has become, in the span of a few brief years, immediate and global.

In every corner of this world, people live off the image on the television screen, and of its message.* But while the news, commentary and information, ever grow in quantity and availability (though not in

* Which also has many negative aspects on society, not least being that most people tend to think in terms of visual images rather than through inquisitive minds.

quality) the existing infrastructure gets strained, particularly in regard to the communications switches and links.

In effect, the revolution brought on by global communications goes far beyond informational instruments and structures. 'We are dealing with a profound and substantial change in the social, economic, moral and cultural spheres,' Dr Vittorio Vaccari suggests. 'It is a revolution which:

- implies and involves the whole fabric of human society
- knows no national or ethnic borderlines, and
- changes the priorities and hierarchies of the established order.'

The argument is valid from the computers used as business tools to the level of household electrical appliances. Ten years ago, developments in the electrical appliance industry focused on reducing physical household labour. Today, emphasis has shifted to the development of *intelligent devices*.

In the home and in the office, intelligent devices incorporate microcomputers and sensors, and they can save mental as well as physical labour. The following section looks at office automation, building automation and different types of appliances, considering the technological developments over the last few years, while keeping in the background the fact that high-performance computers and communications can further promote the current state of the art.

3. Office Automation, Building Automation and the Communications Network

What are the means and tools of office automation which may be most interesting in an intelligent building perspective? First and foremost these are job specific and range from building management services to smart assistants for receptionists and telephone operators.

There are also other duties within the job-specific class. For instance, library and document management services, but these can as well enter into the category of decision support systems (DSS) which increasingly require high-performance communications and computing solutions.

Still another class is that of administration and logistics, through to electronic filing systems for compound storage and retrieval. The automation of administrative and trivial chores has become an integral part of any agile and cost-effective solution.

The office automation perspective which we have just examined overlaps with the communications landscape, and reasonably so. High-performance digital electronic exchanges are necessary to switch and channel voice mail as well as facsimile, and a paging system.

- Local area networks interconnect increasingly powerful workstations – like the ViewStation we discussed in Chapter 8 – with databases and supercomputers acting as servers.
- An internal two-way narrowcasting and broadcasting system is necessary to integrate so far distinct communications services, including entertainment.

The interactive video solutions of the late 1990s will use both fibre-optic and coaxial-based broadband channels of community antenna television (CATV). Both land cables and satellite communications will:

- feed with multimedia information into decision rooms at the corporate level, making teleconferencing a hub of: 'Communicate, don't commute.'
- effectively integrate remote offices into concurrent engineering, concurrent banking and other structures
- enrich residential buildings with agile communications and computing facilities making working at home effectively feasible.

To benefit from economies of mass, closed user groups will be created in a dynamic manner, benefiting from intelligence-enriched security mechanisms. These will evidently interface with the building management system.

One of the major subsystems of building automation will be security, including facilities access monitoring and a well-protected database. Fire prevention monitoring is another key subsystem and so are:

- lighting monitoring
- power supply assurance
- energy control
- water recycling.

Building automation is done on-line, applies sensors to all places where measurements are needed and uses plenty of expert systems for control reasons. Ideally, the information system infrastructure is fully distributed, in the way Figure 12.2 suggests.

As Nippon Telegraph and Telephone was to comment during a meeting in Tokyo, building automation systems consist of knowledge-enriched artefacts to assist management as well as supervisory and control equipment to run the utilities and to serve in crime prevention.

Knowledge modules contribute to better security, premises monitoring, accident prevention and other systems. These developments are not

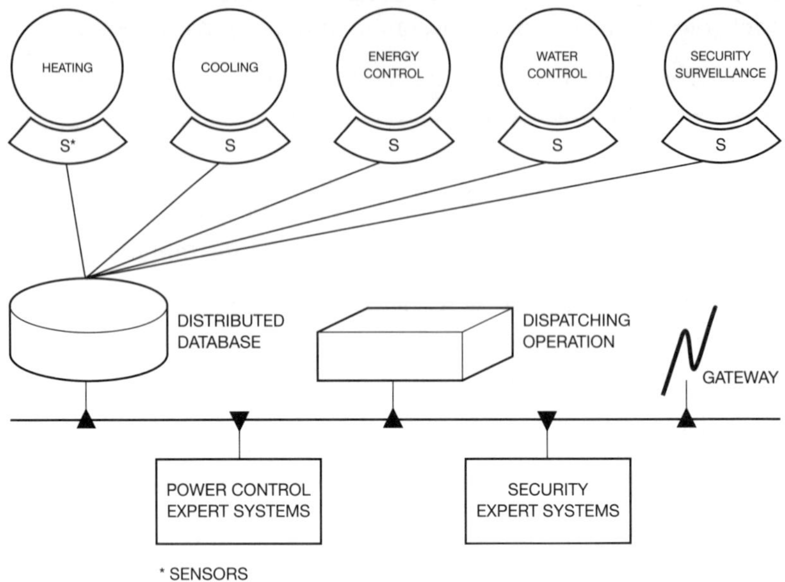

Figure 12.2 Data management for heating automation

due only to technology. They have come about as reflections of the competition for services and for rental facilities that has made it more important than ever to improve:

- the efficiency of office work
- the convenience of the living space.

That is why so much attention is now being paid to making buildings intelligent. The effort has evidently benefited from the advancements in information processing and communications as well as from technology now becoming available at an *affordable cost*. Significant gains have been achieved in cost-effectiveness due to:

- large-scale integration of semiconductor devices
- optical-fibre networks as well as optical storage devices.

As the technology required to build intelligent systems evolves rapidly, the foremost user organizations have put it into use. In so doing, they capitalize on the change in office work characteristics.

Since First World countries (America, Western Europe and Japan) entered an age of stable economic growth, greater importance has been placed on planning and in the domain of concurrent co-operation work than ever before. Therefore, the demand for knowledge-enriched functions in the office to enhance human creativity has increased.

The purpose of making an office building intelligent is to improve efficiency in management and in professional work, as well as to promote innovation, productivity and comfort. When studying what makes a given building intelligent, it is necessary to consider these matters and also reflect from the viewpoint of corporate strategy, identity and symbolism – including the marketing aftermath of advanced solutions.

4. Planning for Solutions which Exploit Microchip Intelligence

In the mid-1970s when microprocessors were still a new subject and their future was not necessarily certain, General Electric effected a far-sighted study. This projected that 10 to 15 years hence practically every one of the company's products will use microprocessor power for better performance, lower cost and competitiveness in a market more demanding than ever.

In the mid-1980s the Japanese undertook a similar study, but their emphasis was on the implementation of fuzzy engineering. The hypothesis being tested was that, whether cast in chips or written in software, fuzzy set models will become commonplace and their usage will amount to one word: *competitiveness*. Knowledge artefacts, the same study found, will differentiate intelligent buildings from those which are dumb or simply smart.

This is a reasonable assumption. Since in the case of industrial buildings the user is the company itself (as landlord, employer and employees) it is wise to build systems which are flexible and can be dynamically adjusted for:

- the type of business as it evolves
- the particular features supported by the building
- the change in the profile and requirements of the tenants of the building.

Along these axes of reference, a leading financial institution classified all its building assets in a matrix as shown in Figure 12.3. One dichotomy has been between head offices and branches; another, among newer and older buildings. The former allowed a full version of building automation plans; for the latter was developed a watered-down version.

This distinction concerned not only the devices to be installed but also the computing features and communications needs to be served. However, no compromises were made regarding workstations, databases and telecommunications needs.

As companies become more information oriented and the importance

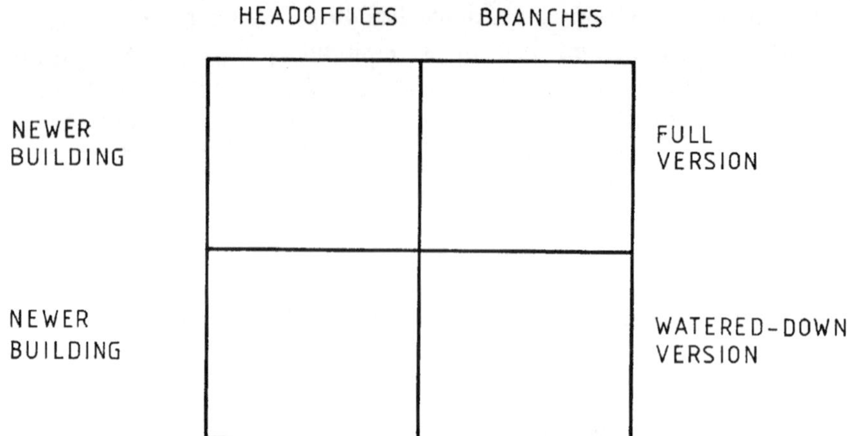

Figure 12.3 Advanced design concept and building assets

of corporate networks is clearly recognized, the range of required capabilities increases. In turn, this calls for:

- any-to-any connectivity between workstations and servers
- remote but secure access to distributed databases
- significant network enhancements
- quick localization of network faults
- provision of artefacts for dealing with the complexity of network operations.

The services we provide today must be suitable for multimedia applications but also be more economical than those already existing. In constructing and improving corporate information networks, various carriers, information media, software and hardware vendors should be used most effectively – leading to the optimization of service contracts.

Network construction techniques with user-dependent conditions, network management know-how and support tools are indispensable. A flexible construction capability is needed to cope with changing requirements and this too is one of the main factors to enter into the building automation equation.

As we will see in the next section, the requirements for embedded intelligence are on the increase. The intelligent building and the intelligent city have functions which exceed the concept of conventional solutions even if the implementation of the new wave of automation does not exhibit the same level of sophistication at home and in business.

The new generation of audio-visual technologies provides an example of the smart house. These are largely related to television receivers, video cassette recorders, audio equipment, broadcasting satellite and receivers, HDTV and optical disks. In terms of TV reception, the last decade has given us:

- high audio quality
- visual picture quality
- large-screen presentation
- on-line personal computers
- accommodation of new media.

Technology has been instrumental in developing, through computers and communications, a home electronics concept but it has also influenced network construction techniques. The overriding goal is the pursuit of a more comfortable, safer and less expensive environment – which expands market perspectives.

Are the products included in the new wave of high-performance solutions something we never had before? The answer is *No*, but they are re-engineered. The so-called new media are a group of products for communications services different from:

- conventional telephone systems
- data collection devices
- radio/television broadcasting.

One form of new media, for example, is a realtime, two-way visual communication system – such as a two-way CATV. As we have seen with the Shuttle example of NYNEX, like the classical CATV it consists of a headend facility and broadband networks provided in a local area. In the headend are included:

- receiving antennas
- the equipment of a television studio
- computer systems
- communication equipment.

The upstream portion can gather request/answer data from subscribers to the headend facility. Communications networks via satellites and optical fibres are particularly useful in this connection, the systems components consisting of:

- operator interfaces
- telemeter and telecontrol
- processors and software.

Two-way solutions can be instrumental due to the fact that people do not just want an automated home. They want a home that is comfortable to live in and able to connect to the outside world, with automation increasing the sense of well-being.

That message is not always easy for automation companies to understand. One of the problems is that there is no single feature able to justify a home-automation solution. It is the *whole system* that should be looked at in an integral manner for the services it can provide. Only then can we find the justification.

5. Towards the Design of Intelligent Cities

Sections 2 to 4 have examined what is meant by intelligent buildings. They are buildings which, in addition to their structural components, have an information and knowledge facility which acts as the system's nerves and brain.

The principles so far examined concern individual buildings and their facilities. However, by grouping several buildings together some of the variables are changing as interconnectivity and interfacing become mandatory. At the same time, the merits of an integrated approach is much more apparent.

Architect Masa Kimura, division manager of NTT, advances the following example which leads toward the concept of an intelligent city. When the monitoring centre of building automation is installed the task of bringing intelligence into the system has only started:

- A consolidated monitoring centre will be the next logical step.
- This will make feasible a policy of developing effective maintenance services.
- By integrating artificial intelligence, the total personnel requirements for maintaining and monitoring the whole group can be reduced.

Significant reductions in manual labour, Masa Kimura advises, cannot be achieved without knowledge-engineering artefacts. The technology is available; all we need to do is to use it.

In a similar manner, the consolidation of information and communications systems can help to save energy. This, too, can be achieved through intelligence-enriched buildings. By endowing them with complementary functions, a greater efficiency can be anticipated. Built in 1986, NTT's 'Shinagawa TWINS'* offers an example of this approach:

- Surplus heat from the computer room is accumulated by the heat storage tank at an underground level (massive water tank).

* Which has a double meaning: Twins, and *T*oward *I*ntelligent *N*etwork *S*ystems.

This is used as a source of heat for office air-conditioning systems. In addition to common energy sources such as electricity and gas as well as solar-heated hot water, the use of atmospheric energy in the air-conditioning system provides further savings.

- The adopted solution economizes some 20 per cent in utilities costs which would have been otherwise necessary.

Further savings have been achieved through the upgrading in performance of the overall building services group by combining the uses and functions of the TWINS buildings.

Another good example on combined building functions is given by the OMNI complex in Atlanta, Georgia. This group of buildings has space for an underground railway station and large car park, which provide for mass transport. It also has an exhibition hall, hotel, international conference rooms, restaurants, and shops surrounding the atrium area.

Figure 12.4 provides a snapshot of the integrated facilities supported

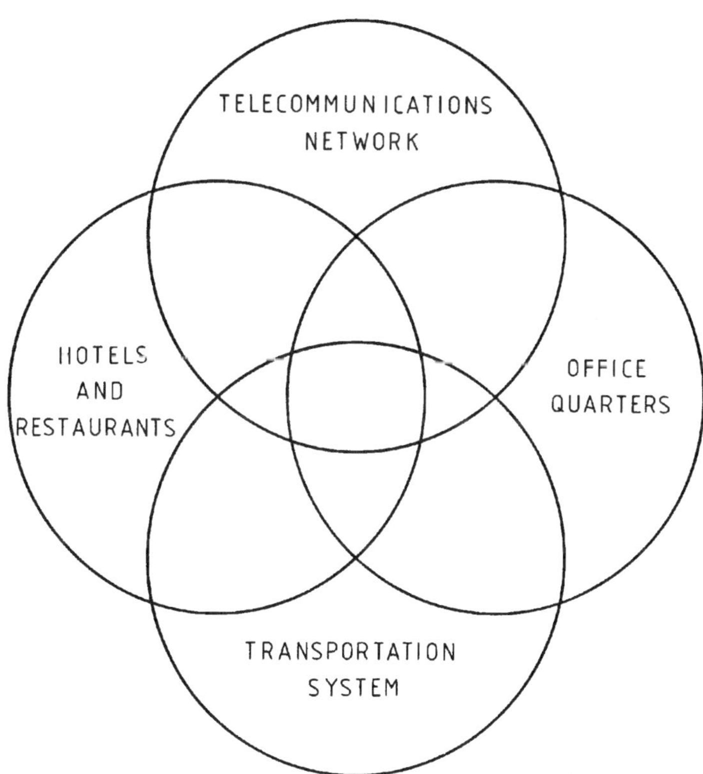

Figure 12.4 A range of functions supported through an integrated approach to building space

by OMNI, as a city within a city. The adopted solution is reinforcing the functions of Atlanta as a commercial hub of the South. But because of a fast-changing technology:

- Many architects now think that this complex already belongs to a past generation of intelligent buildings.
- A basic argument is that its design merits are very dependent on concentrating spatial distance, rather than an intelligence-enriched approach.

Complexes which have as their backbone the new generation intelligent building concept, feature a concentration of high-level information functions. These reinforce the features of consolidating physical distance. New solutions are based on a radical concept of an intelligent system, with corresponding implementation objectives in terms of:

- service diversity
- multiple functionality.

This duality brings into perspective the need for high-performance communications and computing, as well as powerful algorithms to support spacial and temporal management. It also calls for design flexibility able to integrate existing modules into diverse environments such as represented by:

- the old town
- the revamped town
- the new town.

City planning for the second half of the twentieth century was radically influenced by emphasis upon the mass movement of people and high-speed transport. Problems related to *overcoming distances* and the *changes in time values* saw to it that transport networks sprang up all over. But it is mainly the new town which benefited from such facilities.

By contrast, solutions along the line of two-way broadband networks are of significant interest to the old, the revamped and the new town, as they provide significant flexibility with freedom from limitations of:

- time
- distance
- quality
- quantity.

The concept of freedom from time limitations can be shown through voice mail, but there are other examples. For instance, the recording and playback of television broadcasts allows viewers to enjoy programmes outside of broadcast hours.

In the same frame of reference, office work in different time zones can become concurrent through a flexible time framework. In this manner *24-hour functions* can be instituted, extending the concept not only across different continents but also at local level to benefit from services which overcome the barrier of building walls.

Databasing and networking are not the only ways to overcome time and distance limitations. An equally valid example in terms of freedom from distance is the facsimile network. A document requiring a one-time effort to prepare can be transmitted on-line to multiple parties.

- Even a few years ago, documents were sent by express mail.
- Only recently has facsimile, a late nineteenth-century invention, taken hold.

If we look back to post World War II in another field, telegrams were used as means of communicating quickly in case of emergencies. Then in the 1950s the telex network took over, to be overtaken in the early 1980s by electronic mail – with image mail being the answer in the mid-1990s.

6. Freedom from the Limitations of Distance?

The first part of the word *telecommunications* is 'tele' and it means 'distant', underlining that a major functional benefit of electronic communications is the ability to exchange information across distances. This helps in overcoming the long-distance barrier, but does it really free us from the limitations of distance?

Developed in the early 1830s, the concept of telecommunications started with the age of the telegraph and was reinforced in the 1850s to 1880s timeframe with the telephone. Both the telephone and the telegraph have the function of being able to send a signal or voice message to a distant location.

- The telegraph is a point-to-point, one-way network for text and data.
- The telephone started as a point-to-point, two-way network for voice.
- Being more flexible and capillary in its distribution, the telephone network developed into a multidrop networked system of increasingly wider band.

In the present age, this nineteenth-century discovery has been enriched with the transmission of moving images with complex colouring and toning and high fidelity. It is further expanded through the evolving HDTV two-way broadcasting and narrowcasting.

With intelligent terminals, sophisticated software, optical fibres and satellites, telecommunications have taken on new dimensions on a long-distance scale. Today's achievements are tomorrow's competitive offering as we are steadily progressing in terms of transfering R&D results into practical use.

Rapid developments in the telecommunications domain are most important in connection with traffic inside a city and between cities, as communications have become a substitute for transportation. At the same time, however, communications also can be a motivating factor for initiating physical transportation.

These references help to highlight visions of future traffic systems. But we can better understand the risks involved in projections if we bring to mind a couple of historical milestones and their opposite: flops in forecasting. In the traffic exhibition of 1952, in Munich, were introduced some of the prevailing visions of the traffic systems in the year 2000:

- the American dream cars of the 1950s
- fast luxury ocean liners
- turbine-driven mobiles with plexiglass domes
- private helicopters for individual air traffic.

All these projections have dropped from sight but they did have in common what was then technically feasible: the distance between A and B had to be covered in a way aided by existing technology in the fastest, most comfortable and safest way possible.

If we look back to the real development of the last 40 years, and then consider projects now made for the traffic of year 2000 and beyond, we must admit that little has been realized from the technical visions of 1952. The real winner has been telecommunications – and this has happened in polyvalent ways which have passed the test of the fittest.

In 1985, American Airlines asked the consulting firm Booz Allen and Hamilton to study and report on who would be its major competitor by 1995. The answer was: AT&T. It was based on the principle that people will rather communicate than commute given:

- appropriate channel capacity
- software support
- reasonable costs.

American Airlines took up the challenge and by 1992 it had put in place a network of 160,000 computers and terminals – the largest network in the world. Investment banks in Wall Street are suggesting that this operation is so profitable that if American Airlines disposed of its airplanes and concentrated on the network services, its stock will be worth a multiple of its current value.

Such huge networks, however, cannot operate in an efficient manner when served through mainframes and centralized solutions. High effectiveness, flexibility and low cost require fully distributed approaches. Covia, the information systems subsidiary of United Airlines also said just as much.

7. Looking for a Substitute to Physical Transport*

The message to retain from these references is that the traffic of the future is and will continue to be influenced by conditions shaped by what is technically state-of-the-art and what is acceptable in financial terms. Fully distributed telecommunications solutions are instrumental in bridging distances, but *innovation* has to be an integral part of the equation:

- The rail traffic may be improved, but cannot take the weight off of street traffic because it retreats from the rural areas and does not really penetrate the epicentres of the megalopolis.
- Improvements in terms of public traffic for local conditions are limited, even the underground at best helps to surpass the worst impasses.
- The optimization of the existing street traffic through intelligent steering and guidance of automobiles is an approach, but requires multipoint direct communications.

Therefore, what evolves as the bottom line is that without broadband communications and cellular radio an important improvement of the traffic situation, especially in dense areas, cannot be expected. High ecological barriers in terms of auto and bus transports have also to be faced. Aggravating these physical traffic references is the wish of a growing population for an individual home and their own piece of land. This contrasts with the centralized approach of working in condensed areas.

As for air transport and the 1952 futurologists project on individual helicopters, there is a number of major obstacles due to congestion. In fact, such obstacles are on the increase. For instance:

- overcrowded skies, congested airways, too few and overlapping landing and take-off slots in terminals
- even if the airspace problem was not present, there are simply not enough airports with the required number of gates to handle the projected air traffic

* See also Mermaid, the excellent project by NEC, in sections 9 and 10.

- many of the existing airport facilities suffer from ground transportation congestion.

Typically, it requires 10 to 15 years to develop a new airport and there is the issue of aircraft noise which has long been a major concern of the surrounding communities, further restricting the landing and take-off slots.

Other issues are economic. Aircraft fleet expansion and modernization require large capital investments. Growth militates for larger aircraft and more passengers per transport unit, both short and long range. But both the crowded skies and investment constraints put a limit to that business.

These references do not mean that there are absolutely no solutions. Progress has already been made towards reducing the nuisance of airport noise. The large capital needs of airlines lead to more megacarriers, with the number of scheduled airlines declining – an effect also due to various deregulation initiatives.

- Multinational ownership is likely to proliferate and create fewer but financially stronger airlines.
- But is it not also true that the same is valid about communications networks?

If we look more carefully in the global telecommunications arena we will see that there is a growing interest in joint ventures and a soft merging of telecoms. The same is true of the integration of telephony and broadcasting through the development of broadband fibre-optic cable.

8. Freedom from the Limitations of Quality and Quantity

The late Dr Vannevar Bush* was correct in arguing that scientific progress in the modern age is necessary for long-term social and economic progress. Science is beneficial particularly in the longer term, but surely scientific breakthroughs are not sufficient. Something more is needed to contribute to economic prosperity.

This 'something more' is a legitimate subject of a sociology book. Therefore in the present text we will strictly examine the contribution of science and technology in doing away with limitation of quality, by recognizing the critical roles to be played by engineering – taking as an example the system that delivers benefits to city dwellers.

The cornerstone of such a system is concurrent studies which require

* Professor at MIT and scientific adviser to President Truman.

high-performance communications and computing for their completion. This technological component in no way downgrades the fact that, like philosophical enquiry and artistic creation, scientific enquiry has intrinsic values that are important to culture and civilization.

Taking the world of construction technology as an example, Japan's first skyscraper, the Mitsui Kasumigaseki Building, was completed in 1968. To realize the construction of such a high-rising building in an earthquake-prone area required structural calculations which were simply not possible until computers were used for more than data processing chores.

- The advent of simulation and computer experimentation freed skyscraper construction conceptions from qualitative and quantitative limitations.
- If civil engineering calculations are one aspect of the rising city, architectural aesthetics and interior design are another.

Building architecture often reflects something deeper than stone, brick and mortar. It tells much about the history of the way offices work and families live. This has been true through the ages and it is just as valid of the homes of the poor as of those of the wealthy.

The homes of past centuries provided almost no privacy. The habitat of the wealthy people of that time might be exemplified today through magnificent public buildings, complete with large hallways, many bedrooms, baths, parlours, living-rooms, libraries and dining-rooms. But servants were everywhere. Such homes seemed to provide everything except intimacy, resembling a large market-place under one roof.

Gradually, through the centuries, the house took on a different look. It became smaller. It confined itself to being the place where the outside world was excluded, and where there was room only for the family: 'Your house is your castle.'

- But at the same time the family's requirements took on a new perspective as electronic communications crept in.
- Electronic communications promote the concept of automated homes, impacting family as well as economic and industrial life.

Products and services followed that path. Designs of homes of the future, which start finding their way into implementation, call for a cable system to carry all essential services to compatible outlets throughout the house:

- power
- telephone

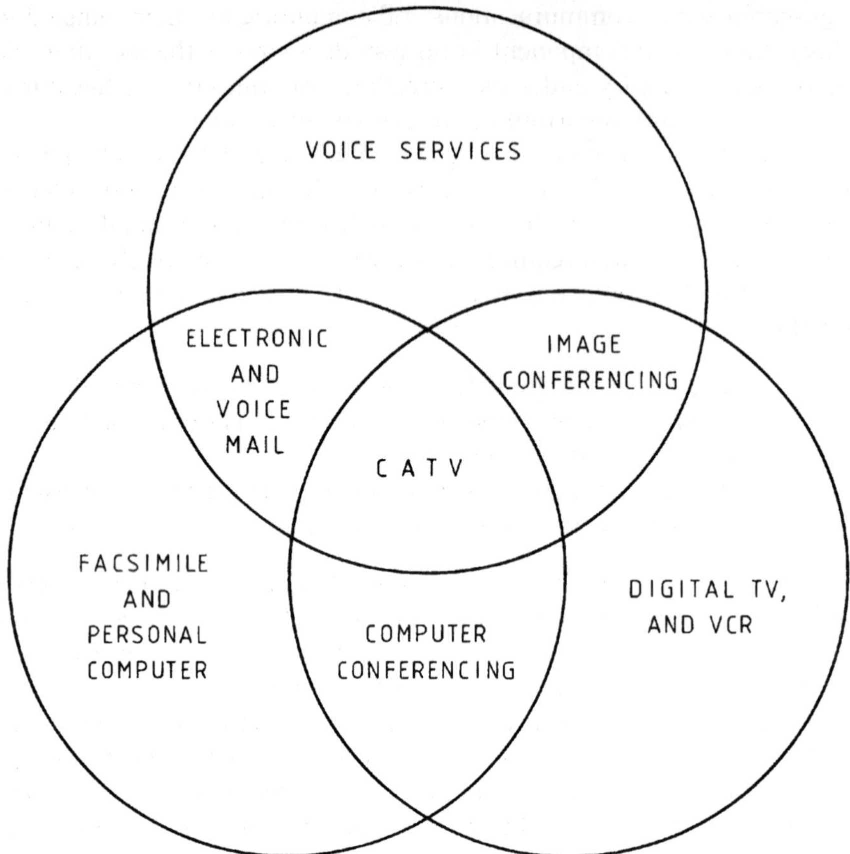

Figure 12.5 Home services supported through communications and computers

- television
- security
- climate
- appliances.

In fact, the infrastructure which makes our house so smart is its wiring. An integrative schema is presented in Figure 12.5 which regroups many services whose walls are now falling.

This unified cable infrastructure enables the user to plug into any outlet, with smart outlets being able to recognize every appliance – supplying it with the proper information and energy level. This does away with the need for special speaker wires, television cables, and telephone jacks – and means children will not get shocked by sticking screwdrivers or utensils into a power line.

This concept started some years ago with the advent of the smart house as a step toward the intelligent building whose investment is justified today in business and industry. It is justified because it is affordable and knowledge-enriched solutions are now providing much richer services at lower costs.

9. Progressing towards Community Intelligence

The implementation of a strategy, 'Communicate, don't commute', necessitates the appropriate infrastructure. But while some teleconferencing systems have been developed, and the word *groupware* has achieved wider use, no truly effective multiparty wide-area conferencing system has yet emerged. The Shuttle of NYNEX is an early species.

The required solution must integrate communication technology and information processing in a way that supports people in widely distributed areas through an increasingly sophisticated range of means. For instance:

- a distributed desk-level conferencing system providing for group collaboration
- an architectural framework for assisting geographically separate group members to work together.

Such groupwork must work in realtime both in a concurrent manner and in different time frames; the way preceding sections have described. It must rest on distributed multimedia databases, high-performance computers, communications and software – with enough embedded intelligence to support groupwork, as outlined in Figure 12.6.

The system shown in Figure 12.6 is geographically distributed, supported by sophisticated information services which rest on both synchronous and asynchronous communications control. Known as Multimedia Environment for Remote Multiple Attendee Interactive Decision-Making (Mermaid) it is a project developed by NEC.

- Mermaid aims to provide widely dispersed group members with an environment supportive of formal or informal multiparty conferences.
- In a way, it may be considered one of the early computers and communications projects targeting community intelligence.

The architecture of Mermaid is a *client-server model* with clients supporting participants by means of knowledge-enriched interfaces and other routines making feasible smooth interaction with the system. Servers supply functions for accomplishing group collaborative work, each server specializing in a given function.

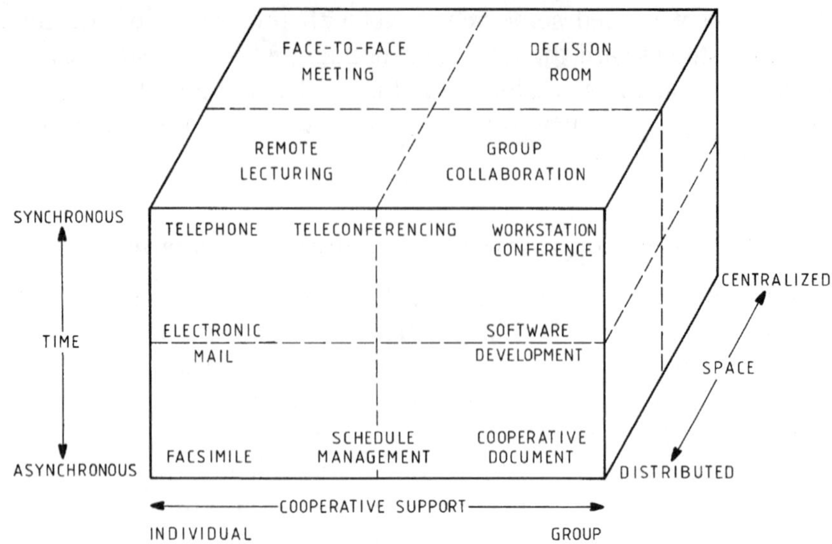

Figure 12.6 The three dimensions of a group collaboration support system

For instance, the Conference Management Server is used to monitor the progress of a conference. It controls convening, opening and closing conferences as well as members joining and leaving, and the conference status as well.

Following a request by a system subscriber, the Conference Information Server provides reference to registered conferences and other events which:

- have been held
- are yet to be held
- are currently held.

An Electronic Bulletin Board contributes the conference's title, date and time, name of chairperson and participants; also, agenda, minutes, advance notices and so on.

The function of the Document File Server is to retrieve and store information in accordance with user requests. It also helps group members to create and process documents, checks the security for retrieving and renewing contents and the like.

The Local Communication Server manages domain issues. A domain is a group of servers and clients to which information is broadcast through a local area network. Each domain contains a local communication server which integrates:

- physical communications media
- software support
- transmission routes.

This function facilitates the work of the other servers acting as a basic communication tool. Knowledge artefacts assist in making the service flexible and adaptable.

The Local Communications Server guarantees the sending and receiving of information to/from the Multidomain Communication Server. It relays information sent from the latter to the clients in its domain, collects information to be sent from any clients within its domain and sends that information where it is due.

The Multidomain Communication Server supports communication among clients by controlling transmission routing and information flow among domains. Software at the client itself provides group members with user-friendly interfaces for comfortable interaction with servers and other clients.

10. Human Windows and Interactive Custom-Made Solutions

Knowledge embedded into the Mermaid modules ensures that the system can be easily customized anywhere within the three-dimensional concept presented in Figure 12.6, in terms of *time*, *space* and co-operative support. This is the type of service few other solutions today make available; therefore it sets the pace for the future.

An important innovation of Mermaid is the five kinds of windows which it supports. First and foremost, as a service facility the *conference window* shows menus for:

- preparing multimedia documents before and after a conference
- convening participants before a conference
- requesting to join a conference
- editing minutes after a conference
- making annotations
- setting different options for choices.

The *shared window* acts as an electronic blackboard. Documents on this blackboard are shared by all the participants. All modifications are shown to all participants almost simultaneously. Such documents can include text graphics, still images, and hand-drawn figures.

The role of the *personal window* is that of an electronic notebook. Such role is similar to that of shared windows, but their document information is not seen by other participants. Personal windows are often used for taking personal conference minutes and for loading and editing personal documents.

Through the *video window* a floor manager* can select the video mode. For instance, displaying a participant or different parties simultaneously by dividing the video window. He or she can also select which person or persons to display.

- The video window is often used for presenting objects.
- Each participant can extend this video window to the full screen.
- He or she does so by clicking a button in the video window with a mouse.

The *status window* shows still pictures of the participants, the manager's name, chair's name, duration of the conference, present time, and so on. The status window also has menus for opening shared and personal windows, requesting the floor, handling the participant's own time of the conference, permitting other participants to leave, and closing a conference.

During a conference, the floor manager can manipulate the shared windows shown on participants' workstation screens, to present documents and other information in realtime. Each participant can manipulate his or her own coloured pointer (allocated from among 256 colours on shared windows) by moving a mouse device.

Conference participants can move the video window to anywhere on the screen and freely change its size. They can extend the video image size in an instant by clicking a mouse. When a participant needs to send a document image during a conference, he or she can input it from an image scanner and deliver it to all other participants.

An imaginative service is that of multiple blackboards and notebooks. A participant can view and handle multiple documents in shared windows and in his or her personal windows at the same time, and cut out a portion of a document and paste it to other documents.

Mermaid provides four modes for floor passing. The floor manager has the right to manipulate shared windows. He or she can perform such operations as opening and closing shared windows, loading compound electronic documents, bringing attention to specific issues, reviewing past minutes and other functions.

Each participant to this computer-based teleconferencing system is served by a client. Each client has the required software for processing the video images of a given participant.

* NEC uses the term *floor-holder*. The floor manager or floor-holder should not be confused with the chairman. The latter chairs the electronic conference; the former holds the electric floor at any specific time and, in some cases, may be the chairman.

- The video signals are transformed into digital signals for transmission purposes,
- Subsequently, they are decoded by the client's equipment before being displayed on a participant's workstation screen.

A participant's video image is delivered through the multidomain communication server. For local communication, a LAN provides the interconnect capability. For communication conducted outside the local domain, the multidomain communication server is used to connect individual LANs together in one global network.

These solutions should not be looked at as self-standing, but as a system. Developments in communications, computers and sophisticated software have a synergy – and the net result is that the total is much greater than the arithmetic sum of the parts. This is what teaches a fast-advancing technology. But are we able to build the social and ethical infrastructure to capitalize on the widening horizon of technological possibilities?

Glossary and Functional Acronyms

access line the circuit that connects a customer to the telephone network.

address class of Internet the A, B and C address classes are Internet address formats suitable for large, medium and small networks.

adjacency a relation between two voxels that are said to be 6-adjacent if they share a face, 18-adjacent if they share a face or an edge, and 26-adjacent if they share a face, an edge, or a vertex.

administrator the person in charge of configuring and maintaining computers and software, for example, database administrator or network administrator.

agent a proactive, generally small but knowledge-enriched computer program that communicates with other programs and end-users via a predefined protocol. An agent is capable of responding to all messages defined by the protocol, and employs the protocol to invoke the services of other agents.

AIN, advanced intelligent network: an architecture developed by Bell Communications Research (Bellcore) for its clients, the US Bell operating companies.

algorithm a step-by-step procedural approach to problem solution (typically mathematical) which leads from variable input data to expected results.

alias an alternate name, created as a convenience in addressing a local network host or user whose unique primary name is long or complicated.

analogue model models reasoning by analogy and emulating the behaviour of a larger system. They can be processed through digital computers, or analogue computers can be used for simulation.

ANSI American National Standards Institute.

AP Application protocol.

API, applications programming interface the common rules that enable an operating system and applications software to communicate. It provides application developers with a common programming environment that can run interchangeably on different vendor's computers. APIs, however, come in different types and forms.

application system an operating system-independent software environment that supports applications and the way they interact with users, other software and other systems.

application-to-application APIs most notable are remote procedure call mechanisms and messaging interfaces. They enable execution on remote machines while hiding the networking details from the programmer.

architecture a grand design which provides for the study, arrangement and interconnection of components within a computers, communications and software environment.

archive a copy of a file put on a storage medium separate from any complete or incremental backup the file may already be on.

ARPA, Advanced Research Project Agency part of the US Department of Defense. Among many other projects sponsored the network architecture research project upon which X.25 and Internet are based.

artefact man-made construct developed for the purpose of emulating operations or behaviour of a certain processor function. With computers this is a piece of software.

ASDL asynchronous digital subscriber loop.

ASIC application-specific integrated circuit.

ATM, asynchronous transfer mode CCITT standard for cell relay, where multimedia information (voice, video, text, graphics, data) is conveyed in fixed-size cells consisting of a 5-byte header and of a 48-byte user information.

atom the smallest unit of a given quantity, such as object size and metrics increments.

ATR advanced telecommunications research.

ATS ATM transmission systems.

AU adaptation unit.

audit record a portion of the audit trail containing a single database look, message block or queue item state change.

audit trail a continuous and chronological log of recoverable events such as step control queue items, database changes, and transaction messages.

bandwidth the range of frequencies characterizing transmission performance and its limits. It is measured as bit rate in a signal line. The greater the bandwidth, the greater the capacity. The term also stands for semantic and information content.

bandwidth compression a technique to reduce the requirements for transmission capacity within the frequency spectrum occupied by signals.

batch in the early days of computing the jobs to be processed were batched up together as the input applicable to a certain job was received. This emulated the way accounting machines worked. Though an awkward and inefficient way, the batch mode is still widely used. The alternative is on-line transaction processing (OLTP).

behaviour mapping matching participant actions to effects in a virtual multimedia environment.

BER, bit error rate the measure of line quality. A BER of 10^{-2} is very low quality; a BER of 10^{-12} is high quality.

binary translation a software technique to change an executable program written for one architecture or operating system into an equivalent program for a different environment.

B-ISDN Broadband ISDN.

bit rate number of bits transmitted per second.

black-box testing testing performed at a device or system level focused on verification and/or a better knowledge of how the system works, by means of input and output protocols.

bridge a means of connecting two similar networks at relatively low protocol levels, such as two LANs at the logical link; for example at the 802.2 level.

broadband a term describing high-bandwidth connections. Generally, it identifies those that can carry voice, data and video channels simultaneously.

broadcasting emission of messages addressed to all suitable receivers.

buffer a staging area for input/output, where arbitrary length transactions are collected into convenient units for computer operations.

byte granularity the appearance that two processors can update adjacent bytes in memory without interfering with one another.

CAD, computer-aided design since the mid-1970s computers have been extensively used for engineering design purposes on-line, interactively, supported through 3-D colour graphics.

call waiting a feature that enables a telephone to time-multiplex calls. If a new call comes in while the user is on another call, the user is alerted with a special tone on the channel.

calling-number delivery a feature that displays the caller's number at the receiver's telephone while the call is ringing.

CAP, competitive access provider an alternative to the local telephone company.

carrier, or **common carrier** A company offering telecommunications to the public on a non-discriminatory basis.

CASE, computer-aided software engineering software development of other software by computers, interactively on-line. There are, however, many different incompatible CASE products.

CATV cable television.

CD-I, compact disc – interactive.

CD-ROM, compact disc – read only memory.

cellular telecommunications technique for radio broadcasting of telephony.

CEO chief executive officer.

certification testing testing to determine the consistency, functional completeness and correctness of a given product, whether hardware or software.

CIM, computer integrated manufacturing computer software instrumental in integrating manufacturing operations.

CISC, complex instruction set computer this is characterized by variable-length instructions, a wide variety of memory addressing modes and instructions that combine one or more memory accesses with arithmetic.

CLASS, custom local area signalling services a set of telephone services for residential and small-business subscribers, including call forwarding, call waiting and three-party conferencing.

client a workstation or any other device requesting services from another processing unit which acts as a server. The client side involves everything relating to the user, from the format of the data as it appears on the screen to the formatting of query and response.

client/server computing a computing solution accomplished through a logical relationship between requesting clients and responding servers – effected through relatively simple sharing of applications, information elements and other services.

CMF, corporate memory facility a term used to denote the use of computers in storing executive decisions, permitting to retrieve both the documentation on a decision which was made and the reasons which led to it.

coaxial cables copper wire typically used to interconnect workstations and servers in a local area network.

common white board or **white board** a window or virtual pad onto which all participants can draw, type and paste pictures.

compilers program statements have to be converted from source language to object code or machine language. This is done by compilers.

concurrency the extent to which multiple users can access the same resources at the same time, without conflict. Concurrent is the occurrence of two or more events within the same time period.

COSINE Cooperation for Open Systems Interconnection Networking in Europe (EUREKA-8).

CPN customer premises network.

CPU, central processing unit the portion of the computer that contains the circuits controlling the interpretation and execution of instructions.

crash a condition whereby the system takes itself out of service because it cannot handle a hardware or software error condition or for other reasons, for instance, the system cannot allocate resources, manage processes or respond to requests for system functions.

cross-modal relationships between different senses such as sight and sound.

CUI, character user interface an old protocol developed for non-intelligent terminals which is based on character presentation in the way that a typewriter works. The modern approach is GUI - graphics user interface.

daemon, or **demon** a supervisory process usually operating in the background, and often perpetual. It performs a local or system-wide function.

DAN desk area network.

data integrity data accuracy and consistency.

data link the communications protocol for the physical media link used to transport data.

database a systematic approach to creating, maintaining and retrieving information typically stored on magnetic and optical supports.

database mining the exploitation of the contents of a database to extract significant information in assessing a given job. For instance for marketing purposes.

database recovery the process of restoring database records to a consistent state, while maintaining data integrity by either reapplying database updates or discarding them.

database server an open system assuring database storage facilities and supplying database processing services to other systems.

datagram a message sent in a packet-switched communications network. The datagram model implies that no connection, such as a virtual circuit, is needed, and the datagram is not required to be delivered in sequence.

DBMS, database management system a generic name for programming products aiming to assist a user organization in managing its database. There are hierarchical, networking, relational and object-oriented DBMS, residing in database servers, managing persistence and integrity of the database, and providing access services.

DDN, defense data network a set of communications capabilities that links together computer systems within the Department of Defense (DOD).

deductive databases typically, a distributed database employing artificial intelligence artefacts for improved management and for better exploitation reasons.

default route entry in the system routing tables that is used when there is no other route to a destination.

deferred update a database update held in main storage or in a retention file until the program reaches a commit point. The uncommitted updates are discarded if rollback occurs.

destination the nearby or remote unit that ultimately receives a file transferred over a network.

device a physical input/output or other unit. A file other than a directory.

dialling sequence the procedure used by a modem on one system to reach another modem on another system. Digits besides the telephone number may be used in a dialling sequence.

direct link a cable that runs directly from a port on one system or device to a port on another system or device.

directory a file that comprises a catalogue of names. It consists of entries that specify further files and consitute a node of the directory tree.

DIS, Draft International Standard specified by ISO, this is a development step representing near final status on a specification. Once a specification has reached DIS status, companies are encouraged to develop actual products based on it.

DIS, distributed information system.

distributed a condition where many parts of a single entity are separated geographically but still operate as a system.

distributed applications application(s) coded modularly so that different routines reside and execute on different systems.

distributed computing an architecture favoured by leading-edge user organizations. It involves a consistent move away from centralized solutions, featuring distributed databases and networked workstations – in short, the client-server model.

distributed databases databases that can be accessed by remote applications or remote users. Such databases may provide various degrees of transparency and accessibility. They are shared across several systems but accessible as if they were whole.

distributed dialogue splitting an application in a way that the dialogue through user interfaces is executed on one system, while other portions are executed on another.

distributed functions splitting an application so that part of its logical functions are executed on one system, while others are executed on another.

distributed processing the process of enabling different applications and data located at remote sites or processors, connected via a communications links, to operate as if they were local.

DMD digital mirror devices.

domain a logical grouping of hosts in a network environment. Hosts in a domain rely on same name servers for certain resource-sharing and security services.

DS, digital service for example, DS-0 means digital service level 0, at 64 KBPS.

DSP, digital signal processors single-minded racehorse chips, which can manipulate realworld sights and sounds far faster than general-purpose microprocessors. They are standard in cellular telephones, hard disk drives and PC sound cards.

DSS, decision support system a generic name for software specifically designed and implemented to help managers and professionals in decision-making.

dumb terminal a terminal, attached to a mainframe or minicomputer which uses the host processor to handle information, possessing no processing capability on its own.

duplexed file a file consisting of two mass storage file copies of the same data.

EDI electronic data interchange.

EDPers computer specialists of the old school mainly trained to work through Cobol on mainframes in batch mode; not always open to new technology and its advantages.

800 service 800 is an area code in the North American dialling plan, which does not correspond to any specific geographical area. Calls to 800 numbers are billed to the receiver.

EIN, European informatics network predecessor of Euronet.

EIS, executive information system a process specifically designed to fit executive requirements on-line through workstations. An alternative but elder name is management information system (MIS).

email electronic mail

email APIs they provide client applications programs with a simple, standardized set of commands to access email servers. They allow spreadsheets, word processors and internal applications routines to send and receive messages transparently.

end-user the user of a computer system who is other than a computer specialist and requires on-line access to databases and other computer resources through his or her networked workstation.

evolutionary plan a scenario selected for realization.

expert systems knowledge-enriched software, the first practical implementation of artificial intelligence. They are designed and implemented for decision support purposes.

facilitator a program that co-ordinates the communication among agents. It provides a reliable network communication layer, routes messages among agents on the basis of message contents and co-ordinates the control of activities involving many agents.

facility deadlock a situation in which two or more run units are queued, each holding a facility required by another queued run unit. Also known as deadly embrace.

FAP, formats and protocols a set of rules that specifies the format, timing, sequence and/or error checking for communication between clients and servers.

FDDI, fibre distributed data interface an ANSI standard specifying a 100-MBPS token-passing network using fibre-optic cable.

FDVDI fibre distributed video/voice and data interface.

federated databases a database architecture which permits the integration of diverse and heterogeneous databases, each one keeping its locality but working together in the execution of global queries or transactions.

FEP, frontend processor a 25-year-old solution advanced, as realtime applications started becoming popular, in order to unload mainframes from communications chores.

fibre optics a transmission medium utilizing a bundle of glass or plastic filaments, operating at gigabits per second and replacing copper cable.

file descriptor a conventional integer quantity that designates an open file within a process.

file name the term stands both for a path name and the last component name in a path name.

file transfer a degree of distributed file access. A process in which users on one system exchange databases with another, usually via communications facilities.

fork the splitting of one process into two – parent process and child, with separate but initially identical data and stack segments.

formatting a process of imposing an addressing scheme on a disk, including the mapping of a disk into tracks and sectors.

frame a reference configuration or subset thereof.

frame relay a modern protocol used across the interface between user devices and network equipment.

framework a set of prefabricated software routines that programmers can use, extend or customize for specific computing solutions. Frameworks are usually built from a collection of objects, so both the design and code of a framework can be reused.

function a set of processes to achieve a specific objective.

functional group a set of functions that may be performed by a single equipment.

functional reference model a set of functions structured into a logical hierarchy and their logical interfaces.

fuzzy engineering a sophisticated relatively new branch of artificial intelligence which in lieu of treating events in a crisp: yes/no, 0/1 fashion, admits intermediate values – that is, tonalties of grey. This enables the handling of vagueness and uncertainty often present in managerial decisions.

gateways a term identifying communications servers which enable two otherwise incompatible networks to interconnect. Gateways perform the functions required for the interconnection of networks beyond the level of bridges.

GBPS gigabit per second.

GIPS giga (billions of) instructions per second.

GIS Geographic Information System.

global schema, or **global view** an approach permitting a global look at the distributed databases. Also, an attempt at making homogeneous so far heterogeneous structures.

GreenSpace or **virtual commons** or **virtual green** a virtual meeting place for collaborative work and information sharing.

GUI – graphic user interface end-user oriented software routines aiming at supporting graphics facilities as contrasted to the more classical character user interface (CUI).

haptic feedback a feedback giving the impression of force and weight.

HDLC high-level data link control.

HDTV high-definition television.

head tracking constant monitoring of head position using a computerized tracking device.

helpdesk a desk put in place by computer user organizations to support end-users when they have queries in terms of their workstations or are confronted with unfamiliar problems.

heterogeneity incompatible vendor hardware and software devices or systems with multiple OS, DBMS, etc. communicating across a variety of protocols.

heterogeneous databases typically incompatible databases because of differences in some of their basic characteristics such as data structures, file structures and DBMS.

heuristics heuristics is in a way the opposite of algorithms. The process features no step-by-step approach, working through trial and error to reach a solution.

hierarchical data model this is the eldest database management structure as reflected in IBM's IMS.

high-performance computing it encompasses advanced computing, communications and software technologies, including multiprocessor

WS, supercomputers, high-speed networks, parallel solutions and systems software integrated and linked over a high-speed network.

HPCC High Performance Computing and Communications Project.

HPPI, high-performance parallel interface a standard defined in ANSI standard X3T9.3/88-023, generally used in supercomputer to workstation linkages.

hub a concentration point of a number of nodes.

hyperlinks associations between objects in a presentation such as images and sounds which can allow the user to navigate interactively in a database, in a threaded way.

ICE information, communication and entertainment.

icons familiar objects, typically a shorthand of graphical representation.

IEEE double-extended format a loosely specified floating-point format with at least 64 significant bits of precision and at least 15 bits of exponent width.

IEEE floating point a form of computer arithmetic specified by IEEE standard 754. Includes rules for denormalized numbers and infinities specifying different modes for rounding results.

image processing computer translation or digitization of image or picture into bits to be stored in the database.

IN intelligent network.

information superhighway optical-fibre based high-bandwidth network infrastructure.

inheritance object-oriented concept by which a class possesses all the methods and variables of the classes above which are on the same branch of the inheritance tree.

inheritance trees tree structure applied to inheritance. It builds from the initial base class and grows branches as new classes are derived.

integration testing testing to ensure that the entities integrate and communicate correctly. It is not directly concerned about the accuracy of the processing results, but with consistency of interface and ability of components to correctly send and receive messages.

integrity constraints specification of properties that must be held by the object to achieve resource consistency.

Intelsat International Telecommunications Satellite Organization.

interactive the ability to carry two-way transmissions and, by extension, presentation. Telephones are interactive; cable TV is not yet.

interactive TV or **video-on-demand** television whose programming can be chosen by the user.

interarrival time time delay from transmitting to receiving site due to finite speed of light and throughput delays in switching.

interface software and hardware means of interconnection of equipment, having defined characteristics. Also, the common boundary of two associated systems.

interface standards different standards organizations, for instance ISO and ANSI, have developed norms for interfaces, such as the interface between applications programs and databases.

internetwork an aggregate made up of two or more networks that communicate through gateways.

interoperability ability of two or more systems to exchange data and to mutually use information that has been exchanged. Also, functional interaction between processing entities on two dissimilar networks. Degree of interoperability is defined by the functions available across the network.

interpreters software routines working on-line and converting directly from one code to another. Therefore, they require significantly more computer power than compilers.

interrupt a break. Also, a signal generated by a hardware condition or a peripheral device that normally terminates a process.

inverted files a DBMS approach used by Adabas and IBM's Stairs to facilitate database searching. It practically doubles the memory requirements.

I/O input/output.

IP, Internet protocol it provides connectionless datagram service at the network layer of the OSI Reference Model.

IPN Intelligent Packet Network.

IPX protocol used by the Novel local area network comparable to but not compatible with TCP/IP.

ISDN integrated services digital network.

ISO, International Standards Organization the organization which co-ordinates all international standards activities, including Open Systems Interconnection (OSI) for multivendor networking.

ISO/X.500 ISO's international standard for global directory services, compliant with the Utility Communications Architecture (UCA).

ITSEC, information technology security evaluation criteria they have been established by the governments of the UK, France, Germany and the Netherlands.

KBPS kilobits per second.

kernel commands basic native commands of an operating system, DBMS or transaction processing monitor. They constitute the shell of the larger system.

LAN, local area network LANs interconnect computers (workstations, file servers, gateways) via telecommunications devices in a single building, complex of buildings, or campus, to form a network of small geographic scope.

LAN management activities required to run day-to-day operations of a LAN, including user enrolment and deletion, user authorization, problem determination and identification, workload management and so on.

LAN operating system software supporting a set of functions designed to manage interoperation of a LAN. Also known as network operating system.

LAPD link access procedure-D.

latency end-to-end time delay required to provide a response to a client's request for a service; the sum of processing time required by the client application, communication code and propagation delays. Also, the mismatch between participant actions and the acknowledging feedback of the action.

leased line or **private line** a dedicated link between the user's location(s) billed at a flat monthly rate. Recommended for heavy traffic routes, it can be provided in a wide range of capacities.

LEC, local exchange carrier the local telephone company which provides the circuits between the user's office and the outside world.

life cycle the period of time from initial product introduction until the time it is retired from service and maintenance is terminated. Also used in reference to the life-cycle costs of a product.

linear processing a memory addressing technique in which all addresses form a single range, from 0 to the largest possible address.

linguistic supports the endowment in languages which comes with an operating system and in cases with the DBMS.

local file a file that can be accessed only by the host for which it is designed.

log file a file that contains records of transactions that occur on the system. Software that spools, generates various log files.

logical LAN one or more physical LANs bridged together, representing a single name space to any client.

long-haul the communications link between metropolitan areas, often involving cross-border and transoceanic connections.

long-recovery a recovery procedure used to restore inconsistent database updates.

MAC, media access control same acronym is used for multiplexed analogue component video for satellite and cable TV transmission.

MAN metropolitan area network.

mapping representation of a real-life situation through simulation. Also, a means of defining how resource requests from users and groups are handled.

mbone, multicast backbone experimental video/audio over the Internet.

MBPS megabits per second.

MBR, memory-based reasoning a database mining approach which uses sophisticated algorithms and heuristics to locate and extract on-line the information needed by the end-user.

MBS Media Broadband Service.

mega 10^6 or millions of ... For instance, megaflops, megastreams.

menu a list of choices from which we make a selection. Choices can be windows to see next, actions to perform, data or other items.

metacomputing concept of distributed computer nodes all of which act together transparently as if they were a single parallel computer.

MIPS, millions of instructions per second a metric often used to measure computer power.

MO, multiplexing opportunity hardware or software resource of a telephone. One MO is needed for each concurrently active call.

modem device that modulates and demodulates data transmitted over communications lines. Originally used to convert the digital signals of a device to analogue pulses and vice versa.

modular constructed with standardized equipment, unit by unit, so that various parts of the system can be replaced or interchanged with ease.

modularity the fact of making modular a computer and communications system, composed of small subsystems which can be combined like a mechano.

module a building block of the modular approach. Also, an implementation, usually in software, of a protocol or other procedure.

MTBF, mean time between failures a statistic reflecting the mean time of system availability. The counterpart of MTOSI.

MTOSI, mean time of system interrupt systems fail and they have to be brought up again. MTOSI is a statistic calculated over a period of time in connection to the interrupts which have taken place.

MTTR, mean time to repair the mean time taken by the repair action which has been necessary.

multimedia the handling of media such as compound electronic documents, text, data, graphics, moving image and voice. Also experiences supporting the display of many types of information, like images, animations, sounds and so on.

multimedia network a system that can carry several forms of communications characterized by multimedia.

multiple instruction issue a high-performance computer implementation technique of starting more than one instruction at once.

multiuser state of the operating system in which multiple users are supported.

multiway calling feature enabling a telephone to join separate, time-multiplexed calls without special hardware. While talking, the user flashes to put the current call on hold and initiate another call.

naming convention a naming convention is relevant for attribute equivalence. Also for specification of the name of an object.

narrowcasting forwarding messages to a defined set of users. Also called distribution.

network hardware and software that constitute interconnections between computer units or systems, permitting communication between them. Also computer communications technologies that link multiple machines to share information and resources across geographically dispersed locations.

network management software routines and procedural steps necessary to operate, maintain and generally look after a network and its performance.

network management APIs APIs giving programmers a standard method of using the services of underlying protocols or management agents, which in turn perform the work of running networks and their components.

networking services sending data from one system to another over a communications medium. Common networking services include file transfer, remote login, remote execution and so on.

neural networks an artificial intelligence artefact which emulates the way in which the neurons of the human nervous system work.

NII National Information Infrastructure.

900 service in calls to a 900 number, the user is billed not only for the call itself, but also for access to the information provided during the connection. Like 800, 900 is an area code in the North American dialling plan, but it does not correspond to any specific geographical area.

911 service calls to 911 provide a toll-free, always available, and an easy-to-remember number to call during emergencies.

nodes nodes are the network's switching centres. A network is composed of links which feature transmission links and nodes.

number portability a process which lets a customer retain the same number when changing carriers.

OA office automation.

object code program instructions that have been translated into machine language to be executed by computer.

object-oriented objects are typically distributed throughout the database environment. Active objects consist of data and commands. Passive objects are data only.

object-oriented software modules software modules which use object orientation either through the appropriate language, object data structures, or both.

ontology specification of a domain of discourse among agents, in the form of definitions of shared vocabulary: classes, relations, functions and object constants.

open file a file that has been opened. A file descriptor. The destination for input, output or both obtained by opening a file or creating a pipe. Open files are shared across forks and persist across executes.

open system one which abides by international standards and norms. Application designed for open systems can run on equipments by different manufacturers.

operational integration integration of several computers and communications media to operate as an aggregate.

operational services computing and communications services provided on behalf of, and across, one or more workgroups. They include problem determination, backup, performance and workload management, configuration, security, output operations and so on.

OPS, operations per second term used as rating of the speed of computers and components, generally taken to mean the usual integer or floating point operations depending on what functional units are included in a particular configuration.

optical fibre see fibre optics.

optimization a process of experimentation and evaluation which enables gaining the best result in terms of a certain variable as, for instance, greater functionality or lower cost.

OS, operating system the program for managing the resources of the computer, including supervisory routines, process scheduling, input/output monitors and the like. Also basic system calls that give applications programmers access to services provided by an operating system.

OSI, Open Systems Interconnection a model developed by the International Standards Organization (ISO). It organizes the network protocols and interfaces as a set of 7 layers, going from the application layer to the physical layer. Each implements a specific set of functions and layers are separated by well-defined interfaces.

out-of-band data transferred in a separate parallel communications channel with a position tracking computer maintaining the connection.

outsourcing third party assumes responsibility of all or part of a company's data processing functions.

owner the user ID of a given process. With a process that creates a file, the owner has distinct permissions.

packet a package of data with a header and, often, a trailer. A packet may or may not be logically complete.

packet-based network communication is based on variable-size blocks of data or packets. Networks typically place a limit on packet size. This is the maximum transfer unit (MTU), which tends to grow with network speed.

parallel processing simultaneous processing by more than one processing unit by a single machine or network, on a single application.

parity a method of checking and correcting communications errors.

password a unique set of characters used to identify a user and give access to a secure system.

PBX, private branch exchange private telephone switching system. A line (or lines) is (are) used as trunk(s) between end-users behind the PBX and the central office that serves them. Today software-based approaches dominate internal switching capabilities.

PCS, personal communication service a digital wireless service that could be inexpensive enough for full-time local calling.

PDA personal digital assistant.

Peta 10^{15} or thousands of trillions of ... For instance petabytes.

physical LAN the hardware of a LAN, comprised of adaptor cards, wires, and other devices – such as computers, printers and so on.

P&L profit and loss.

PMR private mobile radio.

portability the ability to port the same programs from one computer platform to another, typically supported through open systems solutions.

position/orientation tracking constant monitoring of position, usually x, y, z, taw, pitch, roll or quaternians. A computerized tracking device is usually employed.

POTS plain old telephone service.

primitive functions the basic functions of an operating system or other piece of basic software, on which the functioning of this particular programming product rests.

privacy means of ensuring confidentiality of information; protection of end-user's right to privacy of information.

process ID an integer that identifies a process.

program visualization the ability to visualize the modules of a program down to single statements as well as the information elements which they address.

protocol a set of rules and conventions used in the conversation between peer layers on the sending and receiving host. For example, a data link protocol. Also, a statement of procedures used to establish, operate or discontinue communication among two or more functions in functional groups. A set of rules that enable a network entity to understand a communication connection.

prototype a model which functions like the real system it emulates, but is not necessarily optimized. Prototyping is of great help in gaining designer and programmer productivity.

PSN, public switched network acronym also used for people with special needs.

PVN private virtual networks.

QOS, quality of service a measure of performance for a transmission system that reflects availability of service and transmission quality.

queue a line or list formed by items waiting for service in a system.

raster graphics a subfield of computer graphics that represents the scene by a 2-D array, or raster, of pixels stored in a 2-D frame buffer.

ray casting a volume-viewing algorithm in which sight rays are cast from the viewing plane through the volume.

ray tracing, also known as **3-D raster ray tracing**, **discrete ray tracing** or **volumetric ray tracing** a volume-viewing approach in which light behaviour is simulated by recursively tracing individual imaginary rays of light as discrete lines through the scene.

RDA, remote database access a standard for networking providing a way to pass information between clients and servers in a database environment.

reality immersion a home entertainment version of virtual environment, involving realtime simulation.

realspace a sophisticated realtime application in which events happening in widely distributed nodes of a network are cast *as if* in the same spot, usually through high-speed parallel processing. For instance, collapsing all major financial centres into one multidimensional point in time.

realtime the on-line execution of transaction and queries with a very short response time, ideally at subsecond level.

recovery to reconstruct or roll back a database or other files to a consistent state, usually the one prevailing prior to machine downtime.

reference configurations functional groupings and reference points showing possible network implementation(s).

reference point conceptual points at the conjunction of two non-overlapping functional groups.

referential integrity a distributed database must be consistent at all times. Referential integrity rules see to it that if a complex transaction is not executed in its entirety the subtransactions would be rolled back and the information elements in the database would be consistent.

relational data models typically, the relational model is one of flat files and as such it contrasts to the hierarchical model which is expressed in a tree structure.

remote system another system linked to our own over a communications line, directly or through a network.

repeater communication device that amplifies network traffic at the physical layer, for further transmission of amplified signal.

replication a method of keeping copies of an information element at multiple locations synchronized. When a copy is updated, refreshers are automatically sent to other locations. A local, read-write copy is given to users, so read response time is not subject to communication delay.

reseller a company that buys transmission services at bulk rates for resale to the public, for a profit.

restore the act of returning the system to a previous state by copying the contents of a backup media. We can restore an entire aggregate or certain files.

retransmission a duplicate request made by a client for a remote service in the event that no reply for the original request was received from the server. This typically takes place after an NAK (no acknowledgement).

RF radio frequency.

RISC, reduced instruction set computer characterized by fixed-length instructions, simple memory addressing modes and a strict decoupling of load/store memory access instructions from register-to-register arithmetic operations.

rollback a recovery action in which the system reverses (rolls back) the effects of all uncommitted updates. The database returns to the state that existed at the beginning of the recoverable step. Also, the process that removes uncommitted database changes made by one application or user.

router a program that interprets requests for services and directs them to the applicable server. Also, a communication device that redirects network traffic based on network layer address information like the IP portion of TCP/IP.

RPC, remote procedure call a programming technique allowing applications to invoke remote and local procedures in similar manner. It permits software developers to create distributed applications without concern for the physical location of called procedures.

runtime the time operations are being executed by a computer whether in realtime or in batch.

SAA, system applications architecture a business architecture advanced by IBM and based on mainframes under the MVS operating system.

scenario a timed sequence of events showing the stepwise transition in a given implementation, or a change into another possible implementation.

scheduling algorithm an algorithm which has been developed and employed for the reason of scheduling computer resources whether software, hardware or both.

schema a view of the database. An external schema is the view by the user, and internal schema that by the DBMS.

SCP, service control point a computer database that holds information on network services and subscribers, and is separated from the switch making it easier to introduce new services on the network.

SDM space division multiplexing.

seamless database access database access which for any practical purpose is transparent to the end-user in the sense that it is not required to know the details of database functioning or where are stored the information elements.

segment a contiguous range of the address space of a process with consistent store access capabilities.

segmented addressing memory addressing technique in which addresses are broken into two or more parts, hence segments. Elaborate software techniques are needed to extend addressing beyond a single segment.

semaphore a method that allows two or more processes to be synchronized.

server the functions of a database system relating to data management and data maintenance. Also, a program that responds to client request from another system.

shells the kernel or primitive commands of an operating system, DBMS or other piece of basic software.

side effect rules that must be triggered when a query or update operation is issued against an object.

simulator construct which prototypes or emulates a larger system for reasons of experimentation, analysis or optimization.

SMDS, switched multimegabit data service high-speed, packet-switching, datagram-based WAN networking technology offered by the telephone companies.

SMR, specialized mobile radio a two-way, radio-dispatch service being upgraded to provide cellular-like phone services.

SNA, System Network Architecture IBM's group of communications and control routines designed in the early 1970s to be used with mainframes at the vertex of the system.

SONet, synchronous optical network high-speed, up to 2.5 GBPS, synchronous network implemented in the USA and approved as international standard in 1988.

source language the higher-level language in which a computer program has been written.

speed-calling code a special button or short digit sequence that users can associate with dialling numbers of their choice.

spooling collecting and serializing output from multiple processes competing for a single output service.

SQL, structured query language a relational query language that provides an English keyword-oriented set of facilities for query, data definition, data manipulation and data control. It is a programmed interface to a relational database management system.

SS7, signalling system 7 a CCITT standard signalling system that enables calls with a network component to be set up efficiently.

STM synchronous transfer mode.

subarea nodes a network covers a large area and typically is composed of subnetworks, each one having its subarea nodes.

supercomputer a class of general-purpose computers that are faster than their commercial competitors by one or more orders of magnitude.

supercomputing a quantitative and qualitative measure of computer power used in processing activities. Supercomputing can be achieved through networked workstations, not only by supercomputers.

surface rendering indirect approach for visualizing volume primitives by first converting them into an intermediate surface representation and then rendering them to the screen using computer graphics.

swap to move the core of an executing program between main and secondary storage to make room for other processes.

swap area the part of secondary storage to which core images are swapped. The swap area is disjointed from the file system.

switching system consisting of hardware and software, a switching system's primary purpose is to form dynamic connections among transmission channels.

symbol table information in an object file about the names of data and functions in a file. Symbol table and address relocation information are used by the link editor to compile object files.

syntax the format of a command file.

system calls set of system primitive functions through which all computer operations are allocated, initiated, monitored, manipulated and terminated. They are invoked by user processes for system-dependent functions, such as process creation, I/O, and so on.

table an array of data organized in arguments and functions. Each function may be uniquely identified by means of one or more arguments.

tactile feedback information, such as pressure or vibration, displayed by tactors on the skin telephony.

TAN total area network.

TCP, transmission control protocol a transport layer protocol that provides connection-oriented message passing across the network. It is reliable in the sense that packet delivery is guaranteed and that packets arrive at the destination in proper order. TCP operates at the transport layer of the OSI reference model.

TCP/IP, transmission control protocol/Internet protocol a set of protocols for the third and fourth layers of the seven-layer OSI network model which are, respectively, the network and transport layers. It has achieved *de facto* standard status.

TCSEC, trusted computer systems evaluation criteria a set of rules identifying security requirements, and including functionality characteristics.

TDI, trusted DBMS interpretation it interprets TCSEC for different database management systems (DBMS).

TDM time division multiplexing.

TDMA time division multiple access.

telco telephone company.

Telnet the virtual terminal protocol used in Internet.

Tera 10^{12} or trillions of ... For instance teraops.

terminal the endpoint of communications. Also, an abstraction of the lowest common denominator of features within the endpoint components.

threads technique allowing concurrent processing of multiple sequential execution paths, enabing applications to more efficiently exploit the computing power available in a distributed computing system.

3-D three dimensional.

3-D discrete topology the formal topological characterizations of the digital voxel space that conform as closely as possible to the corresponding characterizations used in the topology of the continuous 3-D space.

topology the network configuration. For instance, a tree topology has a hierarchy of many networked hubs.

touch-tone telephone a telephone that transmits dialled digits on the audio channels by varying tones.

transaction a set of one or more units of work operating in unison and altering the contents of information elements in the database.

transparency absence of the need to know whether data is local or remote, or whether a table is unified or distributed. The mechanism is hidden from the user or application programmer.

transport and session level APIs these provide access to transport service protocols such as TCP/IP, OSI TP4 and SNA LU6.2. Transport APIs closely reflect the detailed semantics of underlying transport providers.

trap a technique of detecting and interpreting certain hardware and software conditions through software. A trap is set to catch a signal, or interrupt, and assists in the execution of the next action.

TSIG trusted systems interoperability group.

tune modify the tunable parameters to improve system performance. Also, reconfigure the operating system to incorporate modifications into an executable version.

tunnel a 3-D path of connectivity that penetrates a discrete surface. Surface thickness is defined by the absence of particular tunnels in the surface.

2-D two dimensional.

ULSI ultra large-scale integration.

UMTS Universal mobile telecommunications.

UNI user/network interface.

unit of work set of one or more related requests which must all complete successfully or none of them completes and the operation aborts.

unit testing the smallest, or atomic unit being tested. This is normally completed by the unit developer and would be done prior to integration with the rest of the product.

unlisted number an unlisted dial number is not published in a telephone book and not given out by information operators.

UPT universal personal telecommunications.

URM usage reference model.

user equivalence a user on a remote system who is given the privileges of a user on the local system.

user ID, or **userid** an integer value, usually associated with a login name. The user ID of a process becomes the owner of files created by the process and descendent, forked processes.

utility, also **utility program** a standard permanently available program, generally useful to system functions.

validation determination that final product is correct in terms of specifications, functionality and accuracy of results. This occurs at the end of each phase of the development cycle. Also, validation specifies rules that must hold when a query or update operation against an object is validated or rejected.

vanity number a dialling number with an alphabetic equivalent that is a mnemonic phrase.

VAN value-added network.

VAS value-added services.

VBR variable bit rate.

vector graphics a field of computer graphics that represents the scene by a set of lines (vectors). These are repeatedly redrawn to the screen by a vector generator.

VEOS virtual environment operating system.

version a separate programming product based on an existing one, but containing significant new code or new functions.

video moving images.

video-conferencing on-line interaction using live voice and visual displays.

video dial tone an automatic connection to a network transmitting video. *Also* telephony from a cable television set-top box.

virtual connection preallocated bandwidth in a communications link, which may be transient or long term.

virtual environment computer-simulated realtime environment, with emphasis on human interface.

virtual network a network using the public switching network (PSN) for all its needs, or for a portion of it for service. It is structured so that the user enjoys circuit availability without the fixed cost of a private line.

virtualization the conversion to a virtual reality environment.

visibilization making visible very small and very large items which otherwise may escape the attention of the naked eye.

visistraction the ability to make visible abstract concepts and thought processes which are not quantifiable.

visual programming a programming approach which enables the user to paint on the monitor. The graph being drawn is translated by a compiler, for instance in IF ... THEN ... ELSE statements which are then translated by another compiler into object code such as C or C++. This makes feasible computer programming by end-users without any computer experience.

visualization turning tables and numbers into a visual representation. A method of extracting meaningful information from complex data sets through use of interactive graphics and imaging.

VLSI very large-scale integration.

VOD, video-on-demand see interactive TV.

voice mail a service that stores voice messages for users and enables them to retrieve and hear their messages in various ways.

voice recognition extracting semantic content from spoken word using computer processing.

volume graphics a field of computer graphics employing a volume buffer for scene representation. This process is concerned with synthesizing, manipulating, and rendering scenes, and is the 3-D counterpart of raster graphics.

volume modelling the analysis, synthesis and manipulation of sampled, computed and synthetic objects contained within a volumetric data set.

volume rendering a direct technique for visualizing volume primitives without any intermediate conversion of the volumetric data set to surface representation.

volume visualization a visualization method concerned with the representation, manipulation, and rendering of volumetric data.

volumetric data set the aggregate of voxels constituting the volume.

VOXBIT, voxel block transfer set of operations by which a rectangular subvolume of voxels, known as a room, can be copied within the volume buffer with arbitrary write modes and maskings. Voxbit is the 3-D counterpart of 2-D bit block transfer.

voxel abbreviation for volume element or volume cell. The 3-D conceptual counterpart of the 2-D pixel. Each voxel is a unit of volume and has numeric value(s) associated with it. It represents some measurable properties or independent variables of a real object or phenomenon.

voxel space a 3-D integer grid or lattice of voxels in which the volumetric data set, or object, resides.

voxelization volume synthesis in 3-D. The process of converting a geometric representation of a synthetic model into a set of voxels that best represents that synthetic model within the discrete voxel space.

VPN virtual private network.

VSAM, virtual storage access method a file management system by IBM which predated the advent of DBMS but is still today used by a large number of applications.

VTAM virtual telecommunication access method.

WAN wide area network.

WDM wavelength division multiplexing.

WELL Whole Earth Lectronic Link.

wireless communications means of transferring information without physical signal lines, i.e. through modulated infrared light and radio.

workgroup a group of users working together for an indeterminate length of time – seconds, hours, months, etc. – to achieve goals that are consistent with objectives of the organization.

workgroup computing computer-assisted manipulation of a common database and other resources from remote distributed workstations, as necessary by the workgroup.

workstation desktop, deskbottom, or deskside computer functioning within an on-line network. Non-networked computers should not be called workstations.

workstation services networked services provided to the individual user, usually engineered by the provider of the network.

WWW World Wide Web (the Web).

X.400 a CCITT recommendation specifiying a standard for electronic mail transfer.

X-Open international consortium of computer vendors working to create an internally supported, vendor-independent common applications environment based on industry standards.

X/Open portability guide portability norms written by the X/Open organization.

XTP, express transfer protocol it includes both network and transport layer functions.

X.25 a CCITT standard of the 1970s that defines the packet format for data transfers in a public data network.

Acronyms of Organizations

ANSI American National Standards Institute.
ARPA Advanced Research Project Agency.
CCITT Consultative Committee for International Telephone and Telegraph.
CEPT Conférence Européenne des Poste et Télécommunications.
CNRI Corporation for National Research Initiative.
ECMA European Computer Manufacturers Association.
EIA Electronic Industries Association.
ETSI European Telecommunications Standards Institute.
IEEE Institute of Electrical and Electronics Engineers.
ISO International Standards Organization.
MITI Ministry of International Trade and Industry.
NIST US National Institute of Standards and Technology.
NREN US National Research and Education Network.
NSF National Science Foundation.
NTT Nippon Telegraph and Telephone.

Acknowledgements

The following organizations, their senior executives and system specialists, participated in the 1993 to 1996 research projects which led to the contents of the book and its documentation. But while valuable input comes from these sources, the evaluation and presentation are the authors' own.

United States

Bankers Trust

Dr Carmine Vona, Executive Vice President for Worldwide Technology.
Shalom Brinsy, Senior Vice President, Distributed Networks.
Dan W. Muecke, Vice President, Technology Strategic Planning.
Bob Graham, Vice President, Database Manager.
1 Bankers Trust Plaza, New York, NY 10006

Citibank

Colin Crook, Chairman Corporate Technology Committee.
David Schultzer, Senior Vice President, Information Technology.
Jim Caldarella, Manager, Business Architecture for Global Finance.
Nicholas P. Richards, Database Administrator.
William Brindley, Technology Officer.
Michael R. Veale, Network Connectivity.
Harriet Schabes, Corporate Standards.
Leigh Reeve, Technology for Global Finance.
399 Park Avenue, New York, NY 10043

Morgan Stanley

Gary T. Goehrke, Managing Director, Information Services.
Guy Chiarello, Vice President, Databases.

Robert F. De Young, Principal, Information Technology.
1933 Broadway, New York, NY 10019
Eileen S. Wallace, Vice President, Treasury Department.
Jacqueline T. Brody, Treasury Department.
1251 Avenue of the Americas, New York, NY 10020

Goldman Sachs

Vincent L. Amatulli, Information Technology, Treasury Department.
85 Broad Street, New York, NY 10004

J.J. Kenny Services Inc.

Thomas E. Zielinski, Chief Information Officer.
Ira Kirschner, Database Administrator, Director of System Programming and of the Data Center.
65 Broadway, New York, NY1006

Merrill Lynch

Kevin Sawyer, Director of Distributed Computing Services and Executive in Charge of the Mainframe to Client-Server Conversion Process.
Raymond M. Disco, Treasury/Bank Relations Manager.
World Financial Center, South Tower, New York, NY 10080–6107

Teachers Insurance and Annuity Association/College Retirement Equities Fund (TIAA/CREF)

Charles S. Dvorkin, Vice President and Chief Technology Officer.
Harry D. Perrin, Assistant Vice President, Information Technology.
730 Third Avenue, New York, NY 10017–3206

Financial Accounting Standards Board

Halsey G. Bullen, Project Manager.
Jeannot Blanchet, Project Manager.
Teri L. List, Practice Fellow.
401 Merritt 7, Norwalk, CN 06856

Massachusetts Institute of Technology

Prof. Dr Stuart E. Madnick, Information Technology and Management Science.

Prof. Dr Michael Siegel, Information Technology, Sloan School of Management.
Patricia M. McGinnis, Executive Director, International Financial Services.
Prof. Peter J. Kempthorne, Project on Non-Traditional Methods in Financial Analysis.
Dr Alexander M. Samrov, Project on Non-Traditional Methods in Financial Analysis.
Robert R. Halperin, Executive Director, Center for Coordination Science.
David L. Verrill, Senior Liaison Officer, Industrial Liaison Program.
Sloan School of Management, 50 Memorial Drive, Cambridge, MA 02139

Prof. Dr Kenneth B. Haase, Media Arts and Sciences.
Dr David Zeltzer, Virtual Reality Project.
Ames Street, Cambridge, MA 02139

Santa Fe Institute

Dr Edward A. Knapp, President.
Dr L. Mike Simmons, Jr, Vice President.
Dr Bruce Abell, Vice President Finance.
Prof. Dr Murray Gell-Mann, Theory of Complexity.
Prof. Dr Stuart Kauffman, Models in Biology.
Dr Chris Langton, Artificial Life.
Dr John Miller, Adaptive Computation in Economics.
Dr Blake Le Baron, Non-Traditional Methods in Economics.
Bruce Sawhill, Virtual Reality.
1660 Old Pecos Trail, Santa Fe, NM 87501

School of Engineering, University of California, Los Angeles

Prof. Dr Judea Pearl, Cognitive Systems Laboratory.
Prof. Dr Walter Karplus, Computer Science Department.
Prof. Dr Michael G. Dyer, Artificial Intelligence Laboratory.
Westwood Village, Los Angeles, CA 90024

School of Business Administration, University of Southern California

Dr Bert M. Steece, Dean of Faculty, School of Business Administration.
Dr Alan Rowe, Professor of Management.
Los Angeles, CA 90089–1421

Prediction Company

Dr J. Doyne Farmer, Director of Development.
Dr Norman H. Packard, Director of Research.
Jim McGill, Managing Director.
234 Griffin Street, Santa Fe, NM 87501

Simgraphics Engineering Corp.

Steve Tice, President.
David J. Verso, Chief Operating Officer.
1137 Huntington Drive, South Pasadena, CA 91030–4563

NYNEX Science and Technology, Inc.

Thomas M. Super, Vice President, Research and Development.
Steven Cross, NYNEX Shuttle Project.
Valerie R. Tingle, System Analyst.
Melinda Crews, Public Liaison, NYNEX Laboratories.
500 Westchester Avenue, White Plains, NY 10604

John C. Falco, Sales Manager, NYNEX Systems Marketing.
David J. Annino, Account Executive, NYNEX Systems Marketing.
100 Church Street, New York, NY 10007

Microsoft

Mike McGeehan, Database Specialist.
Andrew Elliott, Marketing Manager.
825, 8th Avenue, New York, NY

Reuters America

Robert Russel, Senior Vice President.
William A.S. Kennedy, Vice President.
Buford Smith, President, Reuters Information Technology.
Richard A. Willis, Manager International Systems Design.
M.A. Sayers, Technical Manager, Central Systems Development.
Alexander Faust, Manager Financial Products USA (Instantlink and Blend).
40 East 52nd Street, New York, NY 10022

Oracle Corporation

Scott Matthews, National Account Manager.
Robert T. Funk, Senior Systems Specialist.

Joseph M. Di Bartolomeo, Systems Specialist.
Dick Dawson, Systems Specialist.
885 Third Avenue, New York, NY 10022

Digital Equipment Corporation

Mike Fishbein, Product Manager, Massively Parallel Systems (MAS-PAR Supercomputer).
Marco Emrich, Technology Manager, NAS.
Robert Passmore, Technical Manager, Storage Systems.
Mark S. Dresdner, DEC Marketing Operations.
146 Main Street, Maynard, MA 01754
(Meeting held at UBS, New York)

Unisys Corporation

Harvey J. Chiat, Director Impact Programs.
Manuel Lavin, Director, Databases.
David A. Goiffon, Software Engineer.
P.O. Box 64942, MS 4463
Saint Paul, MN, 55164–0942
(Meeting held at UBS, New York)

Hewlett Packard

Brad Wilson, Product Manager, Commercial Systems.
Vish Krishnan, Manager R&D Laboratory.
Samir Mathur, Open ODB Manager.
Michael Gupta, Transarc, Tuxedo, Encina Transaction Processing.
Dave Williams, Industry Account Manager.
1911, Pruneridge Avenue, Cupertino, CA 95014

IBM Corporation

Terry Liffick, Software Strategies, Client-Server Architecture.
Paula Cappello, Information Warehouse Framework.
Ed Cobbs, Transaction Processing Systems.
Dr Paul Wilms, Connectivity and Interoperability.
Helen Arzu, IBM Santa Teresa Representative.
Dana L. Stetson, Advisory Marketing IBM New York.
Santa Teresa Laboratory, 555 Bailey Avenue, San José, CA 95141

UBS Securities

A. Ramy Goldstein, Managing Director, Equity Derivative Products.
299 Park Avenue, New York, NY 10171–0026

Union Bank of Switzerland

Dr H. Baumann, Director of Logistics, North American Operations.
Dr Ch. Gabathuler, Director, Information Technology.
Mr Shrikantan, Director, Telecommunications.
Roy M. Darhin, Assistant Vice President.
299 Park Avenue, New York, NY 10171–0026

United Kingdom

Barclays Bank

Peter Golden, Chief Information Officer, Barclays Capital Markets, Treasury, BZW.
Brandon Davies, Director of Financial Engineering.
David J. Parsons, Director Advanced Technology.
Christine E. Irwin, Group Information Systems Technology.
Murray House, 1 Royal Mint Court, London EC3N 4HH

Bank of England

Mark Laycock, Banking Supervision Division.
Threadneedle Street, London EC2R 8AH

Association for Payment Clearing Services (APACS)

J. Michael Williamson, Deputy Chief Executive.
14 Finsbury Square, London EC2A 1BR

Abbey National Bank

Mac Millington, Director of Information Technology.
Chalkdell Drive, Shenley Wood, Milton Keynes MK6 6LA
Anthony W. Elliott, Director of Risk and Credit.
Abbey House, Baker Street, London NW1 6XL

Natwest Securities

Sam B. Gibb, Director of Information Technology.
Don F. Simpson, Director, Global Technology.

Richard E. Gibbs, Director, Equity Derivatives.
135 Bishopsgate, London EC2M 3XT

Oracle Corporation

Geoffrey W. Squire, Executive Vice President and Chief Executive.
Richard Barker, Senior Vice President and Director British Research Laboratories.
Giles Godart-Brown, Senior Support Manager.
Paul A. Gould, Account Executive.
Oracle Park, Bittams Lane, Guildford Road, Chertsey, Surrey KT16 9RG

Virtual Presence

Stuart Cupit, Graphics Engineer.
25 Corsham Street, London N1 6DR

Valbecc Object Technology

Martin Fowler, Ptech Expert.
115 Wilmslow Road, Handforth, Wilmslow, Cheshire SK9 3ER

Scandinavia

Vaerdipapircentralen (VP)

Jens Bache, General Manager.
Mrs Aase Blume, Assistant to the General Manager.
61 Helgeshoj Allé, Postbox 20, 2630 Taastrup, Denmark

Swedish Bankers' Association

Bo Gunnarsson, Manager, Bank Automation Department.
Gösta Fischer, Manager, Bank-Owned Financial Companies Department.
Göran Ahlberg, Manager, Credit Market Affairs Department.
P.O. Box 7603, 10394 Stockholm, Sweden

Skandinaviska Enskilda Banken

Lars Isacsson, Treasurer.
Urban Janeld, Executive Vice President Finance and IT.
Mats Andersson, Director of Computers and Communications.

Gösta Olavi, Manager SEB Data/Koncern Data.
2 Sergels Torg, 10640 Stockholm, Sweden

Securum AB

Anders Nyren, Director of Finance and Accounting.
John Lundgren, Manager of IT.
38 Regeringsg, 5 tr., 10398 Stockholm, Sweden

Sveatornet AB of the Swedish Savings Banks

Gunar M. Carlsson, General Manager.
(Meeting at Swedish Bankers' Association)

Mandamus AB of the Swedish Agricultural Banks

Mrs Marie Martinsson, Credit Department.
(Meeting at Swedish Bankers' Association)

Handelsbanken

Janeric Sundin, Manager, Securities Department.
Jan Aronson, Assistant Manager, Securities Department.
(Meeting at Swedish Bankers' Association)

Gota Banken

Mr Johannsson, Credit Department.
(Meeting at Swedish Bankers' Association)

Irdem AB

Gian Medri, Former Director of Research at Nordbanken.
19 Flintlasvagen, 19154 Sollentuna, Sweden

Austria

Creditanstalt Bankverein

Dr Wolfgang G. Lichtl, Director of Foreign Exchange and Money Markets.
Dr Johann Strobl, Manager, Financial Analysis for Treasury Operations.
3 Julius Tandler-Platz, 1090 Vienna

Bank Austria

Dr Peter Fischer, Director of Treasury.
Peter Gabriel, Deputy General Manager, Trading.
Konrad Schcate, Manager, Financial Engineering.
2 Am Hof, 1010 Vienna.

Association of Austrian Banks and Bankers

Dr Fritz Diwok, Secretary General.
11 Boersengasse, 1013 Vienna

Aktiengesellschaft Fuer Bauwesen

Dr Josef Fritz, General Manager.
2 Lothringenstrasse, 1041 Vienna

Management Data of Creditanstalt

Ing. Guenther Reindl, Vice President, International Banking Software.
Ing. Franz Necas, Project Manager, RICOS.
Mag. Nikolas Goetz, Product Manager, RICOS.
21–25 Althanstrasse, 1090 Vienna

Germany

Deutsche Bundesbank

Eckhard Oechler, Director of Bank Supervision and Legal Matters.
14 Wilhelm Epstein Strasse, D-6000 Frankfurt 50

Deutsche Bank

Peter Gerard, Executive Vice President, Organization and Information Technology.
Herman Seiler, Senior Vice President, Investment Banking and Foreign Exchange Systems.
Dr Kuhn, Investment Banking and Foreign Exchange Systems.
Dr Stefan Kolb, Organization and Technological Development.
12 Koelner Strasse, D–6236 Eschborn

Dresdner Bank

Dr Karsten Wohlenberg, Project Leader Risk Management, Simulation, and Analytics Task Force, Financial Division.

Hans-Peter Liesten, Mathematician.
Susanne Loesken, Organization and IT Department.
43 Mainzer Landstrasse, D–6000 Frankfurt

Commerzbank

Helmut Hoppe, Director Organization and Information Technology.
Hermann Lenz, Director Controllership, Internal Accounting and Management Accounting.
Harald Lux, Manager Organization and Information Technology.
Waldemar Nickel, Manager Systems Planning.
155 Mainzer Landstrasse, D-60261 Frankfurt

Deutscher Sparkassen und Giroverband

Manfred Krueger, Division Manager, Card Strategy.
4 Simrockstrasse, D-5300 Bonn 1
(Telephone interview from Frankfurt)

ABN-AMRO (Holland)

Mr Schilder, Organization and Information Technology.
(Telephone interview from Frankfurt)

Media Systems

Bertram Anderer, Director.
6 Goethestrasse, D-7500 Karlsruhe

Fraunhofer Institute for Computer Graphics

Dr. Ing. Martin Goebel.
Wolfgang Felber.
7 Wilhelminerstrasse, D–6100 Darmstadt

GMD First – Research Institute for Computer Architecture, Software Technology and Graphics

Prof Dr Ing. Wolfgang K. Giloi, General Manager.
Dr Behr, Administrative Director.
Dr Ulrich Bruening, Chief Designer.
Dr Joerg Nolte, Designer of Parallel Operating Systems Software.
Dr Matthias Kessler, Parallel Languages and Parallel Compilers.

Dr Friedrich W. Schroer, New Programming Paradigms.
Dr Thomas Lux, Fluid Dynamics, Weather Prediction and Pollution Control Project.
5 Rudower Chaussee, D–1199 Berlin

Siemens Nixdorf

Wolfgang Weiss, Director of Banking Industry Office.
Bert Kirschbaum, Manager, Dresdner Bank Project.
Mark Miller, Manager Neural Networks Project for UBS and German Banks.
Andrea Vonerden, Business Management Department.
27 Lyoner Strasse, D-6000 Frankfurt 71

UBS Germany

H.-H v. Scheliha, Director, Organization and Information Technology.
Georg Sudhaus, Manager IT for Trading Systems.
Marco Bracco, Trader.
Jaap van Harten, Trader.
52 Bleichstrasse, D-6000 Frankfurt 1

Switzerland

Bank for International Settlements

Claude Sivy, Director, Controllership and Operational Security.
Frederick C. Musch, Secretary General, Basel Committee on Banking Supervision.
2 Centralbankplatz, Basel

Ciba-Geigy AG

Stefan Janovjak, Divisional Information Manager.
Natalie Papezik, Information Architect.
Ciba-Geigy, R-1045, 5.19, 4002 Basle

BZ Bank Zurich

Martin Ebner, President.
Peter Sjostrand, Finance Director.
Olivier Willi, Analyst.
Roger Jenny, Analyst.
50 Sihlstrasse, 8021 Zurich

BZ Trust Aktiengesellschaft

Dr Stefan Holzer, Financial Analyst.
24 Eglirain, 8832 Wilen

Ecole Polytechnique Federal de Lausanne

Prof. Dr Jean-Daniel Nicoud, Director, Microinformatics Laboratory.
Prof. Dr Boi Faltings, Artificial Intelligence.
Prof. Dr Martin J. Hasler, Circuits and Systems.
Dr Ing. Roman Boulic, Computer Graphics.
1015 Lausanne

Eurodis

Albert Mueller, Director.
Beat Erzer, Marketing Manager.
B. Pedrazzini, Systems Engineer.
Reto Albertini, Sales Engineer.
Bahnhofstrasse 58/60, CH–8105 Regensdorf

Olsen and Associates

Dr Richard Olsen, President.
232 Seefeldstrasse, 8008 Zurich

Swiss Bank Corporation

Dr Marcel Rohner, Director, IFD Controlling.
Swiss Bank Centre, 8010 Zurich

Japan

Bank of Japan

Harry Toyama, Councel and Chief Manager, Credit and Market Management Department.
Akira Ieda, Credit and Market Management Department.
2–1–1, Kongoku-Cho, Nihonbashi, Chuo-ku, Tokyo 103

Dai-Ichi Kangyo Bank

Shunsuke Nakasuji, General Manager and Director, Information Technology Division.

Seiichi Hasegawa, Manager International Systems Group.
Takahiro Sekizawa, International Systems Group.
Yukio Hisatomi, Manager Systems Planning Group.
Shigeaki Togawa, Systems Planning Group.
13–3, Shibuya, 2-Chome, Shibuya-ku, Tokyo 150

Fuji Bank

Hideo Tanaka, General Manager Systems Planning Division.
Toshihiko Uzaki, Manager Systems Planning Division.
Takakazu Imai, Systems Planning Division.
Otemachi Financial Centre, 1–5–4 Otemachi, Chiyoda-ku, Tokyo.

Mitsubishi Bank

Akira Watanabe, General Manager, Derivative Products.
Akira Towatari, Manager, Strategic Planning and Administration, Derivative Products.
Takehito Nemoto, Chief Manager, Systems Development Division.
Nobuyuki Yamada, Systems Development Division.
Haruhiko Suzuki, Systems Development Division.
7–1, Marunouchi, 2-Chome, Chiyoda-ku, Tokyo 100

Nomura Research Institute

Tomio Arai, Director, Systems Science Department.
Tomoyuki Ohta, Director, Financial Engineering Group.
Tomohiko Hiruta, Manager, I-STAR Systems Services.
9–1, Nihonbashi, 1-Chome, Chuo-ku, Tokyo 103

Mitsubishi Trust and Banking

Nobuyuki Tanaka, General Manager, Systems Planning Division.
Terufumi Kage, Consultant Systems Planning Division.
9–8 Kohnan, 2-Chome, Minato-ku, Tokyo 108

Sakura Bank

Nobuo Ihara, Senior Vice President and General Manager, Systems Development Office VIII.
Hisao Katayama, Senior Vice President and General Manager, System Development Office VII.
Toshihiko Eda, Senior Systems Engineer, Systems Development Division.
4–2, Kami-Osahi, 4-Chome, Shinagawa-ku, Tokyo 141

Sanyo Securities

Yuji Ozawa, Director, Systems Planning Department.
K. Toyama, Systems Planning Department.
1–8–1, Nihonbashi, Kayabacho, Chuo-ku, Tokyo 103

Centre for Financial Industry Information System Systems (FISC)

Shighehisa Hattori, Executive Director.
Kiyoshi Kumata, Manager, Research Division II.
16th Floor, Ark Mori Building, 12–32, 1-Chome, Akasaka, Minato-ku, Tokyo 107

Laboratory for International Fuzzy Engineering Research (Life)

Prof. Dr Toshiro Terano, Executive Director.
Dr Anca L. Ralescu, Assistant Director.
Shunichi Tani, Fuzzy Control Project Leader.
Siber Hegner Building, 89–1 Yamashita-Cho, Naka-ku, Yokohama-shi 231

Real World Computing Partnership (RWC)

Dr Junichi Shumada, General Manager of RWC.
Hajime Irisawa, Executive Director.
Tsukuba Mitsui Building, 1–6–1 Takezono, Tsukuba-shi, Ibarahi 305

Tokyo University

Prof. Dr Michitaka Hirose, Department of Mechano-Informatics, Faculty of Engineering.
Dr Kensuke Yokoyama, Virtual Reality Project.
3–1, 7-Chome, Hongo Bunkyo-ku, Tokyo 113

Tokyo International University

Prof. Dr Yoshiro Kuratani.
9–1–7–528, Akasaka, Minato-ku, Tokyo 107

Japan Electronic Directory Research Institute

Dr Toshio Yokoi, General Manager.
Mita-Kokusai Building – Annex, 4–28 Mita, 1-Chome, Minato-ku, Tokyo 108

Mitsubishi Research Insitute (MRI)

Masayuki Fujita, Manager, Strategic Information Systems Deptartment.
Hideyuki Morita, Senior Research Associate, Information Science Department.
Akio Sato, Research Associate, Information Science Department.
ARCO Tower, 8–1 Shimomeguro, 1-Chome, Meguro-ku, Tokyo 153

NTT Software

Dr Fukuya Ishino, Senior Vice President.
223–1 Yamashita-Cho, Naka-ku, Yokohama 231

Ryoshin Systems (Systems developer fully owned by Mitsubishi Trust)

Takewo Yuwi, Vice President, Technical Research and Development.
9–8 Kohman, 2-Chome, Minato-ku, Tokyo 108

Sanyo Software Services

Fumio Sato, General Manager, Sales Department 2.
Kanayama Building, 1–2–12 Shinkawa, Chuo-ku, Tokyo 104

Fujitsu Research Institute

Dr Masuteru Sekiguchi, Member of the Board and Director of R&D.
Takao Saito, Director of the Parallel Computing Research Centre.
Dr Hiroyasu Itoh, R&D Department.
Katsuto Kondo, R&D Department.
Satoshi Hamaya, Information Systems and Economics.
9–3 Nakase, 1-Chome, Mihama-ku, Chiba-City 261

NEC

Kotaro Namba, Senior Researcher, NEC Planning Research.
Dr Toshiyuki Nakata, Manager, Computer System Research Laboratory.
Asao Kaneko, Computer System Research Laboratory.
3–13–12 Mita, Minato-ku, Tokyo 108

Toshiba

Dr Makoto Ihara, Manager, Workstation Product Planning and Technical Support Department.

Emi Nakamura, Analyst, Financial Applications Department.
Joshikiyo Nakamura, Financial Sales Manager.
Minami Arai, Deputy Manager, Workstation Systems Division.
1–1, Shibaura, 1-Chome, Minato-ku, Tokyo 105

Microsoft

James Lalonde, Multinational Account Manager, Large Accounts Sales Department.
Sasazuka NA Bldg, 50–1 Sasazuka, 1–Chome, Shibuya-ku, Tokyo 151

Apple Technology

Dr Tsutomu Kobayashi, President.
25 Mori Bldg, 1–40–30 Roppongi, Minato-ku, Tokyo 106

Digital Equipment Japan

Roshio Ishii, Account Manager, Financial Sales Unit 1.
2–1 Kamiogi, 1-Chome, Suginamiku, Tokyo 167

UBS Japan

Dr Peter Brutsche, Executive Vice President and Chief Manager.
Gary P. Eidam, First Vice President, Regional Head of Technology.
Charles Underwood, Vice President, Head of Technical Architecture and Strategy.
Masaki Utsunomiya, Manager, IT Production Facilities.
Yurakucho Building 2F, 1–10–1 Yurakucho, Chiyoda-ku, Tokyo 100

Index